Electromagnetic Fields

Electromagnetic Fields

Sergei A. Schelkunoff

COLUMBIA UNIVERSITY

BLAISDELL PUBLISHING COMPANY

New York • *London*

First Edition, 1963

© Copyright 1963, by Blaisdell Publishing Company,
A Division of **Ginn and Company**
All rights reserved under International and Pan-American Copyright Conventions. Published in New York, Toronto, and London by Blaisdell Publishing Company.

Library of Congress Catalog Card Number: 63–8925

Manufactured in the United States of America

To my wife
Jean Kennedy Schelkunoff

Preface

This text has been prepared for a sequence of two basic courses in electromagnetic field theory. One course can be based upon the first five chapters, the main prerequisites for which are (1) a course in general physics, including sections on electricity and magnetism, and (2) calculus. With this background, students can master these chapters in four semester-hours provided they work hard.

The first part of the book emphasizes the physical aspects of fields rather than mathematical manipulation. It is for this reason that only rather elementary college mathematics is required. More advanced mathematics such as vector analysis, functions of a complex variable, partial differential equations, and special functions are certainly essential in more advanced courses for those who wish to specialize in field theory; but in a basic introductory course this mathematics is unnecessary and would only divert students' attention from the essential characteristics of fields. There is real danger that the use of advanced mathematics in a basic introductory course would encourage pencil pushing at the expense of thinking. The object is to learn to express the physical concepts as simply as possible. Why seek to kill a fly with a 16-inch gun when a fly swatter is available?

There is another danger in relying on too advanced mathematics in an introductory course on fields. Mathematics suggests rigor, and students may get an erroneous idea that rigor assures truth in the domain of physics. What is even worse, they may come to believe that mere algebraic manipulation of symbols constitutes rigor and assures the correctness of the results. The faith in such manipulation can grow to such an extent that students may accept results which are obviously wrong from the physical point of view, without looking over their solutions in search of an error. Students should be encouraged to develop a habit of sound, even more than of rigorous, thinking.

For ready reference, Chapter 1 contains a fairly detailed review of fundamental field concepts. The main purpose, however, is to show the interrelation between static and time-varying fields. This inter-relation is the basis for many approximate methods to follow. In Chapter 2 we obtain the fields of basic sources. The results are important in themselves; they also illustrate fundamental field concepts. In addition we develop approximate techniques for handling the "almost static fields." These techniques enable us to solve many important field problems not amenable to exact analysis. They also illustrate the physical nature of Maxwell's equations. Chapter 3 introduces the ideas of dissipation, storage, and transfer of energy in fields. These ideas are then applied to approximate analysis of cavity resonators and to representations of physical circuit elements by networks of ideal circuit elements. Chapter 4 is devoted to fundamentals of wave propagation in transmission lines and to approximate analysis of certain waveguides. In Chapter 5 we consider waves guided by an infinitely thin semi-infinite wire. The resulting formulas are then used to analyze waves guided by coaxial cones, by diverging cones, and by diverging wires. Finally, the same formulas enable us to obtain the field of an electric current element or an oscillating electric charge. The remainder of the chapter is devoted to some basic applications.

The remaining chapters have been prepared for a more advanced basic course in fields. Here, more mathematical preparation is desirable. Thus for Chapter 6, dealing with normal modes of field distribution and wave propagation, it would be helpful if the student had some knowledge of the method of separation of variables. In Chapter 7 scattering by small objects is considered, and, for the most part, only elementary mathematics is needed. In Chapter 8 we treat coupled oscillations and derive the equivalent networks for certain continuous structures. In Chapter 9 the basic ideas for developing generalized telegraphist's equations are explained and illustrated by simple examples. For the last two chapters some knowledge of Fourier series is essential.

Problems have been designed to develop the ideas and methods in the text still further. For this reason quite a few problems contain suggestions for their solution, and all problems are supplied with answers.

I have deeply appreciated the comments and suggestions made by Professors William H. Huggins and John R. Whinnery who read the first draft of this book. I also wish to thank Mr. Paul R. Karmel for his help with reading the typed copies of the manuscript.

S. A. S.

Columbia University
January 27, 1963

Contents

1. Basic Concepts and Equations

2.   Static and Almost Static Fields

3.   Energy Storage, Dissipation, and Transfer

4.   Waves

5.   Spherical Waves

6.   Normal Modes

7. Reflection and Scattering

8. Coupled Oscillations

9.   Generalized Telegraphist's Equations

Appendix I   Coordinate Systems and Vectors

Electromagnetic Fields

1

Basic Concepts and Equations

1.0 Introduction

The interaction between electric and magnetic fields is at the root of electromagnetic wave propagation in free space—on which depend radio communication, radar, light, noise from outer space, etc. It is at the root of propagation in waveguides, in linear accelerators, in cyclotrons, etc. And it is at the root of wave propagation in cables and overhead transmission lines used in telephone and telegraph communication. The interaction between electric and magnetic fields is responsible for the behavior of *physical* electric circuit elements, electric circuits, and networks at low and at high frequencies. In electric circuit and network theories one studies the behavior of mathematical models which are made up of ideal resistors, inductors, and capacitors. Such ideal circuit elements do not exist in nature. Physical resistors, inductors, and capacitors may be approximated by their ideal counterparts in a restricted frequency range. These physical elements may be approximated much better and in a more extended frequency range by *equivalent networks* of ideal elements. In certain situations they may be represented *exactly* by appropriate equivalent networks. Knowledge of field theory is essential for making reliable approximations and equivalent representations even in ordinary electric networks at low frequencies, not to mention microwave networks. The objective of this book is to provide a physical and mathematical background needed for understanding electric and magnetic fields, the interaction between them as expressed by Maxwell's equations, and the most important consequences of this interaction. Modern physical research and engineering applications require such a knowledge.

Our knowledge of electric and magnetic fields is derived from circumstantial evidence and is based on interpretation of this evidence. We are nearest to "seeing" a *field* when we perform the following experiment. If we scatter iron filings on a sheet of paper at random and bring a bar magnet under the sheet, the filings will rearrange themselves into an ordered pattern along lines diverging from the vicinity of one end of the magnet and converging to the other end. Apparently some sort of invisible force operates in the space around the magnet.

The needle of a magnetic compass aligns itself in the north-south direction. If deflected, the needle tends to return to the original position. If prevented from returning to the original position by a spring, it will exert a force on the spring, either stretching or compressing it. Thus we speak of the earth's *magnetic field* (of force).

On a dry summer day it is not uncommon to receive a shock on touching a doorknob, hear an accompanying crackling noise, and sometimes see a spark. Familiar to many are demonstrations showing that amber rubbed with fur acquires the power of attracting light objects such as pith balls and paper. A few experiments would suffice to show that the field of force around a piece of amber and fur, an *electric field*, has different properties from the field surrounding a bar magnet, even though there are similarities.

It is within the province of physics to present systematically the facts and to formulate the basic concepts related to electricity and magnetism. It is assumed that the reader is familiar with them. To ensure that he understands the terms and the symbols as they are used in this book, we shall summarize and illustrate the principal conclusions, definitions, and equations which are relevant to field theory. In this chapter the order of presentation of basic field concepts, illustrations, and point of view is intended to help the student form mental pictures by an analogy between intangible quantities such as the electric flux density $\bar{D}$ and the "displacement current density" $\partial \bar{D}/\partial t$ and more tangible quantities such as the density of electric current in conductors. The student is advised to become thoroughly familiar with the concept of "displacement current" which is the cornerstone of Maxwell's field theory and its applications. An intuitative understanding of displacement current will enable the student to analyze fields and waves under various conditions, at least qualitatively and often semi-quantitatively.

Special attention should be given to the interrelation between static and time-varying fields. This interrelation is the basis for approximation methods developed in subsequent chapters. In order to stress this idea we have abandoned the conventional grouping of subject matter into "electrostatics," "magnetostatics," etc. Instead, the grouping is arranged to emphasize key ideas, analogies, methods of analysis, and methods of approximation.

1.1 Force, mass, work, energy

We derive our initial ideas about *force* from experience with pushing and pulling, and then extend them to include invisible "forces" such as those of gravitation, electric attraction, and repulsion, etc. The key ideas are expressed in Newton's laws of motion:

1. A body at rest will remain at rest, and a body in motion will continue to move in the same direction and with the same speed, that is, with the same velocity, unless acted upon by some external force.

2. Whenever a force acts upon a body, it produces in the motion of the body an acceleration which is proportional to the force acting and is in the same direction as the force, and is inversely proportional to the mass of the body acted upon.

Quantitatively the second law is expressed as

$$m\,\frac{d\bar{v}}{dt} = \bar{F} \tag{1.1}$$

in all coherent units, that is, in units based on independent and arbitrarily chosen "fundamental" units of length, time, mass, and electric charge (or electric current). In this book we use the MKSC (meter-kilogram-second-coulomb) system of units in which the *meter* is the unit of length, the *kilogram* is the unit of mass m, and second is the unit of time t, the *meter per second* is the unit of velocity $\bar{v}$, and the *meter-kilogram per second per second*, otherwise known as the *newton*, is the unit of force $\bar{F}$. The unit of electric charge, the *coulomb*, will be defined approximately in the next section. Since it is easier to measure accurately electric current, the legal standard is a unit of electric current, the *ampere*, and the coulomb is defined precisely as the *ampere-second*. Hence the MKSC system is usually called the MKSA system.

When motion is in a straight line, equation (1.1) may be written as

$$m\,\frac{dv}{dt} = F, \tag{1.1}$$

where the *speed* v is the magnitude of the velocity vector $\bar{v}$ and F is the magnitude of the force vector $\bar{F}$. Multiplying this equation by the differential ds of the distance traveled by the mass in time dt and integrating, we obtain

$$\int_{s_0}^{s} m \frac{dv}{dt} \, ds = \int_{s_0}^{s} F \, ds,$$

$$\int_{v_0}^{v} mv \, dv = \int_{s_0}^{s} F \, ds,$$

$$\tfrac{1}{2}mv^2 - \tfrac{1}{2}mv_0^2 = \int_{s_0}^{s} F \, ds. \tag{1.2}$$

The quantity on the right of equation (1.2) is called the *work done* by the force in moving the body through the distance $s - s_0$. The quantity $mv^2/2$ is called the kinetic energy of the body. Thus the equation states that the work done equals the increase in kinetic energy.

If a body is lifted against the force of gravity mg (where the acceleration of gravity g equals 9.8 m/sec², more or less, depending on the locality) to the height h, the work done is mgh. It is said that the body has acquired a *potential energy mgh*. If this body is allowed to fall back, the potential energy will be converted to kinetic energy, which in turn will be converted upon impact with the earth into heat and dissipated. The MKSA unit of work and energy is the *newton-meter*, called the *joule*.

More generally, the work W done by a force $\vec{F}$ on a body moving in an arbitrary curvilinear path AB is the line integral of the scalar product

$$W = \int_{AB} \vec{F} \cdot \vec{ds} = \int_{AB} F_s \, ds = \int_{AB} F \cos (\vec{F}, \vec{ds}) \, ds, \tag{1.3}$$

where F_s is the component of $\vec{F}$ tangential to the curve and $(\vec{F}, \vec{ds})$ is the angle between the vector $\vec{F}$ and the differential displacement vector $\vec{ds}$.

According to Newton's theory of gravitation, amply justified by its applications, any two material particles attract each other along the line joining them with a force inversely proportional to the square of the distance between them and directly proportional to their masses:

$$F = -k_g(m_1m_2/r^2). \tag{1.4}$$

The negative sign is included to indicate that the force acts in the direction of *decreasing r*. The gravitational constant k_g equals 6.67 $\times$

10^{-11} meter³ per kilogram-second². It can be shown mathematically that this equation applies to uniformly dense spherical shells if r is the distance between their centers. It is also possible to determine for any body its *center of mass* such that equation (1.4) applies as if the entire mass of each body were concentrated in its center of mass (or center of gravity).

Thus in the space around a material body a force operates on any other material body, and we may say that a mass is surrounded by a *gravitational field*.

1.2 Electric charge, electric field, magnetic field

Historically two kinds of *electric charge*, positive and negative, each conceived as some sort of invisible fluid, were postulated to explain primitive experiments with wax and ebonite rubbed with fur and with bodies brought in contact with them. Simple experiments suffice to demonstrate that charges of the same sign repel each other, those of opposite signs attract, and that equal charges of opposite signs can neutralize each other as far as external action is concerned. Coulomb's law of force between charged particles and bodies is analogous to Newton's law of gravitation

$$F = k_e(q_1 q_2/r^2), \tag{1.5}$$

where q_1 and q_2 are the electric charges on the particles and the force acts along the line joining the particles.

Recent studies indicate that matter and electricity consist of a relatively small number of elementary particles. Particles that are of particular interest to us are electrically neutral particles such as hydrogen atoms, positive electric particles called protons, and negative electric particles called electrons. The mass of a hydrogen atom is 1.67×10^{-27} kg and the force of attraction between two such atoms is given by equation (1.4). A hydrogen atom can be split into a proton and an electron. The forces existing between the various particles are summarized in Figure 1.1. The force between a proton and a hydrogen atom is nearly the same as the force between two hydrogen atoms. The force between an electron and a hydrogen atom is smaller by a factor 1844. This is consistent with an assumption that these forces are gravitational and that the mass of an electron is 1/1844 times the mass of a proton; that is, the mass of an electron is 9.1×10^{-31} kg. A proton and an electron also attract each other with a force inversely proportional to the square of the distance but this force is larger than that given by equation (1.4) by a factor 4×10^{42}.

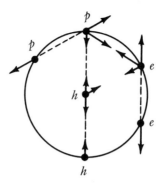

FIGURE 1.1   *A diagram illustrating the directions and, on a greatly compressed scale, the relative magnitudes of: (1) the gravitational forces between an electrically neutral hydrogen atom h and a proton p, an electron e, or another hydrogen atom; and (2) the electric forces between protons and electrons.*

Two protons repel each other with the same force. In the same manner, two electrons repel each other with this force. Thus we assume the existence of two new kinds of "mass" called *electric charge*, positive for the proton and negative for the electron. The signs are chosen to agree with those assigned in early macroscopic experiments in which the electric particles were separated by friction.

No electric charge whose absolute magnitude is smaller than that of a proton or of an electron has ever been observed. Hence this electric charge would be a natural choice for the "unit charge." However, it is too small for ordinary purposes. The practical (MKSA) unit of electric charge, the *coulomb*, has been defined in relation to the practical unit of electric current, the *ampere*. In the past the ampere was defined in relation to certain electro-chemical phenomena; at present it is defined in relation to forces existing between two long parallel wires carrying electric currents. The charge of a proton turns out to be 1.6×10^{-19} coulomb and the charge of an electron -1.6×10^{-19} coulomb. Thus approximately $(5/8) 10^{19}$ electrons, would constitute one coulomb of negative charge. The *electric constant* k_e in equation (1.5) equals approximately 9×10^9 joule-meters per coulomb per coulomb.

There is also an electrically neutral particle, the neutron, whose mass is nearly equal to that of a proton. In the diagram 1.1 we can substitute neutrons for hydrogen atoms to illustrate the difference between gravitational and electric forces.

So far no magnetic particles have been discovered. Primitive experiments show that two thin magnets exert forces on each other consistent with the following assumptions.

1. Each end of one magnet exerts a force on each end of the other.
2. These forces are inversely proportional to the square of the distance between respective pairs of ends.
3. One end of one magnet repels one end of the second and attracts the other with the same force if the distances are the same.
4. The north-seeking ends repel each other; in the same manner south-seeking ends repel. The north-seeking and south-seeking ends attract each other.

At this stage the evidence points to the existence of opposite "magnetic poles" at opposite ends of each thin magnet. Arbitrarily, the north-seeking pole was named "positive" and the south-seeking "negative." Although magnets in common with all material bodies are composed of atoms and hence contain positive and negative electric particles, they are normally electrically neutral and exert no force on an external electric charge because the numbers of opposite particles are the same and the particles are close together. Thus, it appears that there exist "magnetic charges" different from electric charges. However, if we cut a magnet in half, we find that both halves are magnets, each with two poles.

Further experiments have shown that while a stationary electric charge exerts no force on a magnet, an electric current, that is, a moving charge, acts on a magnet and the action is directly proportional to the magnitude of the current. Two wires carrying electric currents also act on each other unless they are perpendicular to each other. Two solenoids, that is, long and thin coils carrying direct electric currents, act on each other and on thin magnets as magnets act on each other. One end of a solenoid is north-seeking and the other south-seeking. If the direction of the current is reversed, the polarity is reversed. On the basis of such evidence it has been concluded that "magnetic" action is a property of a moving electric charge and that the action of a permanent magnet is due to atomic circulating currents.

To summarize:

1. The force between stationary electric particles is given by equation (1.5) and we say that an electric charge is surrounded by an *electric field*. The charge is said to be the source of this field.
2. The force between moving electric particles has two com-

ponents: One is given by equation (1.5) and the other depends not only on their charges but also on their velocities and the angle between directions of motion. Thus it is said that moving charges create a *magnetic field* superimposed on the electric field. In the case of permanent magnets, no external electric field has been observed (except, of course, when they are deliberately charged).

Even though electric charge is granular in nature, we shall consider it a continuous fluid because we shall deal with very large numbers of charged particles which are extremely close. They will be confined to material bodies, conductors, and dielectrics, where their individualities will be lost. It would be quite different in electron streams, where some particles might overtake the others, or fall behind them. The "smoothing" assumption is permissible in electromagnetic field theory wherein we are not concerned with noise phenomena which are attributable to random movements of discrete particles.

1.3   Electric intensity $\vec{E}$

The force $\vec{F}$ on a stationary electric charge q at a point P of a *given* electric field is proportional to the charge. The ratio of this force to the "test charge,"

$$\vec{E} = \vec{F}/q, \tag{1.6}$$

may be taken as a measure of the strength of the field. Various terms are used to denote vector $\vec{E}$: *electric field strength*, *electric field intensity*, or simply *electric intensity* at a point P.

It is essential to note that when a test charge is introduced into an actual electric field for measuring purposes, it may disturb the positions of the charged particles producing the field. The above ratio will then be the electric intensity of the altered field. It will be the intensity of the original field in either of the following cases.

1. The sources of the field are held fixed.
2. Point P is so far away from the sources that the test charge does not affect their positions.
3. The test charge is so small that it does not affect the positions of the sources.

The MKSA unit of electric intensity is *one newton per coulomb* or, as we shall presently see, the *volt per meter*.

From Coulomb's law, equation (1.5), we find that the electric intensity of the field produced by a point charge q has only the radial component (assuming that the center of coordinate system is at the point charge)

$$E_r = k_e q/r^2.$$

If q is positive, $\bar{E}$ points away from the charge; otherwise it points toward the charge as shown in Figure 1.2 (a, b).

The electric intensity of any given distribution of charged particles.

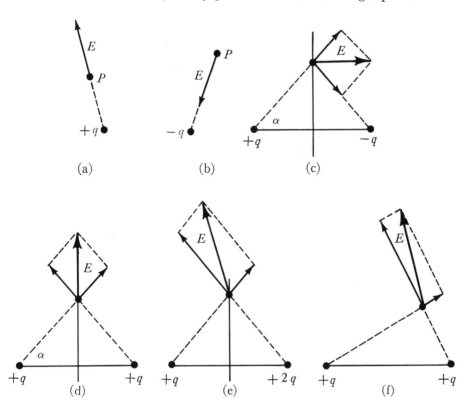

FIGURE 1.2 *Illustrations of vectorial addition of electric intensities.*

may be found by adding vectorially the electric intensities produced by individual particles. Thus, at any point in the plane perpendicular to and bisecting the line joining two equal and opposite charges, the electric intensity is perpendicular to the plane. See Figure 1.2(c). Its magnitude equals that given by the above last equation times 2 cos α. If the charges are of the same sign, $\bar{E}$ is in the plane [Figure 1.2(d)] and the multiplying factor is 2 sin α.

In general vectorial addition becomes complicated [Figure 1.2(e, f)] since the magnitudes of the vectors to be added depend on the magnitudes of the corresponding charges and on the distances involved. In such a case we can add the corresponding Cartesian components of all vectors and then obtain the magnitude and direction of the resultant.

1.4 Electric lines of force

An electric line of force is a line tangential to the electric vector at every point (see Figure 1.3). Such lines are useful for visual representation of fields. If drawn properly, they show not only the direction of the electric intensity but its relative magnitude as well. Electric lines of a single charged particle are radial. For a positive particle they start from the particle and go to infinity, as shown in Figure 1.3(a). For a negative particle they start from infinity and end on the particle. If we draw a certain number of lines, starting them uni-

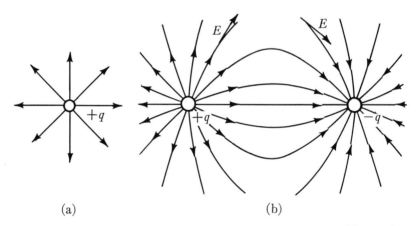

(a)   (b)

FIGURE 1.3   *Electric lines of force: (a) depicting the field produced by a point charge; (b) depicting the field produced by two equal but opposite charges.*

formly around the charge, we note that they are more dense where the field is strong than where the field is weak. The numbers of lines issuing from different particles may be taken proportional to their charges to represent correctly the relative field strengths in the vicinities of the particles. The lines should issue from each particle uniformly in all directions; but as we proceed on each line, always in the direction of the $\vec{E}$ vector, we find that these lines diverge or converge unevenly and exhibit the relative strengths of the field at various points.

Figure 1.3(b) shows two equal and opposite charges where all lines issuing from the positive charge converge to the negative charge. If the positive charge is twice as large, only one half of its lines terminate on the negative charge; the other half go to infinity.

1.5 Electromotive force

The *electromotive force*, or the *voltage*, along a given path AB (Figure 1.4) is the line integral of the tangential component of electric intensity

$$V_{AB} = \int_{AB} E_s \, ds = \int_{AB} \vec{E} \cdot \vec{ds}. \tag{1.7}$$

It is clear that $V_{BA} = -V_{AB}$.

Suppose that a charged particle q is carried along AB. Multiplying equation (1.7) by q, we have

$$qV_{AB} = \int_{AB} q\vec{E} \cdot \vec{ds}. \tag{1.8}$$

Here $q\vec{E}$ is the force acting on q and the line integral is the work done by this force. Hence if $\vec{E}$ does not vary with time, the voltage

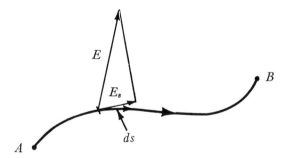

FIGURE 1.4 *An illustration of equation (1.7) which defines the electromotive force (the "voltage") between two points, A and B, along a given curve.*

V_{AB} is the work done by the field per unit charge carried along the path AB. If $\vec{E}$ varies with time but the transit time of the particle is so short that $\vec{E}$ has not changed appreciably in this time, V_{AB} is still substantially the work done by the field per unit charge carried along AB. Otherwise V_{AB} is just the line integral of $\vec{E}$ which plays an important role in electromagnetic theory.

Subsequently, we shall find that in the case of electrostatic fields it is permissible to speak of a *voltage between two points* because the voltage is independent of the path joining the two points. Furthermore, this is often approximately true even for time-variable fields.

Since qV_{AB} is in the nature of work or energy, its unit is the *joule*. Therefore, the unit of electromotive force is one *joule per coulomb*, which is called the *volt*. From equation (1.7) it is clear that the unit of electric intensity may be called the volt/meter as well as the newton/coulomb.

Consider Figure 1.5 which illustrates two parallel coaxial circular plates, equally and oppositely charged, with holes at their centers. Let an electron (whose charge is $-e$) enter the left hole with a speed

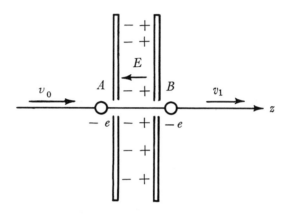

FIGURE 1.5 *An electron moving through an electric field between equally but oppositely charged parallel plates.*

v_0. What is its speed v_1 when it has passed through the right hole? Equation (1.1), Newton's equation of motion, gives

$$m\frac{dv}{dt} = -eE_z,$$

where E_z is the electric intensity along the axis and m is the mass of the electron. From equation (1.2) we find

$$\tfrac{1}{2}mv_1^2 - \tfrac{1}{2}mv_0^2 = -\int_{AB} eE_z\,dz = -eV_{AB} = eV_{BA}.$$

Hence

$$v_1 = [2(e/m)V_{BA} + v_0^2]^{1/2},$$

where $e/m = 1.76 \times 10^{11}$ coulombs per kilogram. If $V_{BA} = 1000$ volts and $v_0 = 0$, then $v_1 = 1.87 \times 10^7$ m/sec. This speed is about 6% of the speed of light and is small enough to justify the use of the "rest mass" of the electron in the above equation. If V_{BA} is so large that v_1 becomes an appreciable fraction of the velocity of light, the relativistic effects should be included.

The voltage between the terminals of a dry cell is of the order of one volt. The voltages between electric power lines, brought into homes, and ground are usually about 110 to 115 volts ("effective" or mean square values since these voltages are alternating). The electric intensity of strong sunlight at the surface of the earth is 713 volts/meter (effective).

1.6 Electric current I and its density $\vec{J}$

In some media, notably metals, there are many easily movable electrons. Such media are called *conductors*. As long as there is an electric field in the interior of a conductor, electric charge will move. This flow of charge is called *electric current*. The movements of individual electrons are erratic; but on the average there will be a drift in the direction of the electric intensity $\vec{E}$. There are so many electrons and they are so close together, that it is convenient to think of the moving charge as a fluid in motion. The *positive* direction of electric current is the direction *opposite* to that in which the electrons are drifting. This convention was adopted long before electrons were discovered, when electric current was thought to be a flow of positive charge. It is convenient to maintain this fiction in order to avoid awkward statements. Thus we shall think of electric current as flow of positive charge even though in reality it is the flow of negative charge in the opposite direction.

The electric current I passing through a given surface is thus defined as the time rate of flow of electric charge

$$I = dq/dt, \tag{1.9}$$

where dq is the charge crossing the surface in time dt.

The *density of electric current* $\vec{J}$, is defined as the limit

$$\vec{J} = \lim(\Delta I/\Delta S)_{max}, \quad \text{as } \Delta S \to 0. \tag{1.10}$$

Here ΔI is the current passing through an element of area ΔS. There will be a particular orientation of this area, namely one perpendicular to the lines of current flow, for which ΔI is maximum.

For this orientation $\Delta I/\Delta S$ is the magnitude of the average current density, and its limit as ΔS approaches zero is the magnitude J of the current density at the point in question. The direction of the vector is the direction of flow at the point.

For any other orientation of the elementary area

$$\Delta I = J(\Delta S) \cos(\vec{J}, \vec{n}), \tag{1.11}$$

where $(\vec{J}, \vec{n})$ is the angle between $\vec{J}$ and the normal $\vec{n}$ to the area ΔS. If the vector element of area is defined by

$$\overrightarrow{\Delta S} = (\Delta S)\vec{n}, \tag{1.12}$$

we can write equation (1.11) as follows:

$$\Delta I = \vec{J} \cdot \overrightarrow{\Delta S}. \tag{1.13}$$

The current passing through any given area can then be expressed in various ways as

$$I = \int \vec{J} \cdot \overrightarrow{dS} = \int J \cos (\vec{J}, \vec{n}) \, dS = \int J_n \, dS, \tag{1.14}$$

where J_n is the component of $\vec{J}$ in the direction normal to dS.

The MKSA unit of current is the *coulomb per second*, called the *ampere*. The unit of current density is the *ampere per square meter*.

The current passing through a 100-watt incandescent lamp is about 10/11 ampere (effective). If the current in a wire one millimeter square is one ampere, the current density is 10^6 amp/m^2.

1.7   Ohm's law and conductivity σ

In metals and some other conducting media the current density is proportional to the electric intensity $\vec{E}$

$$\vec{J} = \sigma \vec{E}. \tag{1.15}$$

The coefficient of proportionality σ is called the *conductivity* of the medium.

This form of "Ohm's Law" is deduced from experiments with homogeneous conductors of uniform cross section (Figure 1.6). It is found that the current I is directly proportional to the voltage V between the ends and the area S of the cross section, and inversely proportional to the length l,

$$I = \sigma V S/l, \tag{1.16}$$

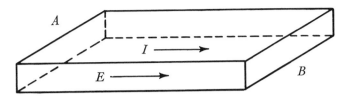

FIGURE 1.6 *Illustrating an experimental verification of Ohm's law.*

where the coefficient of proportionality depends on the substance from which the conductor is made. Since $I/S = J$ and $V/l = E$, we find that equation (1.16) is consistent with equation (1.15). The consequences of equation (1.15) under other varying conditions have been found to agree with measurements.

The ratio $G = I/V$ in equation (1.16) is called the *conductance* of the conductor and its reciprocal $R = V/I$ the *resistance*. Thus for a conductor of uniform cross section

$$G = \sigma S/l, \qquad R = l/\sigma S. \qquad (1.17)$$

The unit of resistance is the *volt per ampere*, called the *ohm*. The unit of conductance, the *ampere per volt*, is called the *mho*. Hence, the unit of conductivity is the *mho per meter*.

Table 1.1 exhibits the wide range of conductivities of various substances

TABLE 1.1

Substance	Conductivity
copper	5.8×10^7
aluminum	3.5×10^7
iron, pure	10^7
carbon (incandescent lamps)	2.5×10^4
sea water	5
soil	0.015
sand	0.002
quartz	8.3×10^{-13}

Very feeble electric fields can maintain strong currents in metals. Quartz, on the other hand, is almost an ideal dielectric (nonconductor).

1.8   Dissipation of energy

When electric charge is moving in a conducting medium, it moves in response to a force. This force is doing work. Consider an element of volume $(\Delta S)(\Delta s)$ with the element of length Δs in the direction of lines of flow and the element of area ΔS at right angles to them. In accordance with equation (1.8) the work done by the field on the charge Δq moving through the distance Δs is $(E \Delta s) \Delta q$. The work done per unit time is $(E \Delta s)(\Delta q / \Delta t) = E J \Delta s \Delta S$. Hence, the work done per unit time per unit volume, that is, the dissipated power per unit volume, is

$$P/v = EJ. \tag{1.18}$$

The principle of conservation of energy demands that this work appear as some form of energy. Experience shows that it appears as heat. Heat is generated whenever an electric current passes through a conducting medium, and it represents the energy consumed in maintaining the electric current. It is said that the latter energy is dissipated in heat. Dissipation of energy is *distributed* throughout the entire volume where there is electric current.

In media obeying Ohm's law equation (1.18) may also be written as

$$P/v = \sigma E^2 = J^2/\sigma. \tag{1.19}$$

Equation (1.18) is more general and it applies even when J is a nonlinear function of E. In nonisotropic media the directions of $\vec{E}$ and $\vec{J}$ are not the same and only that component of $\vec{E}$ is doing work which is in the direction of $\vec{J}$. Hence, for such media

$$P/v = \vec{E} \cdot \vec{J}. \tag{1.20}$$

1.9   Tubes of electric current

Tubes of flow of electric charge or *tubes of electric current* are regions bounded by lines of flow. If the current is steady, there can be no accumulation of charge anywhere in the medium since such an accumulation would develop a time-variable electric field. Thus the same current passes through every cross section of a tube of flow, Figure 1.7

$$\int \vec{J}_1 \cdot \vec{dS}_1 = \int \vec{J}_2 \cdot \vec{dS}_2. \tag{1.21}$$

Also the total current passing through any *closed* surface equals zero

$$\oint \vec{J} \cdot \vec{dS} = \oint J_n \, dS = 0. \qquad (1.22)$$

In later sections we shall develop the concept of a "tube of flow" still further in connection with less tangible field phenomena. It is useful for visualizing abstract mathematical relations.

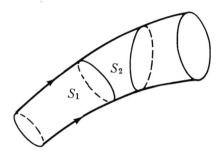

FIGURE 1.7   *A tube of electric current and two of its cross sections.*

1.10   The electric field of a point source of steady electric current

The law of conservation of electric charge requires that if charge is steadily streaming out of a point it must be supplied to this point at the same rate. Also if charge is converging on a point, it must

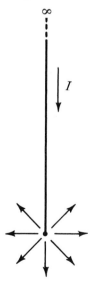

FIGURE 1.8   *A point source of electric current.*

emanate from that point. In Figure 1.8 we have a semi-infinite wire insulated from the surrounding conducting medium except at the end from which the current I in the wire escapes and spreads outward to infinity. If the medium is homogeneous and isotropic, the lines of flow will be radial and the current density J_r will depend only on the distance r from the end of the wire. Hence from equation (1.22), we find

$$4\pi r^2 J_r - I = 0$$

so that in the medium outside the wire

$$J_r = I/4\pi r^2, \quad E_r = J_r/\sigma = I/4\pi\sigma r^2. \tag{1.23}$$

The wire carrying current to the point source need not be straight. The electric field will be the same; but the magnetic field will be altered.

1.11 A dipole source of current or a current element

Equation (1.23) is similar to the equation for the electric intensity of a charged particle. Hence, for two or more point sources of current, we can calculate $\vec{J}$ and $\vec{E}$ by a method suggested in Section 1.3.

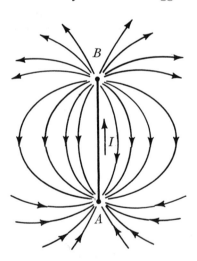

FIGURE 1.9 *A current element consisting of a short wire insulated from the surrounding medium except at the ends A and B. Current emerges from B into the medium and converges to A.*

Consider Figure 1.9 which shows a thin wire of length l, insulated from the surrounding medium except at its ends A and B. Let an electric current I be driven from A to B. This current will emerge from B into the surrounding medium and converge to A. On account of circular symmetry about the axis AB we need consider only the components J_z parallel to AB and J_ρ perpendicular to AB.

Referring to Figure 1.10 and using equation (1.23), we find that

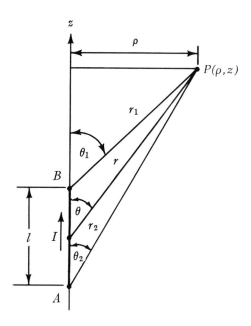

FIGURE 1.10   *A diagram assisting in the calculation of the field of an electric current element.*

the ρ and z components of $\vec{J}$ are

$$J_\rho = \frac{I \sin \theta_1}{4\pi r_1^2} - \frac{I \sin \theta_2}{4\pi r_2^2} \qquad (1.24)$$

and

$$J_z = \frac{I \cos \theta_1}{4\pi r_1^2} - \frac{I \cos \theta_2}{4\pi r_2^2},$$

where

$$r_1 = (r^2 - lr \cos \theta + \tfrac{1}{4}l^2)^{1/2},$$
$$r_2 = (r^2 + lr \cos \theta + \tfrac{1}{4}l^2)^{1/2}, \qquad (1.25)$$

$$r_1 \sin \theta_1 = r_2 \sin \theta_2 = r \sin \theta = \rho,$$

$$r_1 \cos \theta_1 = z - (l/2), \quad r_2 \cos \theta_2 = z + (l/2), \quad r \cos \theta = z.$$

Equations (1.24) become much simpler when l/r approaches zero either because l approaches zero or because r increases indefinitely. In the first instance we shall have a *dipole source* of current, or a *current element*. In the second instance we can say that at large distances the field of any double source of current may be approximated by the field of a dipole source. To obtain the simplified expressions, we shall expand r_1 and r_2 in equations (1.25) in power series of l/r and neglect the terms of order $(l/r)^2$ and higher. For this the binomial series

$$(1 + u)^n = 1 + nu + \frac{n(n-1)}{2!} u^2 + \cdots$$

$$\simeq 1 + nu \quad \text{as} \quad u \to 0$$

is needed. Thus

$$r_1/r = [1 - (l/r) \cos \theta + \tfrac{1}{4}(l/r)^2]^{1/2}$$

$$\simeq 1 - (l/2r) \cos \theta.$$

Hence

$$r_1 \simeq r - \tfrac{1}{2}l \cos \theta,$$

and similarly

$$r_2 \simeq r + \tfrac{1}{2}l \cos \theta.$$

Therefore

$$r_2 - r_1 \simeq l \cos \theta$$

This approximation is quite obvious from the geometric picture.

We now write equations (1.24) as follows:

$$J_\rho = \frac{Ir_1 \sin \theta_1}{4\pi r_1^3} - \frac{Ir_2 \sin \theta_2}{4\pi r_2^3},$$

$$J_z = \frac{Ir_1 \cos \theta_1}{4\pi r_1^3} - \frac{Ir_2 \cos \theta_2}{4\pi r_2^3}.$$

By taking advantage of the last two rows of equations (1.25), we obtain

$$J_\rho = \frac{Ir \sin \theta}{4\pi} \left(\frac{1}{r_1^3} - \frac{1}{r_2^3} \right) = \frac{Ir(r_2^3 - r_1^3) \sin \theta}{4\pi r_1^3 r_2^3}$$

$$= \frac{Ir(r_2 - r_1)(r_2^2 + r_2 r_1 + r_1^2) \sin \theta}{4\pi r_1^3 r_2^3}.$$

As l/r approaches zero, the first-order effect is given by the difference $r_2 - r_1 = l \cos \theta$. In the remaining expressions r_1 and r_2 may be replaced by r.

Similarly,

$$J_z = \frac{Iz}{4\pi}\left(\frac{1}{r_1^3} - \frac{1}{r_2^3}\right) - \frac{Il}{8\pi}\left(\frac{1}{r_1^3} + \frac{1}{r_2^3}\right)$$

which can be analyzed as above.

Thus we find the field of a current element of *moment Il*

$$J_\rho = \frac{3Il \sin \theta \cos \theta}{4\pi r^3}, \qquad J_z = \frac{Il(3 \cos^2 \theta - 1)}{4\pi r^3}.$$

This is also an approximate field for any length l when (l/r) is small compared with unity.

In spherical coordinates (see Appendix I) we have

$$J_r = \quad J_z \cos \theta + J_\rho \sin \theta,$$

$$J_\theta = -J_z \sin \theta + J_\rho \cos \theta,$$

and the field of the current element becomes

$$J_r = \frac{Il \cos \theta}{2\pi r^3}, \qquad J_\theta = \frac{Il \sin \theta}{4\pi r^3}, \qquad (1.26)$$

where r is the distance from the current element and θ is the angle between its axis and the radius.

While the above direct calculation of the current density is straightforward, it is laborious and would involve more work for a larger number of sources. In Chapter 2 we shall introduce the concept of potential which simplifies such calculations and is useful in many other ways.

1.12   Charge distribution in conductors

Conducting bodies are normally electrically neutral. They contain equal numbers of protons and electrons, so distributed that their forces on an external charge cancel and there is no external field. Also, *on the average* there is no internal field. If a quantity of electrons is removed from a body, the body becomes positively charged. It is

negatively charged when there is an excess of electrons. If electrons
are introduced into a conductor, the forces of repulsion will disperse
them. They will keep moving as long as there is an electric intensity
inside the conductor and a tangential component of $\bar{E}$ on the surface.
The normal component of $\bar{E}$ will try to pull them out but unless it is
extremely strong, the electrons will stay on the surface. A *static state*
is reached when the *field inside the conductor and its tangential component on the surface* vanish. Thus in a *static state* the electric field *is
normal* to the surface of any conductor. For example, on a metal
sphere the electrons are distributed uniformly and the field is radial
[Figure 1.11(a)].

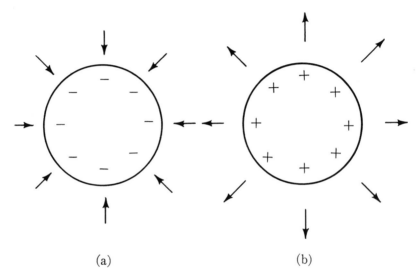

(a)   (b)

FIGURE 1.11   *On a conducting sphere the excess electrons (or their deficiency)
are distributed uniformly at the surface.*

The above argument was based on the excess of electrons. The
same argument applies where there is a deficiency. The protons will
pull the electrons until the positive field inside the conductor disappears so that the deficiency of electrons will exist only on the surface, and there the final distribution will be such that the tangential
component of $\bar{E}$ is zero [Figure 1.11(b)].

If a neutral conductor is introduced in an electric field, the free
electrons are displaced, Figure 1.12(a), in such a way that the
electric intensity due to their displacement *within the conducting
body* is equal and opposite to the original or "impressed" field. Also
the tangential component of the electric field due to the displaced

charge is equal and opposite to the impressed tangential component. This phenomenon is known as "electrostatic induction."

If we introduce a positive charge (electron deficiency) equal to that displaced by the field in Figure 1.12(a), the total displaced charge is then positive and is distributed more densely on one end of the conductor [Figure 1.12(b)].

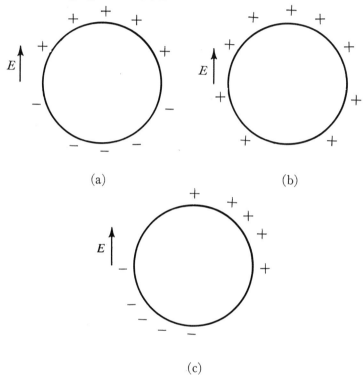

(a)   (b)

(c)

FIGURE 1.12   *The displacement of charge under the influence of an electric field: (a) on a neutral sphere in an isotropic medium, (b) on a positively charged sphere, (c) on a neutral sphere in a nonisotropic medium.*

If the medium outside a metal sphere is crystalline, the electrons are usually displaced in some direction other than that of $\vec{E}$ [Figure 1.12(c)], except when $\vec{E}$ is along a "principal" axis of the medium.

1.13   Faraday's law of electrostatic induction

Faraday discovered that if a charge q is enclosed by a neutral metal sphere, an equal charge of the same sign appears on the external surface of the sphere. He found that the external field is symmetric whether the sphere is concentric with the enclosed charge or not (Figure 1.13). Also, if the charge on the external surface is removed from the sphere by momentarily grounding it, a charge equal and opposite to the enclosed charge will be left on the sphere. This is true regardless of the dielectric (nonconducting) medium surrounding the charge q.

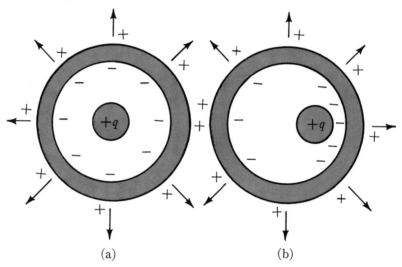

(a)   (b)

FIGURE 1.13 *Illustrating Faraday's experiments with displacement of charge.*

For his experiments, he formed each sphere from two hemispheres so that he could easily enclose a charged body suspended from an insulating string. An electric field was detected with a test charge. The equality of two charges of opposite signs can be easily established by letting them combine and neutralize each other. The equality of like charges can be established by letting them combine with equal charges of opposite sign. And it is always easy to obtain equal and opposite charges.

Faraday's observations are explained in view of present-day knowledge about free electrons in conductors. The enclosed charge will either repel or attract the electrons, depending on its sign. Hence the like charge will always be on the external surface and the opposite charge on the internal surface. When the displacement of charge has taken place, there will be no field in the metallic shell. Hence the charge on the external surface is free to distribute itself according to its own forces.

The fact that the displaced charge is equal to the enclosed charge can be predicted from Coulomb's law. Conversely, *Coulomb's law can be derived from Faraday's law of electrostatic induction.*

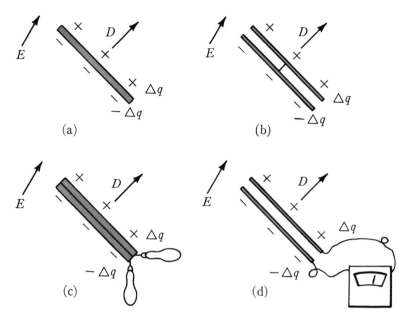

FIGURE 1.14 *Illustrating the definition of the density of electric displacement at a point in an electric field.*

1.14 Electric flux or displacement density $\vec{D}$

The quantity of electric charge displaced on a conductor under the influence of a given electric intensity $\vec{E}$ depends on the area of the conductor exposed to the field, on its shape, and on the surrounding medium. The effect of area can be established by experiments with thin metal plates. Figure 1.14 shows a solid metal plate (a), two thin metal plates connected with a wire (b), two separate metal plates in contact with each other, each having an insulating handle (c), and two metal plates connected through a device (ballistic galvanometer) capable of measuring the time integral of electric current $I(t)$ passing through it or to total charge Δq that has passed through it (d). If the device is connected at time $t = 0$ and if at $t = T$ an essentially static condition has been reached (the interval happens to be extremely short), then

$$\Delta q = \int_0^T I(t) \, dt. \tag{1.27}$$

This quantity is illustrated in Figure 1.15 by the area under the curve representing $I(t)$ as a function of time. In all cases the charge moves until the field in the metal plates (a) and (c) and between

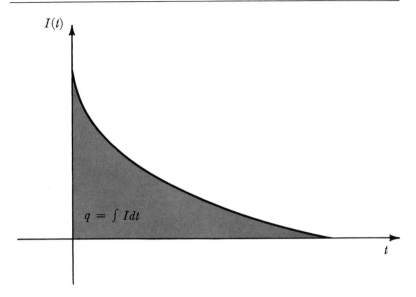

$I(t)$

$q = \int I dt$

t

FIGURE 1.15 *Graphical representation of the time integral of electric current by the area under the curve representing the current $I(t)$ as a function of time t.*

the metal plates (b) and (d) is reduced to zero by the displaced charge. In case (b) the plates can be disconnected while still in the field. In (c) the plates can be separated while still in the field. In either case the displaced charge is trapped and can be measured. Likewise it can be measured in the case (d) by closing the switch connecting originally neutral plates to the device measuring the time integral of electric current. In the latter case an ammeter may be used to measure the time rate of change of the displaced charge if $\bar{E}$ is varying with time, (slowly enough).

With these experiments it is possible to establish the following:

1. The displaced charge Δq depends on the orientation of the test plate.
2. Δq is proportional to the area ΔS of the test plate.
3. When the test plate is perpendicular to a certain unit vector $\bar{d}$, the positive charge displaced in the direction $\bar{d}$ (and the equal negative charge in the opposite direction) is maximum
4. The charge displaced in any other orientation given by the unit normal $\bar{n}$ equals this maximum displaced charge multiplied by the cosine of the angle between $\bar{n}$ and $\bar{d}$.
5. The displaced charge depends not only on the electric

intensity $\vec{E}$ but also on the medium. In pure water, for instance, the displaced charge would be about eighty times as large as in air.

In view of the first four experimental results we conclude that for a complete quantitative description of an electric field we need another vector $\vec{D}$ whose magnitude D is the maximum displaced charge per unit area

$$D = \lim(\Delta q_{max}/\Delta S), \quad \text{as} \quad \Delta S \to 0, \tag{1.28}$$

and whose direction is the direction in which the displaced charge is maximum.

For any other direction $\vec{n}$ the charge Δq displaced across a plate of area ΔS is

$$\Delta q = \vec{D} \cdot \vec{\Delta S} = D \cos (\vec{D}, \vec{n}) \Delta S = D_n \Delta S. \tag{1.29}$$

The unit of $\vec{D}$ is the *coulomb per square meter*.

There is no complete agreement on the modern name for the vector $\vec{D}$. The classical name is "displacement." Another extensively used term is "electric flux density," which suggests the physical fact that D expresses electric charge *displaced per unit* area. We are in favor of calling $\vec{D}$ *electric displacement density* at a given point of the field, thus departing from classical tradition. The advantage of using this term becomes clear when we consider the time rate of change of $\vec{D}$, $\partial \vec{D}/\partial t$ which is expressed in amperes per square meter. In computing magnetic fields produced by electric currents, the quantity $\partial \vec{D}/\partial t$ must be added to the density $\vec{J}$ of the conduction current, and the surface integral of $\partial \vec{D}/\partial t$ must be added to the true electric current. For this reason Maxwell introduced the concept of *displacement current*. By following the classical tradition of calling $\partial \vec{D}/\partial t$ "displacement current," we are adding this "current" to the density of conduction current. This is an awkward use of words. Thus the following terminology is more appropriate.

1. The vector $\vec{D}$ is the *(electric) displacement density*.
2. The vector $\partial \vec{D}/\partial t$ is the *density of displacement current*.
3. The surface integral

$$\Psi = \int \vec{D} \cdot \vec{dS} = \int D_n \, dS \tag{1.30}$$

is the *electric displacement* through the surface of integration (or electric flux).

4. The time rate of change of the electric displacement through a surface is the *(electric) displacement current*

through the surface

$$I_d = \frac{\partial \Psi}{\partial t} = \frac{\partial}{\partial t} \int \vec{D} \cdot \vec{dS} = \frac{\partial}{\partial t} \int D_n \, dS.$$

1.15   Relations between $\vec{D}$ and $\vec{E}$

In free space and in many media $\vec{D}$ is proportional to $\vec{E}$,

$$\vec{D} = \epsilon \vec{E}. \tag{1.31}$$

Such media are called *isotropic*. The coefficient of proportionality ϵ is called the *dielectric constant* of the medium.

In crystalline media where $\vec{D}$ and $\vec{E}$ usually have different directions, the Cartesian components of $\vec{D}$ are linear functions of the Cartesian components of $\vec{E}$.

The unit of ϵ is the *coulomb per volt per meter*. The *coulomb per volt* is the unit of capacitance and is called the *farad*. Hence the unit of ϵ is the *farad per meter*, the same unit as for capacitance per unit length.

In the case of a point charge or a charged metal sphere in an isotropic medium both $\vec{E}$ and $\vec{D}$ are radial. From Faraday's experiment in which the metal sphere is concentric with the enclosed charge and does not alter the geometry of the original field, we have

$$4\pi r^2 D_r = q, \qquad D_r = q/4\pi r^2. \tag{1.32}$$

From this and equation (1.31) we find

$$E_r = q/4\pi\epsilon r^2 \tag{1.33}$$

for a point charge and for an isolated metal sphere.

The dielectric constant of free space is denoted by ϵ_0 and its value is

$$\epsilon_0 = 8.854 \times 10^{-12} \simeq (1/36\pi) 10^{-9} \text{ farad/meter}. \tag{1.34}$$

The ratio

$$\epsilon_r = \epsilon/\epsilon_0 \tag{1.35}$$

is the *relative dielectric constant* of the medium.

Table 1.2 gives relative dielectric constants for a few media.

TABLE 1.2

Media	Relative dielectric constants
Quartz	$\epsilon_r = 4.5$
Sand	$\epsilon_r = 10$
Dry soil	$\epsilon_r = 10$
Wet soil	$\epsilon_r = 30$
Sea water	$\epsilon_r = 78$

In the case of soil and sand, the dielectric constants will vary of course, depending on the sample; the above values are indicative of the order of magnitude only.

1.16 Electric dipole

A pair of equal and opposite charges q and $-q$ (Figure 1.16) when separated by a small distance l constitute an *electric dipole* of *moment* ql. Ideally, q is infinitely large and l infinitely small in such a way that the moment ql is finite. Equations (1.23), (1.32), and (1.33)

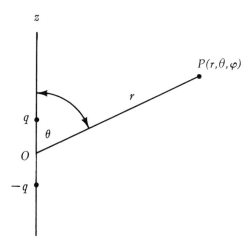

FIGURE 1.16 *An electric dipole along the z axis at the origin of the spherical coordinate system.*

exhibit the analogy between the current I and the charge q as sources of fields in infinite conducting media on the one hand, and in infinite dielectric media on the other. Hence, by analogy with equation (1.26), we have at point P

$$D_r = \frac{ql \cos \theta}{2\pi r^3}, \qquad D_\theta = \frac{ql \sin \theta}{4\pi r^3}$$

$$(1.36)$$

$$E_r = \frac{ql \cos \theta}{2\pi \epsilon r^3}, \qquad E_\theta = \frac{ql \sin \theta}{4\pi \epsilon r^3}.$$

1.17 Magnetic flux density $\vec{B}$

For a quantitative description of electric fields in conducting media, we have introduced two vectors: the electric intensity $\vec{E}$ acting on electric charge and the resulting current density $\vec{J}$. These are obviously different physical quantities. For nonconducting (dielectric) media we have also defined two quantities: the electric intensity $\vec{E}$ and the electric displacement density $\vec{D}$. From our operational definitions of $\vec{D}$ and $\vec{J}$, we will prove that $\partial\vec{D}/\partial t$, the density of displacement current, is related to $\vec{J}$.

Although the operational definitions of $\vec{E}$ and $\vec{D}$ are different, $\vec{D}$ can be defined in terms of $\vec{E}$ on the basis of present-day knowledge about the constitution of matter. Defining $\vec{D}$ in terms of $\vec{E}$ requires a knowledge of appropriate physical theories and considerable mathematical detail. However, such a definition loses sight of the macroscopic meaning of $\vec{D}$, especially in vacuum. Similarly $\vec{J}$ can be defined in terms of $\vec{E}$ and microscopic properties of matter. In effect these definitions are equivalent to a theoretical calculation of the relative dielectric constant ϵ_r and the conductivity σ. In the approach we have adopted, ϵ_r and σ are experimental constants.

In the case of magnetic fields it is also convenient to define two quantities for each point of the field: the magnetic flux density $\vec{B}$ and the magnetic intensity $\vec{H}$. There are two physical aspects to $\vec{B}$. One is particularly important in particle physics and electronics and the other is more prominent in field theory and its applications. In particle dynamics $\vec{B}$ is defined in terms of the force acting on a moving charged particle and thus is analogous to $\vec{E}$. In Maxwell's equations governing the behavior of fields $\vec{H}$ is analogous to $\vec{E}$ and $\vec{B}$ is analogous to $\vec{D}$.

First we shall define $\vec{B}$ from the point of view of particle dynamics. In a pure magnetic field (around a permanent magnet, for instance) no force is exerted on a stationary charge q. When the charge is moving, the force on it is proportional to the product of its speed v and the charge q. The force depends also on a direction of motion. There are two opposite directions such that no force is exerted on a charge moving in these directions. A magnetic needle aligns itself along these directions. Let $\bar{b}$ be a unit vector along this line, in the direction from the south-seeking to the north-seeking end. When the charge is moving in any other direction, the force $\bar{F}_m$ acting on it is perpendicular to this direction and to the unit vector $\bar{b}$. See Figure 1.17(a).

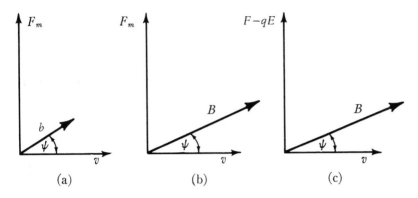

FIGURE 1.17   *An illustration of the force acting on a moving electric charge.*

The magnitude of this force is proportional to the product of qv and the sine of the angle between the velocity $\bar{v}$ and the vector $\bar{b}$. The coefficient of proportionality is defined as the magnitude B of the *magnetic flux density* at the point occupied by q so that $\bar{B} = B\bar{b}$.

In other words, in a pure magnetic field the force on a moving charge is [Figure 1.17(b)]

$$\bar{F}_m = q\bar{v} \times \bar{B}. \tag{1.37}$$

When there is an electric field as well, this equation gives the difference between the total force $\bar{F}$ acting on the particle and the force $q\bar{E}$ which would have been exerted on the particle if it were stationary [Figure 1.17(c)]. Hence, the total force is

$$\bar{F} = q\bar{E} + q\bar{v} \times \bar{B}. \tag{1.38}$$

In light of this operational definition of $\bar{B}$ the name *magnetic flux density* appears to be ill-suited. It might have been more proper to call it "magnetic field strength" or "magnetic intensity." On the other hand, *magnetic flux density* is well suited when we consider the second aspect of $\vec{B}$, which is of primary importance in electromagnetic field theory.

Although from this point of view $\vec{B}$ and $\vec{E}$ are analogous, their physical dimensions are different and they are measured in different units. It is possible to define another quantity

$$\vec{G} = c\vec{B},$$

where c is the speed of light in vacuum, which has the same dimensions as $\vec{E}$ and, therefore, would be measured in volts per meter. By introducing this quantity in equation (1.38) we have

$$\vec{F} = q\vec{E} + q(\vec{v}/c) \times \vec{G}.$$

This quantity $\vec{G}$ would have certain advantages over $\vec{B}$ in particle dynamics. "Gaussian field strength" might be a suitable name for it, to distinguish it from the magnetic flux density $\vec{B}$ and from the magnetic intensity $\vec{H}$.

1.18   The second aspect of $\vec{B}$ and the Faraday-Maxwell law

In accordance with equation (1.37), the free electrons in a conducting wire moving in a magnetic field will experience a force and will be displaced in such a way that the electric intensity

$$\vec{E}^i = \vec{v} \times \vec{B} \qquad\qquad (1.39)$$

induced *in the wire* by the motion of the wire in the magnetic field is annihilated by the electric intensity of the displaced charge. Note that $\vec{E}^i$ exists *only in the moving wire* and is not due to any charge. The displaced charge, on the other hand, creates a distributed electric field. The moving wire is a simple kind of "electric generator" and is a prototype of practical electric generators at low frequencies.

Consider Figure 1.18(a) in which the wire MN, its velocity $\vec{v}$, and magnetic flux density $\vec{B}$ are mutually perpendicular. Assume that $\vec{B}$ is pointing out of the paper and does not vary either in time or in space. Then the induced electric intensity is along the wire, pointing downward. The induced voltage V^i_{MN} causes an equal and opposite voltage V_{NM} due to the displaced charge

$$V_{NM} = V^i_{MN} = Blv, \qquad\qquad (1.40)$$

where l is the length of the wire. If MN is sliding along stationary parallel wires connected to a voltmeter, the induced voltage can be measured. If these leads are connected to a long-period ballistic

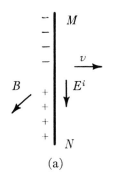

(a)

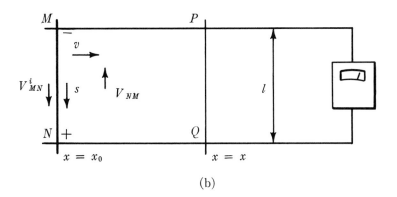

(b)

FIGURE 1.18 *A wire moving in a magnetic field.*

galvanometer as shown in Figure 1.18(b), the *time integral of the induced voltage* can be measured. This time integral is

$$\int_{t_0}^{t} V_{MN}^{i} \, dt = \int_{t_0}^{t} Blv \, dt = \int_{x_0}^{x} Bl \, dx,$$

where MN is at $x = x_0$ when $t = t_0$ and at $x = x$ when $t = t$. Note that the time integral is the same regardless of the speed of the wire. Since we have assumed that B does not depend on x,

$$\int_{t_0}^{t} V_{MN}^{i} \, dt = Bl(x - x_0) = BS, \tag{1.41}$$

where S is the area swept by the wire.

The quantity

$$\Phi = BS \tag{1.42}$$

is called the *magnetic flux* passing through the area of the rectangle $MNQPM$. The time integral of the induced voltage is seen to equal the magnetic flux "cut" by the moving wire.

Suppose now that the magnetic field is static but that B varies from point to point. The induced voltage will be the line integral of the induced intensity

$$V_{MN}^i = \int_{MN} E^i\, ds = \int_0^s Bv\, ds$$

and its time integral will be

$$\int_{t_0}^t V_{MN}^i\, dt = \int_{x_0}^x \int_0^s B\, ds\, dx,$$

where s is taken along the wire. Since the integrand on the right is now by definition (1.42) the magnetic flux through an element of area $dS = ds\, dx$, the integral itself is the magnetic flux through $MNQPM$ which is cut by the moving wire

$$\Phi = \int B\, dS.$$

Let us now remove the remaining restrictions and show that

$$\int_{t_0}^t V_{MN}^i\, dt = \Phi, \tag{1.43}$$

where

$$\Phi = \int B_n\, dS = \int \bar{B} \cdot d\bar{S} \tag{1.44}$$

even when $\bar{B}$ and MN are not perpendicular to $\bar{v}$ (Figure 1.19). Vector $\bar{B}$ can be resolved in two components: $\bar{B}_n$ normal to the plane defined by MN and $\bar{v}$; $\bar{B}_p$ parallel to the plane. The force exerted by the latter on charge in the moving wire is perpendicular to the wire and contributes nothing to the voltage along the wire. The induced intensity due to the normal component is $\bar{v} \times \bar{B}_n \sin \vartheta$. Its magnitude is $vB_n \sin \vartheta$. Hence

$$V_{MN}^i = \int_{MN} vB_n \sin \vartheta\, ds,$$

and

$$\int_{t_0}^t V_{MN}^i\, dt = \int_{NQ} \int_{MN} B_n \sin \vartheta\, ds\, dx,$$

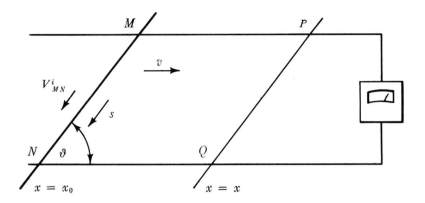

FIGURE 1.19   *A wire moving in a magnetic field.*

where ds is an element of length along MN. Since $\sin \vartheta \, ds \, dx$ equals the area dS of an elementary parallelogram, *the integral on the right is the magnetic flux*, equation (1.44), *crossing the area $MNQPM$ and which is cut by MN in time $t - t_0$. The induced voltage is the time rate with which magnetic flux is cut by the moving wire.*

Let us now calculate the line integral

$$\oint E_s^i \, ds$$

of the induced electric intensity round a conducting loop moving with a velocity $\bar{v}$, illustrated in Figure 1.20. Assume that the integration is in the counterclockwise direction when the positive direction for the magnetic flux through the loop is chosen toward the reader. Considering two elements on the opposite sides of the loop,

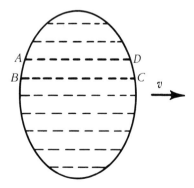

FIGURE 1.20   *A conducting loop moving in a magnetic field.*

AB and CD, we note that V^i_{AB} equals the rate with which the flux is *leaving* the loop while V^i_{DC} equals the rate with which the flux is *entering* the loop so that the *net contribution* $V^i_{AB} + V^i_{CD} = V^i_{AB} - V^i_{DC}$ *to the counterclockwise voltage* equals *the time rate of decrease in* the magnetic flux Φ, linked with the loop. Thus

$$\oint E^i_s \, ds = -\frac{d\Phi}{dt} \tag{1.45}$$

is the voltage induced in the loop if the loop is moving in the field of a stationary magnet. Since motion is relative, equation (1.45) gives the voltage induced in *a stationary loop* by a moving magnet. This is indeed the case. A moving magnet exerts a force on any stationary charge. Thus when the magnetic field at various points is varying with time, there will be generated an electric field and its line integral round a closed curve will be

$$\oint E_s \, ds = -\frac{\partial\Phi}{\partial t} = -\frac{\partial}{\partial t}\int B_n \, dS, \tag{1.46}$$

where the surface integration on the right may be extended over *any surface*, the edge of which is the closed curve of integration on the left. The partial derivative is used here because $\vec{B}$ is now a function of independent space and time variables. This equation was

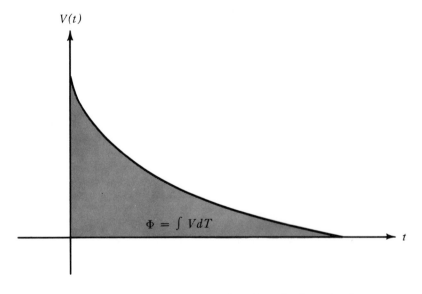

$V(t)$

$\Phi = \int V dT$

t

FIGURE 1.21 *The time integral of the voltage is shown by the area under the curve. The voltage as a function of time is represented by $V(t)$.*

formulated by Maxwell to express experimental results obtained by Faraday. We shall call it the *Faraday-Maxwell Law*.

From equations (1.43) and (1.44) we observe that the unit of magnetic flux is the volt-second. This unit is called the *weber*. Hence the unit of magnetic flux density $\vec{B}$ is the *volt-second per square meter* or the *weber per square meter*. This unit is too large for practical magnetic fields. A convenient subunit is the *gauss* equal to 10^{-4} weber/m² or one weber per square hectometer.

Referring to equations (1.43) and (1.44), we see that with the aid of a ballistic galvanometer we can measure the magnetic flux linked with a small loop by measuring the *time integral* (Figure 1.21) *of the voltage induced in the loop*. Hence we can measure the flux density, that is, the flux per unit area of the loop. This will give the component of $\vec{B}$ normal to the area. We can also determine the particular orientation of the loop for which the flux density is maximum. This will give the magnitude B of magnetic flux density vector, and the normal to the loop will give the direction. This is often used as the operational definition of $\vec{B}$ because it is easier to apply in practice than the one given in the preceding section.

1.19 Magnetic intensity $\vec{H}$

It is an experimental fact that in free space and in some other homogeneous media the vector $\vec{B}$ in the magnetic field around a straight filament of electric current I is tangential to circles coaxial with the filament as represented in Figure 1.22(a). At distances small compared to the length of the filament the magnitude of this vector varies inversely as the distance ρ from the axis of the filament. This suggests that for an infinitely long filament $B_\phi = B$ would vary inversely as ρ for all values of ρ. Thus the product of B_ϕ and the length of the circumference is independent of ρ. It is an experimental fact that *this product is proportional to the current*

$$2\pi\rho B_\phi = \mu I. \tag{1.47}$$

The coefficient of proportionality μ is called the *permeability* of the medium. The permeability of vacuum is denoted by μ_0 and its magnitude is

$$\mu_0 = 4\pi 10^{-7} \frac{\text{volt-second}}{\text{meter-ampere}} \quad \text{or} \quad \frac{\text{henry}}{\text{meter}}. \tag{1.48}$$

In such media the line integral of $\vec{B}$ along *any* closed curve en-

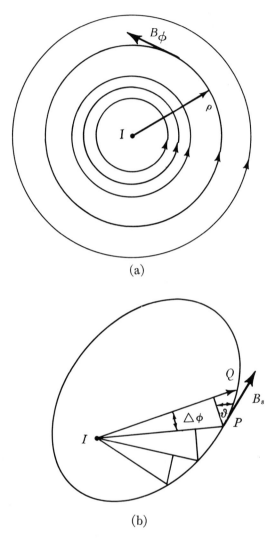

(a)

(b)

FIGURE 1.22   (a) *The magnetic lines of force around a straight current filament; (b) Assisting in the explanation of Ampere's law.*

circling I is proportional to I, Figure 1.22(b),

$$\oint \vec{B} \cdot \vec{ds} = \oint B_s \, ds = \mu I. \qquad (1.49)$$

That this is so for any broken line made up of segments of radii and circles coaxial with the filament is obvious. The radial segments contribute nothing to the integral and the contributions from the circular arcs depend only on the subtended angles $\Delta\phi$. Any curve in a plane normal to the current filament is the limit of such a broken curve and equation (1.49) applies to this limiting curve too. We can also argue that the component of $\vec{B}$ tangential to the curve is $B_s = B_\phi \cos \vartheta$ while the element of length of $ds = \rho \, d\phi/\cos \vartheta$. Hence, the product is $B_s \, ds = B_\phi \rho \, d\phi$. From equation (1.47) we find $B_\phi \rho = \mu I/2\pi$ and the integral of $d\phi$ around a closed curve encircling the filament is 2π. Hence, equation (1.49).

A similar argument shows that equation (1.49) applies to all curves encircling I and not only to curves in planes normal to I. For those closed curves which do not encircle I,

$$\oint B_s \, ds = 0. \tag{1.50}$$

We now introduce another vector, the *magnetic intensity*

$$\vec{H} = \vec{B}/\mu \tag{1.51}$$

which enables us to write equation (1.49) in the form

$$\oint H_s \, ds = I. \tag{1.52}$$

The vector $\vec{H}$ is related directly to the current generating the magnetic field and we might conjecture that equation (1.52) applies to nonhomogeneous media and to nonisotropic media in which $\vec{B}$ is not tangential to circles coaxial with the current. But in order to verify equation (1.52) *experimentally* for such media we need an operational definition of magnetic intensity $\vec{H}$ which is independent of the definition of the magnetic flux density $\vec{B}$.

1.20 Operational definition of $\vec{H}$

Consider a *solenoid*, that is, a closely wound coil carrying current I [Figure 1.23(a)] in air. Suppose that the solenoid is straight and long compared to its diameter. Experiments show that the magnetic field inside such a solenoid is uniform except when the measurements are made close to the winding where there are gaps in the current or near the ends of the solenoid. If the solenoid closely approximates a continuous sheet of circulating current [Figure 1.23(b)], a nearly uniform field is obtained. Experiments further

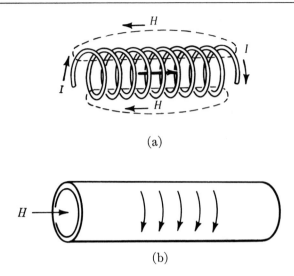

(a)

(b)

FIGURE 1.23   *Assisting in an operational definition of magnetic intensity $\bar{H}$.*

show that a magnetic needle tends to align itself parallel to the axis of the solenoid, and that the torque on the magnet depends only on the *circulating current C per unit length of the solenoid*. This torque is independent of the length of the solenoid, of the shape of the cross section, of the area of the cross section, of the number of turns per unit length N, and of the actual current I_w in the wire as long as $C = NI_w$ is kept constant.

We now define the magnitude H of the *magnetic intensity* inside the solenoid as the *circulating current per unit length*,

$$H \equiv C = NI_w. \tag{1.53}$$

The direction of $\bar{H}$ is taken to be the direction of the force on the north-seeking end of the magnet, that is, parallel to the axis of the solenoid in the direction of the advance of a right-handed screw turned in the direction of circulating current. The unit of $\bar{H}$ is the unit of current per unit length, that is, the *ampere per meter*. Thus the magnetic intensity $\bar{H}$ is directly related to the electric current which generates the field in a laboratory. Any device for measuring $\bar{H}$ can be calibrated by using definition (1.53).

Conceptually, we always relate the magnetic intensity at any point of any magnetic field to the field inside a solenoid. For example, in a solid (which may be nonisotropic), we imagine a thin tunnel with a solenoid in it. There is a circulating current C per unit length of the tunnel for which the component of the magnetic field in the direction of the tunnel will be reduced to zero no matter how this field is being detected. By definition, the $\bar{H}$ component of the field in the solid in the direction of the tunnel is equal and opposite to $\bar{H}$ generated by the solenoid. For any solid, there is a direction of the tunnel for which the generated H will be maximum. Thus we obtain both the magnitude and the direction of $\bar{H}$ in the medium.

When $\bar{B}$ and $\bar{H}$ are defined independently, the relation between them may be obtained either experimentally or from the physical theory of matter. Thus it is found that in some media they are proportional as in equation (1.51) for all values of $\bar{H}$. In other media the proportionality holds only for small values of $\bar{H}$ and the equation becomes nonlinear for the large values. Yet, in other media, the Cartesian components of $\bar{B}$ are linear functions of the Cartesian components of $\bar{H}$.

In a solenoid with 10 turns/cm and with I equal to one ampere, $H = 1000$ amp/meter. With an air-core, $B = 4\pi 10^{-4}$ weber/m² or 4π gauss. This is a rather weak flux density. In the earth's magnetic field B varies from 0.3 gauss at the equator to 0.6 gauss at a pole. In strong sunlight at the surface of the earth, $H = 1.89$ amp/m (effective), and $B = 0.022$ gauss. Flux density of one weber/m², or 10 000 gauss, is strong. The density of 100 000 gauss is very strong.

1.21   Magnetomotive force U and Ampere's law

The line integral of the magnetic intensity along a curve AB is called the *magnetomotive force* along AB,

$$U_{AB} = \int \bar{H} \cdot d\bar{s} = \int H_s \, ds. \qquad (1.54)$$

Experiments indicate that under all circumstances involving closed steady currents, the magnetomotive force round any closed curve equals the total current I linked with the curve

$$\oint H_s \, ds = I = \int J_n \, dS. \qquad (1.55)$$

In this equation the curve of integration on the left is the edge of the surface of integration on the right. It is assumed that, when the handle of a right-handed screw is turned in the direction of integration round the edge, chosen as positive, the screw advances in the positive direction of the normal to the surface of integration. *This is Ampere's Law.*

1.22　Magnetic fields of a point source and a double source of current in an infinite conducting medium

In Section 1.10 we obtained the current density of the field of a point source in an infinite conducting medium. See Figure 1.8. Assume now that the point source is at the origin of the coordinate system (Appendix I, Figures 1 and 2) and that the insulated wire carrying the current to the source is along the positive z axis. On account of circular symmetry the magnetic lines are circles coaxial with the z axis and the magnetic intensity H_ϕ is independent of the angle ϕ. Applying equation (1.55) to a typical circle of latitude of radius $\rho = r \sin \theta$ and to the spherical cap of radius r which surmounts this circle and noting that the radial current density outside the wire is given by equation (1.23), we have

$$2\pi r \sin \theta\, H_\phi = -I + \int_0^\theta \int_0^{2\pi} J_r r^2 \sin \theta\, d\phi\, d\theta$$

$$= -I + \int_0^\theta \int_0^{2\pi} (I/4\pi) \sin \theta\, d\phi\, d\theta$$

$$= -\tfrac{1}{2}(1 + \cos \theta)I.$$

Therefore,

$$H_\phi = -\frac{I(1 + \cos \theta)}{4\pi r \sin \theta}. \tag{1.56}$$

Similarly, we can calculate the magnetic intensity of a current element of moment Il, situated along the z axis at the origin, from J_r given by equation (1.26). Thus

$$2\pi r \sin \theta\, H_\phi = \int_0^\theta \int_0^{2\pi} \frac{Il \cos \theta \sin \theta\, d\phi\, d\theta}{2\pi r} = \frac{Il \sin^2 \theta}{2r}$$

and

$$H_\phi = \frac{Il \sin \theta}{4\pi r^2}. \tag{1.57}$$

1.23　Displacement current and the Ampere-Maxwell law

Steady electric currents can exist only in closed conducting circuits and there is no ambiguity in equation (1.55). On the other hand, the conducting paths do not have to be closed to permit currents varying with time. If a neutral wire is brought into an electric field, the two ends will become oppositely charged (Figure 1.24) and temporary electric currents must have existed during the period of displacement of charge. If the wire is in an electric field varying with time, the flow of charge in it will be taking place continuously. Moving charges generate a magnetic field. In this case, however, the line integral of $\vec{H}$ cannot be given by equation (1.55) as it stands since the closed curve of integration is not "linked" with an open wire. A moving charged particle generates a magnetic field and again equation (1.55) can not be applied as it stands. Maxwell introduced a concept of *displacement current*, which when added to the conduction current constitutes the *total current*. The total current is continuous in space so that equation (1.55) can be applied without ambiguity. Equation (1.55), modified to apply to this total current, represents correctly what happens in time-varying fields.

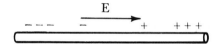

FIGURE 1.24   *A wire in an electric field.*

Displacement "current" is not a real current in the sense of moving charge. To explain the meaning of this concept we shall imagine a few hypothetical simple situations even though it would be impossible to realize them in a laboratory. Subsequently, we can consider some situations that can be realized. Suppose that at the instant $t = 0$ we begin to drive steady electric current I in a semi-infinite wire, Figure 1.25, in a nonconducting medium, toward the end O. Electric charge

$$q = \int_0^t I \, dt = It \tag{1.58}$$

will start accumulating at point O. Equations (1.32) and (1.33) give

$$E_r = \frac{q}{4\pi\epsilon r^2} = \frac{It}{4\pi\epsilon r^2},$$

$$\tag{1.59}$$

$$D_r = \frac{q}{4\pi r^2} = \frac{It}{4\pi r^2}.$$

The electric field is increasing with time and, hence, the force driving the current will have to increase with time. The time derivative of the radial displacement density

$$\frac{\partial D_r}{\partial t} = \frac{I}{4\pi r^2} \tag{1.60}$$

is seen to be constant and its value is given by the same expression as the conduction current density J_r [equation (1.23)] for the case when the medium is conducting. The conduction current in the wire is now "continued" as the radial *displacement current* of density $\partial D_r/\partial t$ in the medium outside. We now modify equation (1.55) which gives the magnetomotive force around a closed curve by including this displacement current density. Thus we obtain the *Ampere-Maxwell law*,

$$\oint H_s \, ds = \int \left(J_n + \frac{\partial D_n}{\partial t}\right) dS. \tag{1.61}$$

Ampere is given the credit for equation (1.55), which is correct when the conduction current is steady and closed. Maxwell is given the credit for introducing displacement current and thus making the equation applicable to time-varying currents in either closed or open conductors.

Using equation (1.60), we now find an expression for the magnetic intensity H_ϕ,

$$H_\phi = -\frac{I(1 + \cos\theta)}{4\pi r \sin\theta} \tag{1.62}$$

of the field generated by a semi-infinite uniform current filament in a dielectric medium. This expression is, of course, identical with expression (1.56) for the same filament in a conducting medium.

From equation (1.36) for an electric dipole of moment ql, we obtain the density of the displacement current at point P in the field of the dipole, Figure 1.26,

$$\frac{\partial D_r}{\partial t} = \frac{\dot{q}l \cos\theta}{2\pi r^3}, \qquad \frac{\partial D_\theta}{\partial t} = \frac{\dot{q}l \sin\theta}{4\pi r^3}. \tag{1.63}$$

Compare these equations with equations (1.25) for the current density of a double source in a conducting medium, from which equation (1.57) for the magnetic field was obtained. A comparison shows that the magnetic intensity of a current element of moment

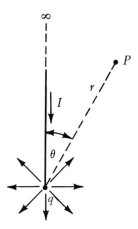

FIGURE 1.25 *A semi-infinite direct-current filament in a dielectric medium and an accumulated charge $q = \int^t I\, dt$.*

$Il = (dq/dt)l$ in a dielectric medium is

$$H_\phi = \frac{Il \sin\theta}{4\pi r^2}. \tag{1.64}$$

The concept of displacement current in vacuum is less tangible than the concept of electric current in a conducting medium where charged material particles are in motion. The most tangible aspect of displacement current is: *If two parallel conducting plates are placed in a time-varying electric field and connected to an ammeter* [Figure 1.14(d)] *there will be an indication of current on the ammeter which can be accepted as the measure of the displacement current in the space occupied by the plates when the plates are removed.* Similarly, the electric intensity $\vec{E}$ is detected only where an electric charge is introduced into the field. In material media *a part of displacement current,* the *polarization current,* consists of motion of bound electrons; but the remainder is just as intangible as displacement current in vacuum.

By analogy, with tubes of true current flow, which are illustrated in Figure 1.7, Section 1.9, we can think of tubes of displacement current and tubes of displacement as regions bounded by lines tangential to $\bar{D}$. The tubes start on positive charges and end on negative charges or at infinity, or they start at infinity and end on negative charges. They may also be completely closed tubes, like doughnuts. The displacement and the displacement current through every cross section of a given tube are the same. The total displacement (or electric flux) through any surface enclosing a charge q equals q. *The displacement* *current through this surface is $\dot{q}$ and thus is equal to the time rate with which the charge is entering the volume enclosed by the surface.* If no charge is enclosed, the tubes of displacement enter the volume and then leave it. The net displacement through such a surface is zero.

Displacement currents in *one* direction are either very feeble or of very short duration. For example, if E increases at the rate of 1 volt/m/sec, the displacement current density in vacuum is $\dot{D} = \epsilon_0 \dot{E} = 8.854 \times 10^{-12}$ amp/m² = 8.854 micro-microamp/m². If E increases at the rate of one volt per micro-microsecond, $\dot{D} = 8.854$ amp/m². This rate of increase cannot be maintained steadily for more than a small fraction of a second since the electric generator would have to develop tremendous internal forces to drive the charge which creates the field.

On the other hand, if the field is alternating, then $E = E_a \sin 2\pi ft$ and $\dot{D} = \epsilon_0 2\pi f E_a \cos 2\pi ft$ so that for high frequencies $\dot{D}$ may be fairly substantial. If $f = 10^{10}$ cycles/sec and $E_a = 100$ volts/m, the amplitude of $\dot{D}$ is 50.5 amp/m².

Displacement currents are important even at low frequencies because they can flow across large areas; conduction currents, however, are usually confined to relatively thin wires. The great dispartity in densities may or may not be compensated by an equally great disparity in the areas across which the currents flow.

1.24   Magnetic field of a moving charge

We shall now calculate the magnetic intensity of a charged particle moving with the speed v. Magnetic lines are circles coaxial with the line of motion. Consider Figure 1.27 which illustrates a typical magnetic line of radius ρ in the plane perpendicular to the line of motion at distance z above the particle. Applying equation (1.61) and noting that there is only a displacement current through the spherical cap of radius r, bounded by the magnetic line, we have

$$H_\phi = \dot{\Psi}/2\pi\rho = \dot{\Psi}/2\pi r \sin \theta,$$

where $\dot{\Psi}$ is the time derivative of the displacement Ψ. Since

$$\Psi = \int_0^\theta \int_0^{2\pi} (q/4\pi r^2) r^2 \sin \theta \, d\phi \, d\theta = \tfrac{1}{2} q (1 - \cos \theta),$$

we have

$$\dot{\Psi} = \tfrac{1}{2} q \sin \theta \, \dot{\theta},$$

where $\dot{\theta}$ is the time rate of change in θ as the particle is moving

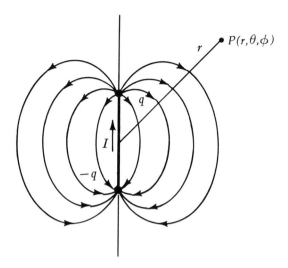

FIGURE 1.26   *An electric current element in a dielectric medium.*

upward with the speed $v = -\dot{z}$. Since

$$\cot \theta = z/\rho,$$

we find

$$-\csc^2\theta \cdot \dot{\theta} = \dot{z}/\rho = -v/\rho,$$

and

$$\dot{\theta} = (v \sin^2\theta)/\rho = (v \sin \theta)/r.$$

By substituting in the expression for $\dot{\psi}$ and then in H_ϕ, we obtain

$$H_\phi = \frac{qv \sin \theta}{4\pi r^2}. \tag{1.65}$$

Comparing this with H_ϕ for an electric current element of moment Il, equation (1.64), we note that, as far as the magnetic field is concerned, the charged particle q moving with the speed v is equivalent to an electric current element of moment $Il = qv$. This is hardly surprising since the movement of the particle may be represented by superimposing a pair of charges, q and $-q$, an infinitesimal distance l apart, on the charge q. See Figure 1.28. The current in this dipole is $I = q/\tau$, where τ is the time required for the charge to move a distance l. Hence the moment $Il = ql/\tau = qv$. Neither I nor l are defined separately; only their product has a meaning. On the other hand, the current density $\bar{J}$ has a perfectly definite meaning. Suppose that the current I of the element is distributed over an infinitesimal volume

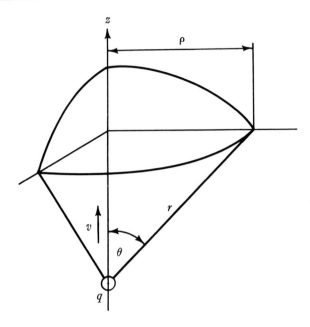

FIGURE 1.27 *Assisting in the calculation of the magnetic field generated by a moving charge.*

Sl, where l is in the direction of current and S is at right angles to it. Then the moment of the current element is $\bar{J}Sl$. This equals the moment of the moving charge $q\bar{v} = \rho Sl\bar{v}$ where ρ is the density of charge. Hence

$$\bar{J} = \rho\bar{v}. \tag{1.66}$$

In deriving equation (1.65) it was assumed that only displacement current is crossing the spherical cap surmounting the magnetic line. This is true as long as the particle itself is not crossing the cap. If it is, we should include the true current density given by equation (1.66) in equation (1.61). The end result is the same.

Equation (1.66) gives the density of *convection current* at any place of a stream of moving charged particles. This density is constant over the volume occupied by each particle and equals zero elsewhere. Frequently we are interested only in the average value of convection current in a stream. This is certainly the case in conducting media where the average value is proportional to the electric intensity, and the convection current is usually called the *conduction current*. [See equation (1.15).]

1.25 The force between two moving charged particles and between two current elements

It is possible now to obtain the force one moving charged particle, q_1, exerts on another particle q_2. First of all there is a force due to the electric field of the first particle. Then there is a force due to the magnetic field. Vector notation is convenient here. Let $\bar{r}_{12}$ be the vector

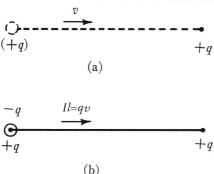

(a)

(b)

FIGURE 1.28 (a) A moving electric charge; (b) an equivalent superposition of an electric current element on a stationary charge.

from the first particle to the second as shown in Figure 1.29. Then the electric intensity of the first particle at the second is

$$\bar{E}_1 = \frac{q_1 \bar{r}_{12}}{4\pi \epsilon r_{12}^3}. \tag{1.67}$$

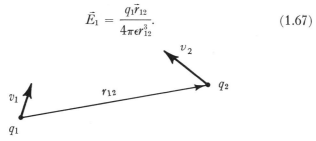

FIGURE 1.29 Two moving point charges.

The magnetic field is given by equation (1.65) and may be written as

$$\bar{H}_1 = \frac{q_1 \bar{v}_1 \times \bar{r}_{12}}{4\pi r_{12}^3}, \qquad \bar{B}_1 = \mu \bar{H} = \frac{\mu q_1 \bar{v}_1 \times \bar{r}_{12}}{4\pi r_{12}^3}. \tag{1.68}$$

The total force $\bar{F}_{12}$ exerted by the first particle on the second is now obtained from these equations and equation (1.38)

$$\bar{F}_{12} = q_2 \bar{E}_1 + q_2 \bar{v}_2 \times \bar{B}_1$$

or

$$\vec{F}_{12} = \frac{q_1 q_2 \vec{r}_{12}}{4\pi \epsilon r_{12}^3} + \frac{\mu q_1 q_2 \vec{v}_2 \times (\vec{v}_1 \times \vec{r}_{12})}{4\pi r_{12}^3}. \tag{1.69}$$

In the case of two current elements of moments $I_1 \vec{l}_1$ and $I_2 \vec{l}_2$, the force due to the magnetic field of the first element on the second is

$$\vec{F}_{12,m} = \frac{\mu I_1 I_2 \vec{l}_2 \times (\vec{l}_1 \times \vec{r}_{12})}{4\pi r_{12}^3}. \tag{1.70}$$

In addition there will be four electric forces between the end charges of the elements.

1.26 Summary of field equations

In the preceding sections we defined and illustrated five field quantities: the electric intensity $\vec{E}$, the density of conduction current $\vec{J}_{cond}$, the electric displacement density $\vec{D}$, the magnetic intensity $\vec{H}$, and the magnetic flux density (or magnetic "displacement" density) $\vec{B}$. In isotropic media these quantities are related as follows:

$$\vec{J}_{cond} = \sigma \vec{E}, \qquad \vec{D} = \epsilon \vec{E}, \qquad \vec{B} = \mu \vec{H}, \tag{1.71}$$

where σ, ϵ, μ are parameters of the media. In iron and some other media the last equation is true only for weak fields. For strong fields the equation is nonlinear. In nonisotropic (crystalline) media the Cartesian components of vectors on the left are linear functions of the Cartesian components of vectors on the right. In other words, we replace the numerical multipliers in equations (1.71) by matrices.

In a stream of electric charge the density of convection current is

$$\vec{J}_{conv} = \rho \vec{v}, \tag{1.72}$$

where ρ is the volume density of charge and $\vec{v}$ is its velocity.

The force exerted by electric and magnetic fields on a charge q is

$$\vec{F} = q\vec{E} + q\vec{v} \times \vec{B}. \tag{1.73}$$

It should be stressed that this equation does not give all the forces which may act on a charged particle. For instance, it does not include forces of gravitation which are generally relatively small. It does not include forces which separate positive and negative charge in chemical dry or liquid cells. It does not include forces which eject electrons in thermal emission. All these other forces are important in electric generators. In this book we shall be concerned mostly with fields *outside* electric generators.

In addition there are two basic equations which connect electric and magnetic quantities and express *the laws of interaction between electric and magnetic fields*:

1. Faraday-Maxwell equation

$$\oint E_s \, ds = -\frac{\partial}{\partial t} \int B_n \, dS \qquad (1.74)$$

and

2. Ampere-Maxwell equation

$$\oint H_s \, ds = \int J_n \, dS + \frac{\partial}{\partial t} \int D_n \, dS, \qquad (1.75)$$

where

$$\bar{J} = \bar{J}_{cond} + \bar{J}_{conv}.$$

The integrations on the right are performed over any surface while the integrations on the left are extended over the edge of this surface, [Figure 1.30(a)]. The algebraic signs in these equations are determined by the right-hand rule, Figure 1.30(b, c), with respect to the

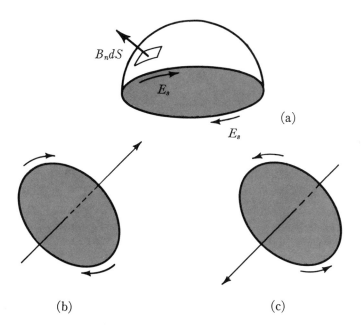

FIGURE 1.30 (a) The right-hand rule with respect to the positive directions of "flux" and round a closed curve encircling it: (b) if the observer is looking in the arbitrarily chosen positive direction of the flux, then the positive direction round a curve encircling it is clockwise; (c) if the positive flux is toward the observer, the positive direction round the curve is counterclockwise.

positive direction of the normal to the surface of integration and the positive direction of integration round its edge. (If the handle of a right-handed corkscrew is turned in the positive direction of integration, the corkscrew will advance in the direction of the positive normal.)

Equations (1.74) and (1.75) apply to all media. In media for which equations (1.71) are valid, we have:

1. FARADAY-MAXWELL EQUATION

$$\oint E_s \, ds = -\frac{\partial}{\partial t} \int \mu H_n \, dS \tag{1.76}$$

and

2. AMPERE-MAXWELL EQUATION

$$\oint H_s \, ds = \int \sigma E_n \, dS + \frac{\partial}{\partial t} \int \epsilon E_n \, dS. \tag{1.77}$$

These are the equations for *source-free* regions, which are of primary concern in this book. The sources or electric generators will be surrounded by closed surfaces and their effect on the external fields will be expressed by appropriate boundary conditions.

Equations (1.74) and (1.75) are *independent* field equations. We can derive other equations which *must* be true if equations (1.74) and (1.75) are true. The surface of integration may be an almost closed surface with just a small hole in it as shown in Figure 1.31.

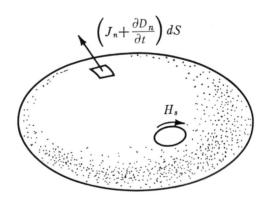

FIGURE 1.31 *Application of the Ampere-Maxwell equation to an almost closed surface with a shrinking hole.*

Let us apply equation (1.75) to such a surface and assume that the hole shrinks to a point. The line integral must vanish in the limit if

$\bar{H}$ is *finite*. Therefore, the total current leaving *any closed surface* is zero

$$\oint J_n \, dS + \frac{\partial}{\partial t} \oint D_n \, dS = 0. \tag{1.78}$$

Equation (1.78) is not really a consequence of equation (1.75). It is a consequence of our definition of "displacement current," the purpose of which was to make the tubes of "total current" closed so that Ampere's equation (1.55) for steady currents would apply to time-varying currents. [See equation (1.61)]. The definition involves a hypothesis that displacement currents generate magnetic fields just as true flow of electric charge does. This hypothesis has been confirmed by experience.

Rearranging the terms in equation (1.78), we have

$$\frac{\partial}{\partial t} \oint D_n \, dS = -\oint J_n \, dS,$$

where the right-hand side represents the time rate with which electric charge *is entering* the volume enclosed *either by way of conductors or as a stream of charged particles*. Hence if we integrate this equation from an instant when there was no charge in the interior of the closed surface to the instant when the flow of charge stops, we have

$$\oint D_n \, dS = q, \tag{1.79}$$

where q is the charge in the interior. Again, this equation is not so much a consequence of equation (1.75) *as a prerequisite for it*.

In the same manner, we obtain from equation (1.74)

$$\frac{\partial}{\partial t} \oint B_n \, dS = 0 \tag{1.80}$$

and since there are no magnetic charges

$$\oint B_n \, dS = 0. \tag{1.81}$$

There are occasions when it is desirable to postulate magnetic charges. Then equation (1.81) will be similar to equation (1.79).

Equations (1.74) and (1.75) or (1.76) and (1.77) express the *interaction between electric and magnetic fields. They form the foundation of electromagnetic field theory and of all its applications. We shall* refer to them frequently throughout this book and they must be thoroughly understood. It is strongly recommended that they be remembered in the following verbal forms.

1. AMPERE-MAXWELL LAW. *The total electric current (the sum of convection, conduction, and displacement currents) passing through a given surface equals the magnetomotive force (the line integral of the magnetic intensity) round the edge of the surface.*

2. FARADAY-MAXWELL LAW. *The magnetic displacement current (the time rate of change of magnetic flux) passing through a given surface equals the negative of the electromotive force or the "voltage" (the line integral of the electric intensity) round the edge of the surface.*

There are no free magnetic particles and there can be no magnetic convection or conduction current. It is possible, however, to express the condition of magnetized bodies in terms of equivalent magnetic charge. If this is done, another term appears in the Faraday-Maxwell equation similar to that of true electric current in the Ampere-Maxwell equation. It is convenient sometimes to introduce such a term deliberately to facilitate mathematical solutions of certain problems.

Another obvious but important observation is that *the voltage round a closed curve is the sum of the voltages along the arcs into which*

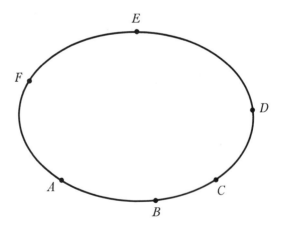

FIGURE 1.32 *Referring to equations (1.82) and (1.83).*

the curve may be subdivided. See Figure 1.32. Then, the Faraday-Maxwell equation may be stated as follows:

$$V_{AB} + V_{BC} + V_{CD} + V_{DE} + V_{EF} + V_{FA} = -\frac{\partial \Phi}{\partial t}, \qquad (1.82)$$

where Φ is the total magnetic flux linked with the curve. Similarly, we can state the Ampere-Maxwell equation as the *sum of magneto-motive forces round a closed curve*

$$U_{AB} + U_{BC} + U_{CD} + U_{DE} + U_{EF} + U_{FA} = I + \frac{\partial \Psi}{\partial t}, \qquad (1.83)$$

where I is the total true (convection plus conduction) current and $\partial \Psi / \partial t$ the total displacement current linked with the curve.

Two additional tautological statements come from the definition of the "average" of a given quantity. Thus the average electric intensity tangential to a given closed curve is

$$E_{\tan}^{\mathrm{av}} = \frac{1}{l} \oint E_s \, ds,$$

where l is the length of the curve. Similarly, the average intensity of the component normal to a surface is

$$E_{\mathrm{nor}}^{\mathrm{av}} = \frac{1}{S} \int E_n \, dS.$$

Maxwell's equations (1.76) and (1.77), without the convection current, may then be written as follows:

$$l E_{\tan}^{\mathrm{av}} = -\mu S \frac{\partial H_{\mathrm{nor}}^{\mathrm{av}}}{\partial t},$$

$$l H_{\tan}^{\mathrm{av}} = S\left(\sigma E_{\mathrm{nor}}^{\mathrm{av}} + \epsilon \frac{\partial E_{\mathrm{nor}}^{\mathrm{av}}}{\partial t} \right).$$

Here it has been tacitly assumed that μ, σ, and ϵ are constant throughout the region. Otherwise the expressions on the right-hand side should be in terms of $B_{\mathrm{nor}}^{\mathrm{av}}$, $J_{\mathrm{nor}}^{\mathrm{av}}$, and $D_{\mathrm{nor}}^{\mathrm{av}}$.

1.27 Boundary conditions

Maxwell's equations (1.74) and (1.75) are assumed to be general and applicable to all closed circuits, either small or large, and to all media, either homogeneous or nonhomogeneous, either isotropic or nonisotropic. They have been formulated on the basis of experimental evidence, but no matter how great the number of experiments or how varied the experiments, it is impossible to claim that the equations have been established in the most general form that we stated. However, so far all the conclusions that have been made from these equations over many years have been confirmed experimentally. Mathematical restrictions on Maxwell's integral equations are: The field quantities must be integrable and the time derivatives of the integrals on the right of equations (1.74) and (1.75) must exist. In situations which can be realized physically these mathematical restrictions are not severe. The field quantities may be discontinuous for instance, without invalidating the equations. The field quantities may even be infinite provided their integrals exist.

If the field quantities are continuous and differentiable, the integral equations can be converted into a set of partial differential equations This conversion may be accomplished by applying the integral equations to infinitesimal circuits. When the parameters of a medium, μ, σ, and ϵ are continuous, there is no reason why these requirements should not be satisfied. On the other hand, at an interface between two media where one or more of these parameters change abruptly, the field quantities cannot all be continuous. Equations (1.71) show that if some are continuous, others have to be discontinuous. From the integral equations we can find those quantities which must be continuous.

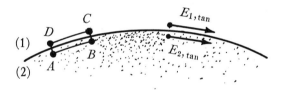

FIGURE 1.33   *The interface between two media.*

Consider two media (Figure 1.33) and a narrow rectangle straddling the interface. Let $AB = DC = l$ and $BC = AD = s$. From the Faraday-Maxwell law we have

$$V_{AB} + V_{BC} + V_{CD} + V_{DA} = -ls \frac{\partial}{\partial t} B_{\text{nor}}^{\text{av}}.$$

As s approaches zero the right-hand side as well as V_{BC} and V_{DA} approaches zero. Thus $V_{AB} \rightarrow -V_{CD} = V_{DC}$. This is true for any l no matter how small; but as l approaches zero, V_{AB}/l approaches the tangential component of $\bar{E}_2$ and V_{DC}/l the tangential component of

$\vec{E}_1$. Hence, the *tangential component of electric intensity must be continuous at the interface between two media*

$$E_{2,\tan} = E_{1,\tan}. \qquad (1.84)$$

Similarly, the *tangential component of magnetic intensity must be continuous at the interface between two media*

$$H_{2,\tan} = H_{1,\tan}. \qquad (1.85)$$

Applying equation (1.78) to a thin pillbox [Figure 1.34(a)] with one broad face in one medium and the other face in the other medium

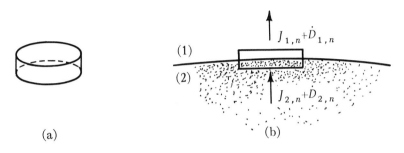

(1)

(2)

$J_{1,n}+\dot{D}_{1,n}$

$J_{2,n}+\dot{D}_{2,n}$

(a)   (b)

FIGURE 1.34   (a) *A thin "pill box" or a "wafer"; (b) a pill box straddling the interface between two media.*

[Figure 1.34(b)], we find that the *normal component of the total electric current density must be continuous at the interface between two media*

$$J_{2,n} + \frac{\partial}{\partial t} D_{2,n} = J_{1,n} + \frac{\partial}{\partial t} D_{1,n}. \qquad (1.86)$$

In the same manner, we find from equation (1.81) that the *normal component of the magnetic flux density must be continuous at the interface between two media*

$$B_{2,\text{nor}} = B_{1,\text{nor}}. \qquad (1.87)$$

Similarly, from equation (1.79) we find that the *normal component of the displacement density is discontinuous across the interface between two media* and that the *discontinuity equals the surface density of free electric charge on the surface*

$$D_{1,\text{nor}} - D_{2,\text{nor}} = q_S. \qquad (1.88)$$

If there is no free surface charge, then the normal component of the displacement density is continuous across the interface between two media

$$D_{1,\text{nor}} = D_{2,\text{nor}}. \tag{1.89}$$

1.28 Discontinuities

The vectors $\bar{E}$ and $\bar{D}$ on two sides of an infinite uniform sheet of charge of density q_s per unit area, imbedded in a homogeneous isotropic medium (Figure 1.35) are equal and oppositely directed. From equation (1.88) we obtain their magnitudes

$$D_1 = \tfrac{1}{2}q_s, \qquad E_1 = q_s/2\epsilon. \tag{1.90}$$

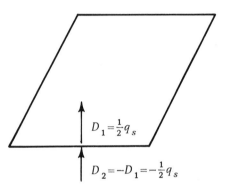

FIGURE 1.35   *A uniformly charged plane sheet.*

We have assumed, of course, that there are no other charges present. Otherwise we have only equation (1.88).

Equation (1.77) implies that the tangential component of $\bar{H}$ is

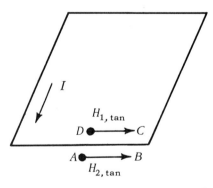

FIGURE 1.36   *A uniform plane current sheet.*

discontinuous across an electric current sheet. See Figure 1.36.

Let C be the current per unit width of the sheet, perpendicular to the flow lines. Then the magnetomotive force round a narrow rectangle $ABCDA$ is

$$U_{AB} + U_{BC} + U_{CD} + U_{DA} = Cl,$$

where l is the length of AB, chosen to be infinitesimal while the length of BC is an infinitesimal of higher order. Thus the mmf U_{BC} and U_{DA} are infinitesimals of higher order and the equation becomes

$$lH_{2,\tan} - lH_{1,\tan} = Cl$$

or

$$H_{2,\tan} - H_{1,\tan} = C. \tag{1.91}$$

If the current sheet is plane, then from symmetry considerations

$$H_{2,\tan} = -H_{1,\tan} = \tfrac{1}{2}C. \tag{1.92}$$

A practical approximation to an ideal current sheet is current in a thin conducting sheet. Here equations (1.91) and (1.92) apply to $H_{\tan}$ on the two sides of the sheet, Figure 1.37. In passing through the sheet of finite thickness $H_{\tan}$ changes rapidly but continuously.

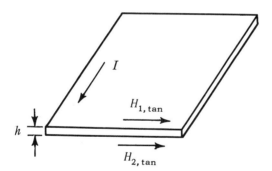

FIGURE 1.37 *An infinite, thin conducting plate carrying uniform current.*

If the thickness of the sheet is h and the conductivity σ, the current C per unit width is

$$C = \sigma E h$$

and approaches zero with h. Let us suppose that the conductivity increases indefinitely while E and h approach zero in such a way that the product remains constant. In this way, we arrive at a mathematical concept of a *perfectly conducting sheet* capable of supporting electric current while tangential electric intensity is zero. It is a very useful concept.

1.29   Step-by-step calculation of electromagnetic fields

We have seen that static electric fields are produced in dielectrics by static distributions of charge and in conductors by steady electric currents. The latter are accompanied by static magnetic fields. Let us denote this combination of static electric and magnetic fields by $\bar{E}^{(0)}$ and $\bar{H}^{(0)}$. Assuming that there are no convection currents, Maxwell's equations (1.76) and (1.77) yield

$$\oint E_s^{(0)} \, ds = 0,$$

$$\oint H_n^{(0)} \, ds = \int \sigma E_s^{(0)} \, dS. \tag{1.93}$$

The electric field in dielectric regions is entirely independent of the magnetic field. The magnetic field depends only on the electric field in conducting regions of space.

Let us now assume that these fields begin to vary slowly. We do not expect that the spatial distribution of these fields will be changed radically; but we do expect that the terms depending on time derivatives will produce small changes in the spatial distribution, depending on the time derivatives of the original static fields. Let us denote these "correction fields" by $\bar{E}^{(1)}$ and $\bar{H}^{(1)}$. Then from the same equations we have

$$\oint E_s^{(1)} \, ds = -\frac{\partial}{\partial t} \int \mu H_n^{(0)} \, dS,$$

$$\oint H_s^{(1)} \, ds = \int \sigma E_n^{(1)} \, dS + \frac{\partial}{\partial t} \int \epsilon E_n^{(0)} \, dS. \tag{1.94}$$

Since these correction fields may in general also vary with time, we will calculate the second-order correction fields, $\bar{E}^{(2)}$ and $\bar{H}^{(2)}$, from

$$\oint E_s^{(2)} \, ds = -\frac{\partial}{\partial t} \int \mu H_n^{(1)} \, dS,$$

$$\oint H_s^{(2)} \, ds = \int \sigma E_n^{(2)} \, dS + \frac{\partial}{\partial t} \int \epsilon E_n^{(1)} \, dS. \tag{1.95}$$

In principle this step-by-step calculation of successive correction fields may be continued indefinitely. Thus we express the solutions of Maxwell's equations as follows:

$$\vec{E} = \vec{E}^{(0)} + \vec{E}^{(1)} + \vec{E}^{(2)} + \cdots + \vec{E}^{(m)} + \cdots,$$

$$\vec{H} = \vec{H}^{(0)} + \vec{H}^{(1)} + \vec{H}^{(2)} + \cdots + \vec{H}^{(m)} + \cdots,$$
(1.96)

where

$$\oint E_s^{(m+1)}\, ds = -\frac{\partial}{\partial t} \int \mu H_n^{(m)}\, dS,$$

(1.97)

$$\oint H_s^{(m+1)}\, ds = \int \sigma E_n^{(m+1)}\, dS + \frac{\partial}{\partial t} \int \epsilon E_n^{(m)}\, dS.$$

Adding term by term the infinite sequence of equations (1.93), (1.94), (1.95), etc., we have

$$\oint [E_s^{(0)} + E_s^{(1)} + E_s^{(2)} + \cdots]\, ds = -\frac{\partial}{\partial t} \int \mu [H_n^{(0)} + H_n^{(1)}$$

$$+ H_n^{(2)} + \cdots]\, ds,$$

that is,

$$\oint E_s\, ds = -\frac{\partial}{\partial t} \int \mu H_n\, dS.$$

Similarly, we find that series (1.96) formally satisfy the Ampere-Maxwell equation.

In the next few chapters we shall apply this *step-by-step method* to specific problems. We shall find that although in certain situations we can evaluate the successive terms indefinitely, under most conditions we can evaluate only the first few terms—sometimes exactly and sometimes only approximately. The method has serious limitations which will be pointed out when a suitable occasion arises; but it furnishes insight into the behavior of electromagnetic fields as they start varying faster and faster. When used *judiciously*, the step-by-step method yields good approximations when exact solutions are hard, or impossible, to obtain.

2

Static and Almost Static Fields

2.0 Introduction

In this chapter we analyze the fields of several basic sources which are shown in Figure 2.18 in connection with a summary of the results in Section 2.11. A glance at this figure, before studying the details, will be helpful. Then we consider the properties of fields *in the large* and introduce quantities which later will be identified as "circuit parameters," "lumped," and "distributed." Finally, we develop approximate techniques for handling "almost static fields." Such fields include the effects of the first-time derivatives of $\bar{E}$ and $\bar{H}$. A field can actually be varying very fast and still be almost static if it is confined to a "sufficiently small" region of space. The precise meaning of "almost static" and "sufficiently small" will be considered in Section 3.13.

2.1 Potential

For *static* electric and magnetic fields Maxwell's equations (1.76) and (1.77) become

$$\oint E_s \, ds = 0, \tag{2.1}$$

$$\oint H_s \, ds = \int J_n \, dS = I, \tag{2.2}$$

where $\bar{J}$ is the conduction current density, J_n its normal component, and I is the total conduction current linked with the circuit of integration on the left. Equation (2.1) implies that the electromotive force from any point A of the field to any other point B [Figure 2.1(a)] is independent of the path along which it is taken. Hence, we can choose a fixed reference point B and define for any other point A a *unique* quantity V_A equal to the electromotive force from A to the reference point. This quantity is called the *potential* V_A of the field at point A. The reference point is often chosen at infinity.

62

Consider Figure 2.1(b) which shows a third point C. Since $V_{AB} = V_{AC} + V_{CB}$ or $V_A = V_{AC} + V_C$, we conclude that $V_{AC} = V_A - V_C$. Thus the electromotive force from A to C equals the *potential drop* from A to C.

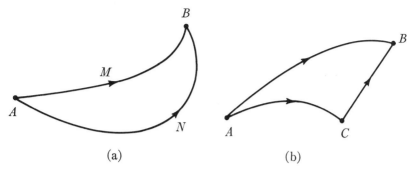

(a)   (b)

FIGURE 2.1   *Assisting in the definition of electric potential.*

The potential of the field of a point charge with respect to infinity can be found by integrating equation (1.33) along a radius (since the emf does not depend on the path of integration)

$$V = \int_r^\infty \frac{q\,dr}{4\pi\epsilon r^2} = -\frac{q}{4\pi\epsilon r}\bigg|_r^\infty = \frac{q}{4\pi\epsilon r}. \tag{2.3}$$

This is also the potential outside a charged spherical conductor. The potential inside is constant since in the interior of a conductor no static field can exist.

The lines and surfaces of equal potential are called *equipotential lines* and *equipotential surfaces*. Together with the lines of force they form a good pictorial representation of the field, which is similar to a topographic map on which the contour lines are loci of points of equal height. Just as in the case of topographic maps, it is customary to draw equipotential lines corresponding to equal increments (or decrements) in potential. Thus Figure 2.2 shows that where the equipotential lines are close the field is strong and where the lines are far apart the field is weak. Figure 2.3 represents a map of the cross section of the field of a charged conducting strip. The equipotential lines are confocal ellipses and the lines of force confocal hyperbolas. The lines of force are seen to be the lines of steepest descent.

In the case of a static charge distribution, the potential on the surface of any conductor must be constant because if it were not constant, there would be a tangential component of $\bar{E}$ and a flow of

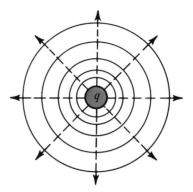

FIGURE 2.2   *A cross section of a charged sphere, equipotential lines (circles), and lines of force (radii).*

charge. In electrostatic fields conducting surfaces are equipotential surfaces. Any equipotential surface may be replaced by conducting surface without disturbing the field. For example, a very thin uncharged conducting elliptic cylinder confocal with the edges of the conducting strip in Figure 2.3 will not disturb the field.

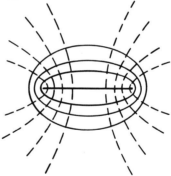

FIGURE 2.3   *A cross section of a thin charged conducting strip, equipotential lines (ellipses), and lines of force (hyperbolas).*

The potential of any given charge distribution is found by adding the potentials of the individual charged particles,

$$V = \sum \frac{q_n}{4\pi\epsilon r_n}, \tag{2.4}$$

where r_n is the distance from the nth particle to a typical point in the field. If the distribution is continuous, we subdivide it into infinitesimal volume (or surface, or line) elements of charge and integrate.

Thus

$$V(x, y, z) = \int \frac{\rho(u, v, w) \, d\tau}{4\pi\epsilon r_{12}}, \qquad (2.5)$$

where ρ is the volume density of charge and r_{12} is the distance between the element of charge at point (u, v, w) and a point $P(x, y, z)$ of the field

$$r_{12} = [(x - u)^2 + (y - v)^2 + (z - w)^2]^{1/2}.$$

These results follow immediately from the definition of potential. Since the electric intensity of a system of charged particles is the vector sum of the electric intensities of the individual particles

$$\vec{E} = \vec{E}_1 + \vec{E}_2 + \vec{E}_3 + \cdots,$$

the potential of the system is

$$V = \int_{AB} \vec{E} \cdot \vec{ds} = \int_{AB} (\vec{E}_1 + \vec{E}_2 + \vec{E}_3 + \cdots) \cdot \vec{ds}$$

$$= \int_{AB} \vec{E}_1 \cdot \vec{ds} + \int_{AB} \vec{E}_2 \cdot \vec{ds} + \int_{AB} \vec{E}_3 \cdot \vec{ds} + \cdots$$

$$= V_1 + V_2 + V_3 + \cdots,$$

the sum of the individual potentials.

Reciprocally, we can obtain the electric intensity from the potential. Consider a point A with the potential V and a neighboring point P with the potential $V + dV$ as shown in Figure 2.4. By definition, the

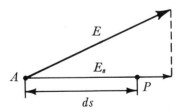

FIGURE 2.4   *Two infinitely close points A and P, the electric intensity E at point A, and its component E_s in the direction AP.*

emf $E_s \, ds$ from A to P equals the potential drop, $-dV$, from A to P

$$E_s \, ds = -dV.$$

Hence

$$E_s = -\frac{dV}{ds},\tag{2.6}$$

that is, the *component of $\bar{E}$ in a given direction equals the negative of the derivative of the potential in that direction.*

In particular, the Cartesian components of $\bar{E}$ are

$$E_x = -\frac{\partial V}{\partial x}, \qquad E_y = -\frac{\partial V}{\partial y}, \qquad E_x = -\frac{\partial V}{\partial z}.\tag{2.7}$$

Equation (2.6) implies that $\bar{E}$ is in the direction of the maximum derivative of the potential. The maximum derivative of a scalar function V, taken with its direction, is a vector, called the *gradient* of V and is denoted by grad V. Thus we can write

$$\bar{E} = -\mathrm{grad}\ V.\tag{2.8}$$

It is important to remember that the concept of potential is based on equation (2.1) and does not apply in all its generality to time-variable fields. However, if strong magnetic fields are confined to certain regions, then equation (2.1) is approximately true *outside* these regions. Also in certain regions we may have strong time-variable electric fields and relatively weak magnetic fields. In such regions equation (2.1) is also approximately true and we can introduce the concept of *local potential*.

2.2 Calculation of electric fields

If the distribution of electric charge in an infinite dielectric medium (or the distribution of sources of current in an infinite conducting medium) is *known*, the calculation of electric intensity is straightforward. In Section 1.11, for instance, we obtained the field of a double current source by adding the components of the vector current densities of the individual point sources. Let us solve the same problem with the aid of the potential function. To obtain the potential for a point source we integrate E_r given by equation (1.23). The integration is similar to that in equation (2.3) and we have

$$V = \frac{I}{4\pi\sigma r}.\tag{2.9}$$

Using the notation of Section 1.11, we write the potential for two point sources, I at point B and $-I$ at point A (see Figure 2.5) which are separated by distance l

$$V = \frac{I}{4\pi\sigma r_1} - \frac{I}{4\pi\sigma r_2} = \frac{I(r_2 - r_1)}{4\pi\sigma r_1 r_2}.$$

As point P moves farther and farther away from the sources, the lines AP, OP, and BP become more nearly parallel and

$$r_2 - r \rightarrow \tfrac{1}{2}l \cos\theta,$$

$$r_1 - r \rightarrow -\tfrac{1}{2}l \cos\theta,$$

$$r_2 - r_1 \rightarrow l \cos\theta,$$

$$r_1 r_2 \rightarrow r^2 - \tfrac{1}{4}l^2 \cos^2\theta.$$

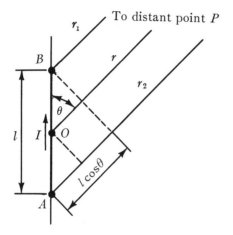

FIGURE 2.5   A current element in a conducting medium.

Hence at distances large compared with l, the potential equals approximately

$$V = \frac{Il \cos\theta}{4\pi\sigma r^2}. \tag{2.10}$$

The error is of the order of $(l/r)^2$. For an infinitesimal l equation (2.10) is exact at all distances.

The above method of obtaining equation 2.10 suggests that for the infinitesimal dipole $V = -l\partial V_0/\partial z$, where $V_0 = I/4\pi\sigma r$.

The element of length along the radius OP is $ds_r = dr$, and along the meridian of radius r we have $ds_\theta = rd\theta$. Using Equations (2.6) and (2.10) ,we have

$$E_r = -\frac{\partial V}{\partial r} = \frac{Il \cos\theta}{2\pi\sigma r^3},$$

$$E_\theta = -\frac{\partial V}{r\partial\theta} = \frac{Il \sin\theta}{4\pi\sigma r^3}.$$

Thus the calculations are less laborious if we use the potential function.

Potential of a uniformly charged line filament

As our second example we choose a uniformly charged filament OA of length l, no longer small. See Figure 2.6. The potential and the field are independent of the angle ϕ between half-planes issuing from

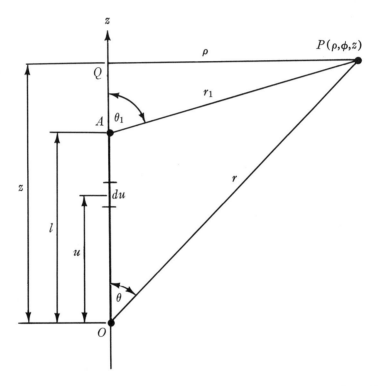

FIGURE 2.6 *Assisting in the calculation of the potential of a uniform line charge OA.*

the filament. If q is the charge per unit length, the element of charge at distance u from the origin is $q\, du$ and

$$V = \int_0^l \frac{q\, du}{4\pi\epsilon\sqrt{\rho^2 + (u - z)^2}}.$$

By introducing a new variable of integration $v = u - z$, we have

$$V = \int_{-z}^{l-z} \frac{q \, dv}{4\pi\epsilon\sqrt{\rho^2 + v^2}}.$$

Since

$$\frac{d[v + \sqrt{\rho^2 + v^2}]}{v + \sqrt{\rho^2 + v^2}} = \frac{dv}{\sqrt{\rho^2 + v^2}},$$

we obtain

$$V = \frac{q}{4\pi\epsilon} \ln \frac{l - z + r_1}{-z + r} = \frac{q}{4\pi\epsilon} \ln \frac{(l - z + r_1)(z + r)}{\rho^2}, \qquad (2.11)$$

where

$$r = \sqrt{\rho^2 + z^2}, \qquad r_1 = \sqrt{\rho^2 + (l - z)^2}.$$

If we multiply the numerator and the denominator in the first expression by $(r + z)(r_1 - l + z)$, we obtain a third form

$$V = \frac{q}{4\pi\epsilon} \ln \frac{r + z}{r_1 - l + z}.$$

Therefore

$$\frac{l - z + r_1}{-z + r} = \frac{r + z}{r_1 - l + z} = \exp\,(4\pi\epsilon V/q) \equiv k,$$

and

$$l - z + r_1 = -kz + kr, \qquad r + z = kr_1 - kl + kz.$$

By adding and rearranging the terms, we obtain

$$(k - 1)(r + r_1) = (k + 1)l.$$

Thus

$$r + r_1 = \frac{k + 1}{k - 1}\, l = l \coth \frac{2\pi\epsilon V}{q}.$$

Hence the equipotential lines are ellipses confocal with the ends of the charged filament, equipotential surfaces are prolate spheroids, and electric lines are confocal hyperbolas. Thus the map of the field in a radial plane resembles the one in Figure 2.3.

Let us now examine the potential on a thin cylinder $\rho = a, 0 < z < l$, around the filament. Not too near the ends we may neglect a^2 in comparison with z^2 and $(l - z)^2$. Hence, approximately

$$V \simeq \frac{q}{4\pi\epsilon} \ln \frac{4z(l - z)}{a^2}. \qquad (2.12)$$

At the ends $z = 0, l$ we have

$$V \simeq \frac{q}{4\pi\epsilon} \ln \frac{2l}{a}.$$

Half way between the ends

$$V = \frac{q}{2\pi\epsilon} \ln \frac{l}{a}.$$

Thus the potential at the ends is about half the potential in the middle and approaches one half as l increases or a decreases since $\ln(l/a)$ becomes much greater than $\ln 2$. If z_1 is the distance from the middle, equation (2.12) becomes

$$V \simeq \frac{q}{2\pi\epsilon} \ln \frac{l}{a} + \frac{q}{4\pi\epsilon} \ln \left(1 - \frac{4z_1^2}{l^2}\right), \qquad (2.13)$$

which shows that as l/a increases, the potential will be substantially constant over an increasing central portion of the cylinder and then drop to half of its value more rapidly near the ends.

Potential of two equally and oppositely charged filaments

The potential of a pair of equal and oppositely charged filaments [Figure 2.7(a)] may be obtained from equation (2.11). The lower and upper limits in the integral for the potential V^- of the lower filament are $-l$ and zero to begin with and $-l - z$ and $-z$ after the change in the variable of integration. Hence

$$V^- = -\frac{q}{4\pi\epsilon} \ln \frac{-z + r}{-l - z + r_2} = -\frac{q}{4\pi\epsilon} \ln \frac{l + z + r_2}{z + r},$$

where

$$r_2 = \sqrt{\rho^2 + (l + z)^2}.$$

Adding this to V in equation (2.11), we find the potential of both filaments

$$V = \frac{q}{4\pi\epsilon} \ln \frac{(l - z + r_1)(z + r)^2}{\rho^2(l + z + r_2)}. \qquad (2.14)$$

Axial cross sections of two equipotential surfaces are shown in Figure 2.7(b). Near point O the equipotential surfaces are conical. Assuming that ρ and z are small compared with l, the above equation becomes

$$V = \frac{q}{2\pi\epsilon} \ln \frac{z + \sqrt{\rho^2 + z^2}}{\rho}.$$

If $z = k\rho$, V is constant; but $z = k\rho$ is the equation of a cone.

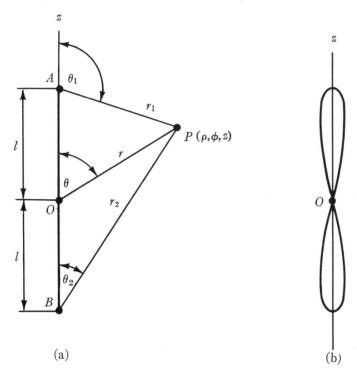

(a)

(b)

FIGURE 2.7 (a) *Two uniformly but oppositely charged filaments; (b) an axial cross section of two equipotential surfaces.*

Two perfectly conducting surfaces, if coinciding with the equipotential surfaces whose cross sections are shown in Figure 2.7(b), will not disturb the field. If they are maintained at equal and opposite potentials, the potential outside is given by equation (2.14).

On the surface of a thin cylinder $\rho = a$, $-l < z < l$, about the charged filaments, we can neglect ρ^2 in the expressions for r, r_1, and r_2, provided we are not near the ends or the middle of the cylinder. Hence for $z > 0$, we have

$$V = \frac{q}{4\pi\epsilon} \ln \frac{4z^2(l - z)}{a^2(l + z)} = \frac{q}{2\pi\epsilon} \ln \frac{2z}{a} + \frac{q}{4\pi\epsilon} \ln \frac{l - z}{l + z}.$$

From symmetry considerations

$$V(-z) = -V(z).$$

Thus the potential drop between points equidistant from the middle is

$$V(z) - V(-z) = \frac{q}{\pi\epsilon}\ln\frac{2z}{a} + \frac{q}{2\pi\epsilon}\ln\frac{l-z}{l+z}$$

$$= \frac{q}{\pi\epsilon}\ln\frac{2l}{a} + \frac{q}{\pi\epsilon}\ln\frac{z}{l} + \frac{q}{2\pi\epsilon}\ln\frac{l-z}{l+z}. \qquad (2.15)$$

As $2l/a$ increases, the potential differences becomes substantially constant over increasing portions of the cylinders, excluding the decreasing central and end sections.

2.3 Calculation of charge distributions

Frequently there are problems in which something is known about fields and one has to find charge distributions. For instance, two wires (an antenna) may be connected to a generator. See Figure 2.8(a). The impressed electromotive force V^i in the generator drives

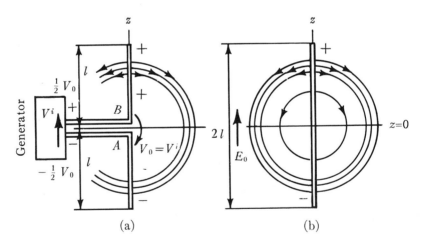

(a)   (b)

FIGURE 2.8   *(a) Two conducting wires connected to a generator; (b) a conducting wire in a uniform electric field.*

electric charge from one wire to the other. In the static case, we know only that the potentials of the wires are constant and the potential difference V_0 is equal and opposite to V^i. In a symmetric arrangement the potentials of the wires will be equal and opposite. In the time-variable case, we know the electromotive force between the input terminals of the antenna, $V_{BA} = V^i$, and the component of electric intensity tangential to the wires is very small. From this information we have to find the charge (and current) distribution in the wires. Once we find it we can calculate the field.

Another example is shown in Figure 2.8(b). A wire is in a static or time-variable field. We want to know what happens in the wire and its effect on the field. The wire may be broken in the middle and connected to a device absorbing energy (a receiving antenna). Exact solution of such problems is possible only in a few special cases and even then only with the aid of special mathematical methods. Usually we have to be satisfied with approximate solutions.

While the calculation of fields from given charge distributions is straightforward, the solution of inverse problems which we are considering in this and the following sections requires varying degrees of imagination. There is no single method applicable to all problems. One has to take advantage of special conditions. He who solved a given problem or a class of problems for the first time had to be inventive. Consider, for instance, the calculation of charge $q(z)$ per unit length on the wires diverging from A, B in opposite directions, as shown in Figure 2.8(a), from the given potentials. By swinging the wires about A and B, we can make them parallel. Reciprocally, parallel wires can be swung apart. Thus we have related problems and the solution of one might help us solve the other. Let us see to what extent it does.

If the length of parallel wires is considerably greater than the distance s between their axes, we expect substantially uniform charge distributions except near the ends. The field of each wire by itself is radial. If q is the charge per unit length, the radial displacement density is $q/2\pi\rho_1$, where ρ_1 is the distance from the axis. Hence, the radial electric intensity is $q/2\pi\epsilon\rho_1$. Similarly, the radial electric intensity of the field produced by the other charged wire is $-q/2\pi\epsilon\rho_2$ where ρ_2 is the distance from *its* axis. Of course, the charge on one wire attracts the opposite charge on the other wire, and there is some nonuniformity in charge distribution round the axis of each wire. But if s is fairly large in comparison with the diameters of the wires, the nonuniformity is small. Hence the mean voltage between the wires is

$$V_0 = \int_a^s (q/2\pi\epsilon\rho_1)\,d\rho_1 + \int_s^a (-q/2\pi\epsilon\rho_2)\,d\rho_2$$

$$= (q/\pi\epsilon)\,\ln(s/a).$$

From this equation we find the charge per unit length

$$q = CV_0, \qquad C = \pi\epsilon/\ln(s/a).$$

In the theory of "circuits with distributed parameters" the quantity C is called the "capacitance per unit length."

The equation indicates that the capacitance between the opposite elements of two wires depends only on the ratio, s/a, of the mean distance between the elements to the radius. If we use the same formula for the capacitance between the corresponding oppositely charged elements, as we swing the wires apart to obtain the configuration shown in Figure 2.8(a), we obtain

$$q(z) = C(z)V_0, \qquad C(z) = \pi\epsilon/\ln(2z/a)$$

since $2z$ is the distance between the elements. Let us look at the situation from another angle. The potential of a charged particle decreases as the distance from the particle increases. Hence, the potential at any point on a thin wire will be determined primarily by the charge density (per unit length) at that point. Since the potential is constant along each wire, the charge density $q(z)$, where z is the distance from A, B, must be approximately constant. We can use, therefore, prior knowledge of equation (2.15) for the potential of two uniformly charged filaments and adjust it to make $V(z) - V(-z) = V_0$ by assuming

$$q(z) = \frac{V_0}{A(z)}, \tag{2.16}$$

where

$$A(z) = \frac{1}{\pi\epsilon}\ln\frac{2l}{a} + \frac{1}{\pi\epsilon}\ln\frac{z}{l} + \frac{1}{2\pi\epsilon}\ln\frac{l-z}{l+z}$$

$$= \frac{q}{\pi\epsilon}\ln\frac{2z}{a} + \frac{1}{2\pi\epsilon}\ln\frac{l-z}{l+z}.$$

Since $A(z)$ is the reciprocal of $C(z)$, we observe that this result agrees with the previous one except near the ends of the wires.

As already noted, $A(z)$ becomes more nearly independent of z as a/l decreases and may be further approximated by its average value,

$$A_0 = \frac{1}{l}\int_0^l A(z)\,dz = \frac{1}{\pi\epsilon}\left(\ln\frac{l}{a} - 1\right). \tag{2.17}$$

Let us try a third approach. Suppose that $q(u)$ is the unknown charge density per unit length on the upper wire, at distance u from the midpoint of AB. The potential *on and in the wire* is $V_0/2$. We express therefore the potential of the surface charge, *on the axis* of the wire at distance z, and equate it to $V_0/2$. Thus

$$\tfrac{1}{2}V_0 = \int_s^{l+s} \frac{q(u)\,du}{4\pi\epsilon\sqrt{a^2 + (u-z)^2}} + \int_{-l-s}^{-s} \frac{q(u)\,du}{4\pi\epsilon\sqrt{a^2 + (u-z)^2}},$$

where $2s$ is the distance AB. Here we take advantage of the fact that the potential is constant throughout a conducting body to avoid a double integral which would arise from surface integration. The only approximation in this integral equation for the unknown function is that we did not include the potentials of the charges on the flat ends of the wires. No method is known for solving this particular type of integral equation exactly. To solve it approximately, we note that the integrand is large in the vicinity of $u = z$, where $q(u) = q(z)$. We replace, therefore, $q(u)$ by $q(z)$ and take the latter outside the integral signs. The integrals can then be evaluated as in the preceding section. The effect of s is negligible and we obtain equation (2.16). The charge density, $q(z)$, thus found, varies slowly with z. This is another reason why our approximation of $q(u)$ by $q(z)$ is justified.

It is possible to formulate an iterative procedure for obtaining a series solution of the above integral equation; but this is beyond the scope of this text and quite unnecessary for practical purposes.

To solve the problem shown in Figure 2.8(b), we observe that if the impressed field is uniform, its potential with reference to the central plane is $-E_0z$. Since the total potential of the wire must be constant, the potential of the field due to the charge displaced by E_0 must be

$$V(z) = E_0z.$$

The integral equation for the unknown charge density becomes

$$V(z) = E_0z = \int_{-l}^{l} \frac{q(u)\,du}{4\pi\epsilon\sqrt{a^2 + (u-z)^2}}.$$

As in the preceding problem, we replace $q(u)$ by $q(z)$ and obtain

$$q(z) = \frac{E_0z}{A_1(z)}, \tag{2.18}$$

where

$$A_1(z) = \frac{1}{4\pi\epsilon} \ln \frac{l - z + \sqrt{a^2 + (l - z)^2}}{-l - z + \sqrt{a^2 + (l + z)^2}}$$

$$= \frac{1}{4\pi\epsilon} \ln \frac{[l - z + \sqrt{a^2 + (l - z)^2}][l + z + \sqrt{a^2 + (l + z)^2}]}{a^2}$$

$$\simeq \frac{1}{4\pi\epsilon} \ln \frac{4(l^2 - z^2)}{a^2}$$

$$\simeq \frac{1}{2\pi\epsilon} \ln \frac{2l}{a} + \frac{1}{4\pi\epsilon} \ln \left(1 - \frac{z^2}{l^2}\right).$$

When l/a is large, $A_1(z)$ is approximately equal to $\frac{1}{2}A(z)$. In fact, if in the foregoing integral we had replaced $q(u)$ by $-q(z)$ in the interval $(-l, 0)$, where we know that the charge is negative, we would have obtained $\frac{1}{2}A(z)$ in the denominator of equation (2.18). This would be a better approximation (based, of course, on a better understanding of the physical situation).

We see that under the influence of the impressed field the wire has become similar to a dipole or has become "polarized."

2.4   Metal sphere in uniform electric field

If a neutral metal sphere is placed in a uniform electric field of intensity E_0 [Figure 2.9(a)], the charge on it will be displaced and the field affected correspondingly. The tangential component of the total $\vec{E}$ must vanish on the surface of the sphere. For the impressed field we have

$$E_r^i = E_0 \cos \theta, \qquad E_\theta^i = -E_0 \sin \theta. \tag{2.19}$$

The θ component of the *reflected field* due to the displaced charge must vary as $\sin \theta$ or else the total E_θ will not vanish for all values of θ. Referring to equation (1.36), we find that the field of an electric dipole has the proper dependence on θ and we assume the reflected field to be of that form,

$$E_r^r = \frac{A \cos \theta}{2\pi\epsilon_0 r^3}, \qquad E_\theta^r = \frac{A \sin \theta}{4\pi\epsilon_0 r^3}. \tag{2.20}$$

Hence at $r = a$

$$E_\theta^i + E_\theta^r = -E_0 \sin \theta + \frac{A \sin \theta}{4\pi\epsilon_0 a^3} = 0.$$

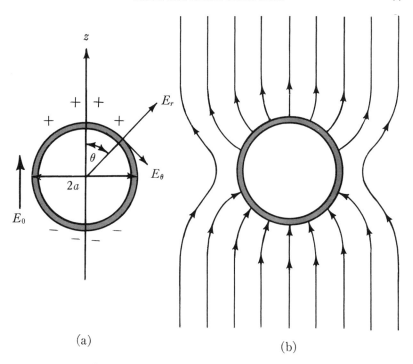

FIGURE 2.9 (a) A metal sphere introduced into an originally uniform electric field; (b) the lines of force in the presence of the sphere.

Thus we find the unknown constant

$$A = 4\pi\epsilon_0 a^3 E_0. \tag{2.21}$$

The sphere in a uniform electric field acts as a dipole of moment A for $r > a$.

For $r < a$ the total field vanishes. There the displaced charge produces a field equal and opposite to the impressed field. The quantity A/E_0 is called the *polarizability* of the sphere.

Once A has been determined, we can obtain other characteristics of the polarized sphere. The potential of an electric current dipole is given by equation (2.10). By analogy, we obtain the potential of an electrostatic dipole,

$$V = \frac{A \cos\theta}{4\pi\epsilon_0 r^2} = \frac{a^3 E_0 \cos\theta}{r^2}. \tag{2.22}$$

The surface density q_S of the displaced charge equals the discontinuity in the radial displacement density [see equation (1.88)] at $r = a$. Thus

$$q_S = D_r = \epsilon_0(E_r^i + E_r^r) = 3\epsilon_0 E_0 \cos\theta.$$

The total displaced charge on the upper hemisphere is

$$q = \int_0^{2\pi} \int_0^{\pi/2} q_S a^2 \sin\theta \, d\theta \, d\phi = 3\pi\epsilon_0 a^2 E_0.$$

Figure 2.9(b) illustrates the lines of force in the total field.

There is another reason for assuming that the field of displaced charge *might be* of the dipole type, equations 2.20. On account of symmetry conditions, to every element of displaced charge at (a, θ) there corresponds an element of opposite charge at $(a, \pi - \theta)$. The two elements form a dipole of finite separation $2a\cos\theta$. At a large distance r from the center of the sphere, the field of such a dipole becomes indistinguishable from the field of an infinitesimal dipole of the same moment situated at the center of the sphere. Hence, for $r \gg a$, the field of an entire displaced charge is of dipole type and, pending subsequent verification (or rejection), we could assume tentatively that the field of the displaced charge is given by equations 2.20 everywhere outside the conducting sphere. The foregoing calculations show that this assumption is indeed consistent with the conditions which must prevail inside and on the surface of the conducting sphere.

A question might be raised whether there exists a different charge distribution or a different field of the same charge distribution which also satisfies the required conditions in the presence of the same impressed field $\vec{E}_0$. Let this different reflected field be $\vec{E}_1^r$ while the one we found is $\vec{E}^r$. The total fields in the two cases are $\vec{E}_0 + \vec{E}^r$ and $\vec{E}_0 + \vec{E}_1^r$. The difference between them is $\vec{E}^r - \vec{E}_1^r$. If this difference did not vanish, we would have to conclude either that electric charges in a conductor could separate spontaneously without any impressed forces or that a static electric field can exist without any charge. Furthermore, this would mean that if we were to create a field in a certain region in a laboratory and then introduce a metal sphere, a charged particle at a given point would be acted upon by two different forces or by one force on Mondays, Wednesdays, and Fridays and by another on Tuesdays and Thursdays. This is absurd and we conclude that there is a unique response of a metal sphere to an impressed field. Once we have determined a solution which satisfies all the physical conditions of a given situation, the solution must represent the reality.

If the impressed electric field is varying slowly at the rate $\dot{E}_0$, then in the first approximation we may assume that it is still distributed uniformly in space and that the reflected field is still given by equations (2.20) with the moment A varying at the time rate $\dot{A}$. The total time-varying electric field generates a magnetic field. That part of the latter which is produced by reflected field can be calculated very easily on account of its symmetry about the z axis passing through the center of the sphere. In this field, magnetic lines are circles of radius $\rho = r \sin \theta$. The magnetomotive force round a typical circle is $2\pi\rho H_\varphi = 2\pi r \sin \theta H_\varphi$. By the Ampere-Maxwell law, this mmf should equal the total electric current linked with the circle. This current can be obtained by integrating the radial displacement current density over a portion of the spherical surface of radius r, concentric with the origin, which is enclosed by the circle. The integration is exactly the same which led to equations (1.57) and (1.64) for magnetic intensities of fields produced by electric current elements in conducting and in dielectric media. Thus we have

$$H_\varphi = \frac{\dot{A} \sin \theta}{4\pi r^2} = \frac{\epsilon_0 a^3 \dot{E}_0 \sin \theta}{r^2}, \qquad r \geq a.$$

The intensity of the magnetic field produced by the time-varying *impressed* field can also be obtained *if* we know that it is symmetric and if we know its axis of symmetry. Uniform static and slowly varying fields do not have to be symmetric. For instance, consider two parallel metal plates of arbitrary shape, large in comparison with the distance between them and connected to an electric generator. Between the plates, not too close to their edges, the electric field is substantially uniform. But there is no axis of symmetry and the preceding method of calculating magnetic intensity is inapplicable. We can, of course, calculate the mmf round any circle; but we can not assume that the magnetic intensity is tangential to the circle and that its magnitude is the same at various points.

If, however, the plates are circular and have a common axis, then the magnetic lines are circles coaxial with this axis. The mmf round a typical magnetic line of radius ρ_1, is $2\pi\rho_1 H_{\varphi_1}$, where φ_1 is the angle round the axis. The electric displacement current linked with this line is $\pi\rho_1^2\epsilon_0\dot{E}_0$. Therefore

$$H_{\varphi_1} = \tfrac{1}{2}\epsilon_0\rho_1\dot{E}_0.$$

Note that while the electric field is uniform, the magnetic field is not. Of course, if $\dot{E}_0$ is not constant, the magnetic field will vary with time and will generate an electric field E_1 which will be superimposed on E_0. This additional field will be proportional to $\ddot{E}_0$ and nonuniform.

The metal sphere which we have been discussing in this section could be centered either on the axis of the plates or off the axis. In the former case $\rho_1 = \rho = r \sin \theta$ and the lines of the total magnetic field are circles. In the latter case, the total magnetic field is the sum of two circularly symmetric fields with different axes of symmetry. The lines of the total field are no longer circles.

2.5   Dielectric sphere in uniform electric field

In the case of a dielectric sphere in a uniform field, Figure 2.10, boundary conditions (see Section 1.27) require that the tangential component of $\bar{E}$ and the normal component of $\bar{D}$ be continuous across the surface of the sphere. As noted in the preceding problem, these conditions can be satisfied only if the corresponding quantities vary with θ in conformity to the impressed field, equation (2.19). There

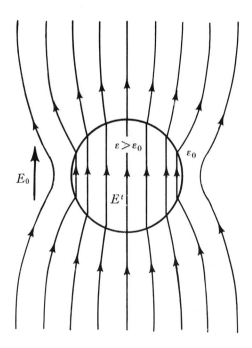

FIGURE 2.10   *A dielectric sphere in an originally uniform electric field and a sketch of lines of electric displacement.*

are two types of fields which have the required dependence on θ: (1)

a uniform field with lines parallel to the impressed field, and (2) a dipole field, equations (2.20). The dipole field becomes infinite when $r = 0$ and therefore cannot exist in the interior of the sphere since we have no point charges at the center to cause such behavior. The effect of the dielectric sphere on the external impressed field must decrease with increasing distance from the sphere and, hence, must be represented by a dipole type of field. Thus, outside the sphere, we add to the impressed field a reflected field given by equations (2.20). Inside the sphere we assume a *transmitted* field

$$E_r^t = B \cos \theta, \qquad E_\theta^t = -B \sin \theta. \qquad (2.23)$$

The boundary conditions are

$$E_\theta^i(a, \theta) + E_\theta^r(a, \theta) = E_\theta^t(a, \theta),$$

$$D_r^i(a, \theta) + D_r^r(a, \theta) = D_r^t(a, \theta).$$

Substituting from equations (2.19), (2.20), and (2.23) and cancelling $\sin \theta$ and $\cos \theta$, we have

$$-E_0 + \frac{A}{4\pi \epsilon_0 a^3} = -B,$$

$$\epsilon_0 E_0 + \frac{A}{2\pi a^3} = \epsilon B.$$

Solving

$$A = \frac{4\pi a^3 \epsilon_0 (\epsilon - \epsilon_0) E_0}{2\epsilon_0 + \epsilon}, \qquad B = \frac{3\epsilon_0 E_0}{2\epsilon_0 + \epsilon}. \qquad (2.24)$$

Thus the larger the ratio (ϵ/ϵ_0) is, the smaller the electric intensity B inside the sphere is. Externally the dielectric sphere acts as a dipole of moment A. Note that the ratio of this moment to the dipole moment of a conducting sphere is $(\epsilon - \epsilon_0)/(\epsilon + 2\epsilon_0)$. The dipole moment per unit volume of the sphere is

$$P = A/(4\pi a^3/3) = \frac{3\epsilon_0 (\epsilon - \epsilon_0) E_0}{2\epsilon_0 + \epsilon}. \qquad (2.25)$$

The fact that the dielectric sphere acts as a dipole is not surprising. All material media contain protons and electrons. In conductors there are numerous free electrons and the impressed electrostatic field displaces them to the surface. In dielectrics the electrons are bound for the most part (all of them are bound in perfect dielectrics). The impressed field, however, displaces the bound electrons with reference to the protons, thus forming tiny dipoles throughout the dielectric. We expect also a surface layer of displaced bound electrons on the bottom hemisphere and a layer of positive charge on the top, similar to free surface charges on the conducting sphere. In both cases the field of the displaced charge *opposes* the impressed field in the interior of the sphere. In the metal sphere the opposing field is exactly equal to the impressed field and the total internal field vanishes. This is, in fact, the condition from which we find the amount of displaced charge. In the dielectric sphere the opposing field weakens the total field but does not destroy it altogether.

Displacement of bound electrons in dielectrics or the *polarization* of dielectrics by the impressed field is responsible for the values of dielectric constants higher than that of vacuum. Thus inside the sphere

$$E_z^t = B = \frac{3\epsilon_0}{2\epsilon_0 + \epsilon} E_0, \qquad D_z^t = \frac{3\epsilon_0 \epsilon}{2\epsilon_0 + \epsilon} E_0.$$

The difference

$$D_z^t - \epsilon_0 E_z^t = \frac{3\epsilon_0(\epsilon - \epsilon_0)}{2\epsilon_0 + \epsilon} E_0$$

equals the dipole moment per unit volume, called the *polarization P*, equation (2.25). Thus in the interior of the sphere

$$D = \epsilon_0 E + P. \tag{2.26}$$

It is possible to prove that this equation is general. Alternatively this equation can be used *to define P*. Subsequently it can be shown that *P* is the dipole moment per unit volume.

2.6 Proximity effect

If charged conducting bodies are very far apart, the potential and the field at any point is essentially the sum of the potentials and the fields of the individual bodies, calculated on the assumption that the other bodies are not present. Thus the potential of two equally and oppositely charged spheres, *A* and *B*, shown in Figure 2.11 is

$$V^{(0)} = V_1^{(0)} + V_2^{(0)} = \frac{q}{4\pi\epsilon_0 r_1} - \frac{q}{4\pi\epsilon_0 r_2}. \tag{2.27}$$

The superscript "zero" serves to remind us that we have a "zero-order" approximation, good only if the distance *l* between the centers of the spheres is large in comparison with the diameter *2a* of each sphere.

Because of the attraction between opposite charges, the charge distributions will not be uniform. The nonuniformity increases as $l/2a$ decreases. This *proximity effect* can be calculated approximately from the result obtained in Section 2.4 when $l/2a$ is still so large that the field of one sphere is nearly uniform in the region occupied by the other. The electric intensity E_0 produced by the charge on

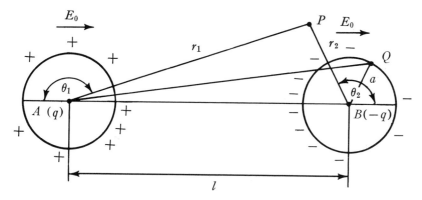

FIGURE 2.11 *Illustrating the calculation of the proximity effect of two equally but oppositely charged spheres.*

sphere A at the center of sphere B is

$$E_0 = \frac{q}{4\pi\epsilon_0 l^2}. \tag{2.28}$$

This is also the electric intensity produced by the charge on B at the center of A. This is a mean value of the electric intensity impressed by one charged sphere on the other. Under its influence, some positive charge on each sphere is shifted to the right and equal negative charge is shifted to the left. This "dipole type" displacement of charge is superimposed on the original uniform distribution of charge, thus producing greater charge densities on the sides of A and B which face each other. The moment A of each dipole is obtained from equations (2.21) and (2.28)

$$A = q(a^3/l^2).$$

The potential of each dipole is

$$V_d = \frac{A \cos\theta}{4\pi\epsilon_0 r^2} = \frac{qa^3 \cos\theta}{4\pi\epsilon_0 l^2 r^2}$$

where r is the distance from its center and θ is the angle between a typical direction and the dipole axis from the negative to the positive charge. For the dipole superimposed on B this angle equals θ_2; for the dipole superimposed on A the angle equals $\pi - \theta$. Adding the dipole potentials to the potential given by equation (2.27), we have the next approximation to the potential produced by two charged spheres

$$V^{(1)} = \frac{q}{4\pi\epsilon_0 r_1} - \frac{q}{4\pi\epsilon_0 r_2} - \frac{qa^3 \cos\theta_1}{4\pi\epsilon_0 l^2 r_1^2} + \frac{qa^3 \cos\theta_2}{4\pi\epsilon_0 l^2 r_2^2}. \qquad (2.29)$$

Let us now calculate the potential at a point Q on sphere B. There $r_2 = a$ and

$$r_1^{-1} = (l^2 + 2\,al\,\cos\theta_2 + a^2)^{-1/2}$$

$$= l^{-1}[1 + (2a/l)\,\cos\theta_2 + (a/l)^2]^{-1/2}$$

$$\simeq l^{-1} - (a/l^2)\,\cos\theta_2.$$

Hence, the first and the fourth terms in equation (2.29) add to $q/4\pi\epsilon_0 l$. Therefore on B

$$V_B^{(1)} = \frac{q}{4\pi\epsilon_0 l} - \frac{q}{4\pi\epsilon_0 a} - \frac{qa^3 \cos\theta_1}{4\pi\epsilon_0 l^2 r_1^2}. \qquad (2.30)$$

In absolute value the second term is the largest. Relatively to it, the first is of the order of a/l; and the third of the order of $(a^4/l^2 r_1^2)$. Even when the distance between the centers of the spheres equals only two diameters, the largest value of the last term is less than one per cent of the principal term.

The *exact* potential of B must be constant, of course. We can take only the first two terms in equation (2.30) and consider the third as indicative of the magnitude of error we make. But $\cos\theta_1$ does not differ much from -1 and r_1 is comparable to l. So we shall have a better approximation if we let $\cos\theta_1 = -1$, $r_2 = l$ instead of dropping the term altogether. Thus the potential of B is approximately

$$V_B = -\frac{q}{4\pi\epsilon_0 a}\left(1 - \frac{a}{l} - \frac{a^4}{l^4}\right). \qquad (2.31)$$

The potential of A is

$$V_A = -V_B = \frac{q}{4\pi\epsilon_0 a}\left(1 - \frac{a}{l} - \frac{a^4}{l^4}\right).$$

Thus the capacitance between the spheres is

$$C = q/(V_A - V_B) = 2\pi\epsilon_0 a \left(1 - \frac{a}{l} - \frac{a^4}{l^4}\right)^{-1}. \qquad (2.32)$$

2.7   Magnetic scalar potential

The existence of electric potential is a direct consequence of equation
(2.1) which states that the electromotive force round every closed
curve in the static field vanishes. The magnetomotive force, on the
other hand, vanishes only when the curve is not linked with electric
current. This means that magnetic potential can be defined only for
regions free from electric current. This restricts the usefulness of the
concept in the case of magnetic fields.

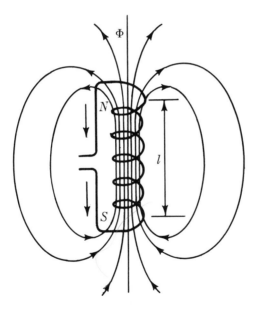

FIGURE 2.12   *A closely wound solenoid and magnetic lines of force.*

The magnetic analog of an electric dipole is a short and very thin
closely wound solenoid. See Figure 2.12. Inside the solenoid magnetic
lines are substantially straight except in the vicinity of the ends.
By analogy with the electric dipole we obtain [see equations (1.36)]

the following equations for the magnetic field *outside* the solenoid

$$B_r = \frac{\Phi l \cos \theta}{2\pi r^3}, \qquad B_\theta = \frac{\Phi l \sin \theta}{4\pi r^3}$$

$$\tag{2.33}$$

$$H_r = \frac{\Phi l \cos \theta}{2\pi \mu r^3}, \qquad H_\theta = \frac{\Phi l \sin \theta}{4\pi \mu r^3},$$

where Φ is the magnetic flux emerging from one end of the solenoid and converging to the other. The quantity Φl is the *moment* of the solenoid or of the *magnetic dipole*. Similarly, by analogy with equation (2.10) for a double current source (or a similar equation for an electrostatic dipole) we have the potential of the magnetic dipole,

$$U = \frac{\Phi l \cos \theta}{4\pi \mu r^2}. \tag{2.34}$$

The magnetic dipole resembles more closely an electric current element shown in Figure 1.9 than an electrostatic dipole shown in Figure 1.16. Magnetic lines and lines of current flow are closed. Inside the solenoid magnetic flux is from the south-seeking end to the north-seeking. Equation (2.34) is valid only *outside* the solenoid.

If we imagine a semi-infinite, thin solenoid, we shall have a *magnetic point source* with a radial magnetic field and a potential similar to the electric potential of a point charge, equation (2.3), or the potential of a point current source, equation (2.9). But this potential is of no help in the calculation of magnetic fields generated by given current distributions. In such a calculation the current distributions are subdivided into current elements of moment $Il = J \, d\tau$ (see Section 1.23). Magnetic lines of the field of an element are circles coaxial with the element and the magnetic intensity is given by equation (1.64). The individual element is surrounded by displacement current. In general the magnetomotive force around closed curves does not vanish and the potential in the above sense does not exist for a single element even though it may exist for the entire current distribution, at least in current-free regions (see Section 2.10).

2.8   Magnetic vector potential*

In vector analysis it is shown that any vector whose flux through any closed surface vanishes everywhere is the "curl" of another vector.

* This section is optional and may be omitted.

Magnetic flux density $\vec{B}$ is such a vector (Section 1.26), and we have

$$\vec{B} = \text{curl } \vec{A}. \tag{2.35}$$

The vector $\vec{A}$ is called the *magnetic vector potential*. When so introduced, this vector has no physical significance. Actually no matter how we introduce it, it remains an auxiliary mathematical function, a convenient computational "gimmick." The following derivation may make the concept seem less abstract.

The magnetic intensity of a current element in an infinite *nonconducting* medium as shown in Figure 2.13(a) is [equation (1.64)]

$$H_\phi = \frac{Il \sin \theta}{4\pi r^2} = \frac{Il\rho}{4\pi r^3},$$

where Il is the moment of the element. The magnetic flux through the

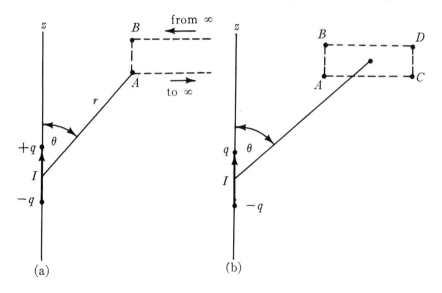

FIGURE 2.13 *Assisting the analysis of the field produced by an electric current element.*

rectangle $A \infty BA$ shown in the figure where $AB = \Delta z$, is

$$\Delta\Phi = \frac{\mu Il\Delta z}{4\pi} \int_\rho^\infty \rho(\rho^2 + z^2)^{-3/2}\, d\rho$$

$$= \frac{\mu Il\Delta z}{4\pi}(\rho^2 + z^2)^{-1/2} = \frac{\mu Il\Delta z}{4\pi r}.$$

Suppose that I starts varying with time. According to the Faraday-Maxwell law, the time derivative of $\Delta\Phi$ will create an electric field which will be superimposed on the field of the end charges of the current element. The total *counterclockwise* emf round the circuit $A \infty BA$ equals the time derivative of $\Delta\Phi$. The question is: How is it distributed round the circuit? There is no symmetry or anything else to guide us. The student will now understand the statement made in Section 1.29 that the step-by-step method of calculating time-variable fields cannot, as a rule, be carried on indefinitely if we use Maxwell's laws in integral form.

Let us assume tentatively that the entire emf is along AB. In other words we assume that the electric field created by magnetic current is given by a vector $\vec{F}$ *parallel* to the current element. Then the *clockwise* emf is $F_z\Delta z$ and from the above result

$$F_z = -\frac{\mu \dot{I} l}{4\pi r}, \qquad F_\rho = F_\varphi = 0. \tag{2.36}$$

To be on the safe side we denote our "error" by $\vec{G}$ so that the true electric field is

$$\vec{E} = \vec{F} + \vec{G}, \tag{2.37}$$

where $\vec{G}$ may have ρ and z components. From considerations of symmetry all ϕ components in our case should equal zero. The clockwise emf round $AB \infty A$ is

$$\oint \vec{E}\cdot\vec{ds} = \oint \vec{F}\cdot\vec{ds} + \oint \vec{G}\cdot\vec{ds} = -\frac{\partial}{\partial t}(\Delta\Phi).$$

Vector $\vec{F}$ was defined so that its line integral equals the right-hand side term. Therefore

$$\oint \vec{G}\cdot\vec{ds} = 0. \tag{2.38}$$

In certain calculations of the work done in establishing magnetic fields one has to integrate $\dot{E}_s I$ round a closed circuit when I is the same in all parts of the circuit. In such cases we can replace E_s by F_s since the integral of G_s cancels out. Note also that equation (2.38) implies that $\vec{G}$ is the gradient of some scalar potential function.

The integral of $\vec{F}$ round an infinitesimal closed circuit such as $ACDBA$ in Figure 2.13(b) divided by the area enclosed, is the component of curl $\vec{F}$ in the direction perpendicular to the area (see Appendix I). In our example this is also the component of $\vec{B}$ in that direction. Thus

$$\dot{\vec{B}} = \text{curl } \vec{F} = \text{curl } \frac{\mu \dot{I}\vec{l}}{4\pi r}.$$

Taking the time integral, we obtain

$$\vec{B} = \text{curl } \frac{\mu I l}{4\pi r}$$

for the current element of vector moment $I\vec{l}$. The magnetic vector potential

$$\vec{A} = \frac{\mu I \vec{l}}{4\pi r} \tag{2.39}$$

of the current element has thus been obtained. In calculating magnetic fields, it is easiest to add the vectors parallel to current elements and then obtain $\vec{B}$ by differentiation. Nevertheless the calculations are lengthy and one should take advantage of possible simplifications in each specific case, as we shall in the next two sections.

In a homogeneous isotropic medium H is also the curl of a vector $\vec{A}/\mu$.

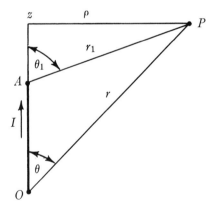

FIGURE 2.14 *Illustrating the calculation of the magnetic field produced by a straight, uniform, electric current filament.*

2.9 Straight uniform current filaments

The field of a straight uniform current filament shown in Figure 2.14 can be calculated from the field, equations (1.62), of a semi-infinite current filament. This field is the sum of the field of current I .

from point O to infinity and the field of current $-I$ from A to infinity. Thus

$$H_\varphi = \frac{I(1 + \cos \theta)}{4\pi r \sin \theta} - \frac{I(1 + \cos \theta_1)}{4\pi r_1 \sin \theta_1}.$$

Since $r \sin \theta = r_1 \sin \theta_1 = \rho$, we have

$$H_\varphi = \frac{I(\cos \theta - \cos \theta_1)}{4\pi\rho}. \tag{2.40}$$

In the vicinity of the filament not too near the ends, $\theta \simeq 0$ and $\theta_1 \simeq \pi$; thus

$$H_\varphi \simeq \frac{I}{2\pi\rho}. \tag{2.41}$$

The longer the filament is, the greater is the range of ρ in which the approximation is valid. The equation is exact for all values of ρ if the filament is infinite in length.

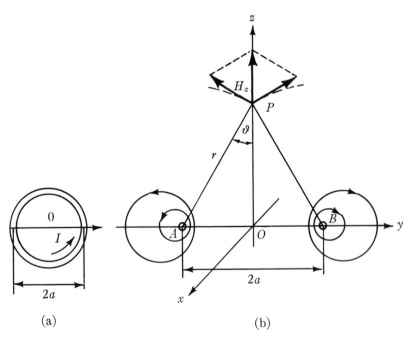

FIGURE 2.15 *(a) A circular turn of wire carrying uniform current I. (b) Illustrating magnetic lines of force, linked with the wire and the calculation of the magnetic intensity on the axis of the ring.*

2.10 Circulating current

The exact field of a circular turn of wire [see Figure 2.15(a)] carrying current I can be expressed as an elliptic integral. The solution is much simpler for distances large compared with the diameter of the loop. First we obtain the field on the axis of the loop, Figure 2.15(b). For each current element, $\bar{H}$ is perpendicular to the radius AP and its magnitude is $I\,ds/4\pi r^2$ [see Equation (1.63) and note that point P is in the equatorial plane of the element, $\theta = \pi/2$]. The component of this $\bar{H}$ along OP is $(I\,ds/4\pi r^2)\sin\vartheta$. The radial components cancel on account of symmetry. Since $\sin\vartheta = a/r$, we have, for the whole loop

$$H_z = \frac{a^2 I}{2r^3} = \frac{SI}{2\pi(a^2 + z^2)^{3/2}}, \qquad (2.42)$$

where S is the area of the loop.

At distances large compared with $2a$, the field should be the same as that of the magnetic dipole of proper moment. On the axis, H_z is the radial component (in spherical coordinates) and we can identify the moment Φl in equations (2.33) by setting $\theta = 0$ and comparing with equation (2.42). Thus we find $\Phi l = \mu I S$ and the complete field

$$H_r = \frac{IS\cos\theta}{2\pi r^3}, \qquad H_\theta = \frac{IS\sin\theta}{4\pi r^3}, \qquad (2.43)$$

where r is now the distance from the center of the ring and θ is the angle between the radius and the axis of the ring. The product IS is called the *area moment* of the circulating current as contrasted with the equivalent *dipole moment* μIS.

A thin solenoid and a current ring have the same fields at points not too close to them; but they are expressed differently. In a solenoid we have a given magnetic flux but not the current. As the radius of the solenoid approaches zero, the current in the winding must be increased indefinitely in order to maintain the same field. On the other hand, in a ring we have given current but not the flux. The radius of the wire making the ring does not enter the expressions for the field as long as this radius is a small fraction of the radius of the ring. In fact, in deriving equations (2.43) we have tacitly assumed that the radius of the wire is zero. In this case, the magnetic intensity in the immediate vicinity of the wire equals $I/2\pi\rho$ where ρ is the distance from the axis of the wire. Hence the magnetic flux linked with the wire is infinite.

If the electric current is varying with time, the magnetic intensity and the magnetic flux density will also vary. Hence a circle coaxial with either the solenoid or the current ring is linked with magnetic displacement current (that is, the time rate of change of magnetic flux) and there will exist, in accordance with the Faraday-Maxwell equation (1.76), an electromotive force round the circle. If the coordinates of the circle are r and θ, the radius is $r \sin \theta$. By symmetry the electric intensity is uniform round the circle, and the emf is $2\pi r \sin \theta E_\phi$. The radial magnetic flux linked with the circle may be obtained by integrating B_r over the spherical cap of radius r surmounting the circle. Such an integration was performed in Section 1.22 where we obtained the magnetic field of a current dipole and used it subsequently in Section 1.23 to obtain the magnetic field produced by the electric displacement current of a time-variable electric dipole in a dielectric medium. Thus noting the differences in the algebraic signs in Maxwell's equations, we have

$$E_\phi = -\frac{\dot{\Phi} l \sin \theta}{4\pi r^2} = -\frac{\mu \dot{I} S \sin \theta}{4\pi r^2}. \tag{2.44}$$

Comparing equations (2.43) with equations (2.33) and (2.34) we have the scalar magnetic potential of the circulating current

$$U = \frac{I S \cos \theta}{4\pi r^2}. \tag{2.45}$$

The *solid angle* Ω of a cone is defined as the ratio of the area intercepted by the cone on the surface of a sphere, centered at the apex

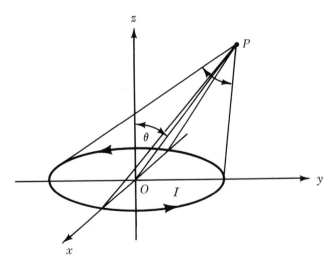

FIGURE 2.16 *A cone, with its apex at point P, subtended by a circular ring in the xy plane and illustrating the definition of the solid angle.*

of the cone, to the square of the radius. Assume that the loop is infinitesimal and imagine a cone from some point P subtended by the loop as in Figure 2.16. The area intercepted on the surface of the sphere of radius r centered at P, is $dS \cos \theta$, where dS is the area of the loop, and its ratio to the square of the radius is $(dS/r^2) \cos \theta$. By definition, this is the solid angle of the infinitesimal cone $d\Omega$. Hence the potential of an infinitesimal circulating current may be written as

$$U = I \, d\Omega/4\pi. \tag{2.46}$$

Consider a current loop of an arbitrary shape [see Figure 2.17].

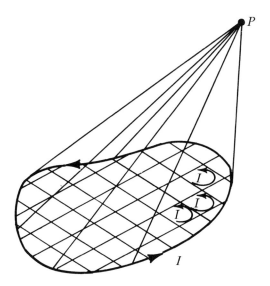

FIGURE 2.17   *A cone subtended by a current loop of arbitrary shape.*

On any surface bounded by this loop we imagine crisscross lines subdividing the surface into infinitesimal elements of area. Imagine a circulating current I round the boundary of each element. These currents cancel on the boundaries common to the elements. What is left is the circulating current round the boundary of the entire area. For each element we have equation (2.46). Integrating, we have for an arbitrary closed current

$$U = I\Omega/4\pi. \tag{2.47}$$

Magnetic scalar potential, when it exists, is a many-valued function of position. Imagine a circular ring, for instance. If we start with $\Omega = 0$ at infinity and approach the ring, Ω will increase. If we approach the plane of the ring *outside* the ring, Ω will approach zero again; but if we approach it inside the ring, Ω will approach 2π. As we pass through the plane of the ring, it will keep increasing. It is the *exterior* solid angle that we use to preserve the continuity of potential. Then if we approach the plane of the ring from below but outside the ring, Ω will approach 4π, where originally it was zero. At all points, U has an infinite number of values differing by nI, where n is an integer. This is as it should be. The line integral of $\bar{H}$ round a closed curve linked with current I once must equal I or $-I$; but this integral is also the magnetomotive force, and therefore the change in magnetic potential, round the curve. When obtaining $\bar{H}$ by differentiation we have to change U continuously, and the constant nI does not affect $\bar{H}$.

2.11   Comparison of electric and magnetic fields

By now it should be clear that many similarities exist between electric fields in conducting and nonconducting media and between electric and magnetic fields. There are also important differences. Analogies are very useful both in thinking and in calculations; but serious errors can be made if the differences are forgotten.

Figure 2.18 illustrates the following: (a) a point source of electric conduction current I in a conducting medium; (b) a point charge in a dielectric medium; (c) a point source of electric displacement current $I = \dot{q}$ in a dielectric medium; (d) a point source of magnetic flux, Φ; (e) a point source of magnetic current, $\dot{\Phi}$; (f) conduction current between perfectly conducting concentric spheres; (g) electrostatic field between conducting spheres, not necessarily perfect; (h) electric displacement current between perfectly conducting spheres; (i) a double source of current Il in a conducting medium; (j) an electrostatic dipole of moment ql; (k) an electric current element of moment $I = \dot{q}l$ in a dielectric medium; (l) a magnetic dipole (solenoid) of moment Φl; (m) a magnetic current element of moment $\dot{\Phi}l$; (n) a ring of current of area moment IS; (o) a ring of slowly-varying current; (p) two closely spaced parallel plates (double layer of charge) with a voltage V between them so that the area moment is VS; and (q) a double layer with a slowly varying voltage.

Most of these sources shown in Figure 2.18 and their fields are idealizations of physical sources and their fields. The field of a point charge in an infinite space is an idealization of the field of a small charge far removed from other bodies. The field of a point source of **direct** current in an infinite conducting medium is an idealization **of current** issuing from an open end of a thin insulated wire submerged in a large metal tank filled with some conducting fluid, for example. The other end of the wire and tank may be connected to the terminals of a direct current generator. Case (c), however, in which we assume *direct* displacement current emerging from the end of a semi-infinite wire, can best be described as a mathematical model of a purely hypothetical physical situation, rather than an idealization. To produce this situation in a laboratory we would need tremendous voltages (increasing at tremendous rates) applied continuously along the wire in a way that would neutralize the radial field voltage at the wire itself. Otherwise, the uncompensated voltage distribution on the wire would produce displacement current issuing all along the wire. This would be superposed on the radial displacement current emerging from the end of the wire. Such a continuous distribution of driving generators is not necessary in case (a) in which the wire can be insulated from the conducting medium. However, there is no substance with zero dielectric constant which could "insulate" the wire from a dielectric medium. Nevertheless, the hypothetical case (c) will help us obtain the field of the corresponding time-variable source and many other fields which are physically realizable and of great practical importance. Similarly, the current element in free space, case (k), is an abstraction, a mathematical model of a hypothetical physical source. Using its field, we can calculate the field of any physically realizable distribution.

The electric fields of point sources (a), (b), and (c) are, column by column

$$J_r = \frac{I}{4\pi r^2}, \qquad D_r = \frac{q}{4\pi r^2}, \qquad \dot{D}_r = \frac{I}{4\pi r^2}$$

$$E_r = \frac{I}{4\pi\sigma r^2}, \qquad E_r = \frac{q}{4\pi\epsilon r^2}, \qquad E_r = \frac{\int^t I\, dt}{4\pi\epsilon r^2} \qquad (2.48)$$

$$V = \frac{I}{4\pi\sigma r}, \qquad V = \frac{q}{4\pi\epsilon r}, \qquad V \text{ does not exist}$$

Here the analogy is almost complete. On the other hand, for magnetic fields we have

$$H_\varphi = -\frac{I(1 + \cos\theta)}{4\pi r \sin\theta}, \qquad \dot{H} = 0, \qquad H_\varphi = -\frac{I(1 + \cos\theta)}{4\pi r \sin\theta}. \qquad (2.49)$$

There is no magnetic field in the electrostatic case, and in (c) V does not exist when I is time variable.

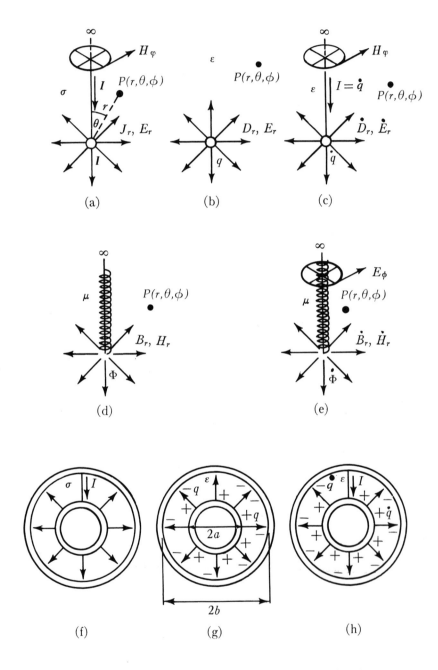

FIGURE 2.18   *Analogies between electric and magnetic fields.*

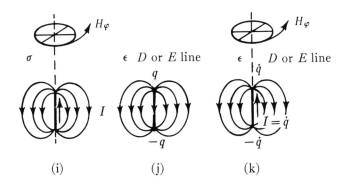

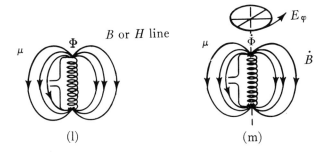

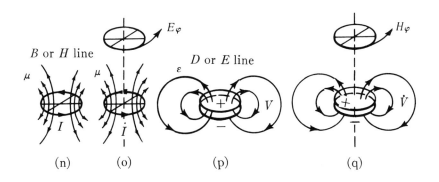

FIGURE 2.18 *Analogies between electric and magnetic fields.*

The magnetic fields of point sources (d) and (e) are, column by column,

$$B_r = \frac{\Phi}{4\pi r^2}, \qquad \dot{B}_r = \frac{\dot{\Phi}}{4\pi r^2}$$

$$H_r = \frac{\Phi}{4\pi \mu r^2} \qquad \dot{H}_r = \frac{\dot{\Phi}}{4\pi \mu r^2} \qquad (2.50)$$

$$U = \frac{\Phi}{4\pi \mu r} \qquad U = \text{does not exist.}$$

The analogy with equations (2.48) is unmistakable. The field of a magnetic point charge has been omitted because in the real world magnetic charge does not exist. On occasions it is convenient, however, to introduce fictitious magnetic charge in which case we have a third set of equations corresponding to the middle column in equations (2.48).

There is no electric field in the magnetostatic case; but in the time-variable case we have

$$E_\phi = \frac{\dot{\Phi}(1 + \cos \theta)}{4\pi r \sin \theta}. \qquad (2.51)$$

This equation is analogous to equation (2.49) *except for the difference in algebraic sign*. The difference arises from a similar difference in Maxwell's equations.

In (a), (b), and (c) since there is no electric field tangential to the spheres to begin with, we can introduce perfectly conducting spheres concentric with the point sources without disturbing the fields. Thus the fields between the spheres, (f), (g), and (h), will be given by equations (2.48) and (2.49). In (f) and (h) we can connect the "feed wires" to the spheres and disconnect the remaining wire portions. The fields inside the interior sphere and outside the exterior sphere will disappear and only those between them will remain. The reason for requiring perfect conductivity of the spheres becomes clear when we note that currents have to flow in them and an E_θ field would appear if the spheres were not perfectly conducting. If the conductivity σ between the spheres is much smaller than the conductivity of the spheres, E_θ will be much smaller than E_r and we have a good approximation to the ideal case.

In (g) the spheres need not be perfect since there is no current. Originally there is the charge q of the point source, $-q$ on the inside surface of the interior sphere, q on the outside surface, $-q$ on the inside surface of the exterior sphere, and q on its outside surface. Connecting the latter to ground, we remove the exterior field. Connecting the point charge to the interior sphere, we remove the field inside it. Thus only the charge q on the outer surface of the interior sphere and $-q$ on the inner surface of the exterior sphere will remain.

There are no physical magnetic analogs of (f), (g), and (h).

The fields of a double current source in an infinite conducting medium (i), of an electrostatic dipole (j), and of a current element in a dielectric medium (k) are, column by column,

$$V = \frac{Il \cos \theta}{4\pi\sigma r^2}, \qquad V = \frac{ql \cos \theta}{4\pi\epsilon r^2}, \qquad V \text{ does not exist}$$

$$E_r = \frac{Il \cos \theta}{2\pi\sigma r^3}, \qquad E_r = \frac{ql \cos \theta}{2\pi\epsilon r^3}, \qquad E_r = \frac{ql \cos \theta}{2\pi\epsilon r^3} \qquad (2.52)$$

$$E_\theta = \frac{Il \sin \theta}{4\pi\sigma r^3}, \qquad E_\theta = \frac{ql \sin \theta}{4\pi\epsilon r^3}, \qquad E_\theta = \frac{ql \sin \theta}{4\pi\epsilon r^3}$$

$$H_\varphi = \frac{Il \sin \theta}{4\pi r^2}, \qquad \vec{H} = 0, \qquad H_\varphi = \frac{Il \sin \theta}{4\pi r^2},$$

where in the third column $I = \dot{q}$ or $q = \int I \, dt$.

Similarly the fields of a magnetic dipole (l) and magnetic current element (m) are

$$U = \frac{\Phi l \cos \theta}{4\pi\mu r^2} \qquad U \text{ does not exist}$$

$$H_r = \frac{\Phi l \cos \theta}{2\pi\mu r^3}, \qquad H_r = \frac{\Phi l \cos \theta}{2\pi\mu r^3} \qquad (2.53)$$

$$H_\theta = \frac{\Phi l \sin \theta}{4\pi\mu r^3}, \qquad H_\theta = \frac{\Phi l \sin \theta}{4\pi\mu r^2}$$

$$\vec{E} = 0, \qquad E_\varphi = -\frac{\dot{\Phi} l \sin \theta}{4\pi r^2}.$$

Fields of the circulating currents, constant (n) and time variable
(o) are

$$H_r = \frac{IS \cos \theta}{2\pi r^3}, \qquad H_r = \frac{IS \cos \theta}{2\pi r^3}$$

$$H_\theta = \frac{IS \sin \theta}{4\pi r^3}, \qquad H_\theta = \frac{IS \sin \theta}{4\pi r^3} \qquad (2.54)$$

$$\vec{E} = 0, \qquad E_\varphi = -\frac{\mu \dot{I} S \sin \theta}{4\pi r^2}.$$

The scalar magnetic potential in case (n) is many-valued. From
equations (2.53) we obtain its "principal" value by letting $\Phi l = \mu I S$.

Finally, we have double layers of electric charge, (p) and (q),
analogs of circulating currents, whose fields are

$$E_r = \frac{VS \cos \theta}{2\pi r^3}, \qquad E_r = \frac{VS \cos \theta}{2\pi r^3}$$

$$E_\theta = \frac{VS \sin \theta}{4\pi r^3}, \qquad E_\theta = \frac{VS \sin \theta}{4\pi r^3} \qquad (2.55)$$

$$\vec{H} = 0, \qquad H_\varphi = \frac{\epsilon \dot{V} S \sin \theta}{4\pi r^2}.$$

The magnetic fields of a solenoid and a current ring are similar
but expressed in terms of two different quantities, dipole moment
Φl and area moment IS. We can express the magnetic flux Φ in terms
of the current I in the winding; but then we have to introduce the
number of turns per unit length n and the area S of the cross section
of the solenoid. These three parameters I, n, and S are conveniently
expressed by one parameter Φ. As S approaches zero, I has to increase
indefinitely to maintain a constant Φ. Similarly we can express I in a
current ring in terms of Φ; but then we have to introduce another
parameter, the radius of the wire. In fact, equations (2.54) are valid
when the radius of the wire is infinitesimal so that the magnetic flux
Φ is infinite.

Analogously, the fields of an electric dipole and a double layer are
similar but one is expressed in terms of the dipole moment ql and the
other in terms of the area moment VS. The dipole moment is finite
for point charges when the voltage between them is infinite. The area
moment is finite when the thickness of the double layer is infinitesimal
and the charges are infinite. There is no "area" connected with the
dipole.

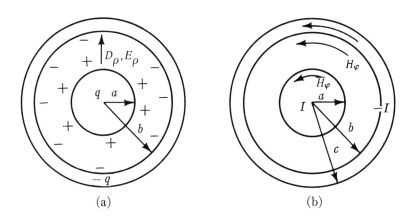

FIGURE 2.19   *A cross section of two coaxial cylinders: (a) equally but oppositely charged; (b) carrying equal but opposite currents.*

Two infinitely long, coaxial metal cylinders are shown in Figure 2.19. In (a) they are equally and oppositely charged; in (b) they carry equal and opposite currents, with current I in the inner cylinder flowing out of the page. In case (a) the field exists only between the cylinders. If q is the charge per unit length, the radial displacement per unit length is q and the displacement density is $q/2\pi\rho$ where ρ is the distance from the axis. Thus

$$D_\rho = \frac{q}{2\pi\rho}, \qquad E_\rho = \frac{q}{2\pi\epsilon\rho}. \qquad (2.56)$$

The magnetic field (b) on the other hand, exists not only between the cylinders but *in* the cylinders as well. The magnetomotive force round a circle of radius ρ equals the enclosed current and hence we have

$$H_\varphi = \frac{I\rho}{2\pi a^2}, \qquad 0 \le \rho \le a$$

$$= \frac{I}{2\pi\rho} \qquad a \le \rho \le b \qquad (2.57)$$

$$= \frac{I(c^2 - \rho^2)}{2\pi\rho(c^2 - b^2)}, \qquad b \le \rho \le c$$

$$= 0, \qquad \rho \ge c.$$

If, in cases (a) and (b) b approaches infinity and a approaches zero, we have an infinitely long filament of either charge or current in free space.

2.12 Images

In problems studied so far, we have dealt, for the most part, with fields in infinite homogeneous media. In mixed media even the field of a point source is considerably more complex and more powerful methods are needed for their calculation. Some cases, however, can be solved by elementary methods. One of these is the case of two semi-infinite homogeneous media separated by a plane boundary.

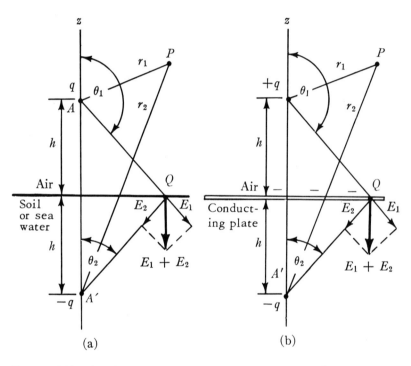

FIGURE 2.20 *A point charge q at A and its image $-q$ at A': (a) above and below the plane interface between air (or some dielectric) and a conducting medium; (b) above and below a conducting plate.*

Consider a charge q at point A above ground or sea water at height h as shown in Figure 2.20(a). Soil and sea water are conductors, even though poor conductors as compared to metals. Hence the charge at A will pull a charge of opposite sign to the surface until the electric field below the surface is reduced to zero and the tangential component on the surface also becomes equal to zero. Similarly if the charge is above a thin conducting plane, Figure 2.20(b), a charge of opposite sign will be pulled (from infinity) until the component tangential to the plane vanishes. This is the essential condition which the field in the upper half space must fulfill. To the original field of the point charge at A, we must add another field which will make the total tangential component on the conducting surface equal to zero. To find this field we imagine a charge $-q$ at the mirror image point A' below the surface. The resultant field of both charges satisfies the above requirement. Thus we have the required potential *above* the interface

$$V = \frac{q}{4\pi\epsilon_0 r_1} - \frac{q}{4\pi\epsilon_0 r_2}, \qquad z \geq 0. \qquad (2.58)$$

The first term is the potential of the point charge q at A as it would exist in an infinite medium. The second term is the potential of the surface charge so distributed that it makes the total potential constant on the surface. The differential of V in a direction tangent to the surface, and thus the tangential component of the electric field, is zero on the surface. *As far as the upper region is concerned*, this added potential equals the potential of the *image charge* $-q$ below the surface. This image charge is a *virtual source*, not a real source, since actually there is no charge at A'.

The potential of the surface charge in the upper and lower half spaces is symmetric about the surface. Therefore, *in the lower half space* the surface charge potential is equal to the potential of a virtual charge $-q$ at point A which thus cancels the potential of the real charge.

The density of the surface charge equals the normal component of the total $\vec{D}$ at the surface

$$q_S = D_z = -\epsilon_0 \frac{\partial V}{\partial z} = -\frac{q \cos\theta_2}{2\pi(h^2 + \rho^2)}, \qquad (2.59)$$

where ρ is the distance from the axis AA' and θ_2 is the angle indicated in Figure 2.20.

In the case of two semi-infinite dielectric media, air and pure water for instance (Figure 2.21) the field of a point charge in one medium will penetrate the other. This field will displace the bound electrons, and at the interface between two media a layer of bound charge will appear. Since the impressed field of the point charge at A is the same as in the preceding problem, we conjecture that the bound surface charge will be distributed in the same manner as the free charge on a conducting plane and that *above the interface* the

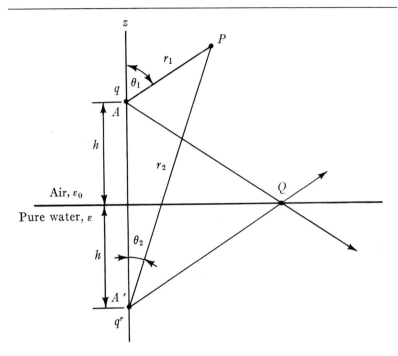

FIGURE 2.21   *A point charge q at A and its image q^r at A' in the plane interface between two pure dielectrics, air and pure water, for example.*

field of this surface charge, the reflected field, might be the same as that which would be produced by some image charge q^r at A'. The *transmitted field* below the interface is the sum of the field of the surface charge and the impressed field. We conjecture that this field might be the same as that which would be produced by some charge q^t at A. Thus we assume the potential of the total field as follows:

$$V = \frac{q}{4\pi\epsilon_0 r_1} + \frac{q^r}{4\pi\epsilon_0 r_2}, \qquad z \geq 0$$

$$\text{(2.60)}$$

$$= \frac{q^t}{4\pi\epsilon r_1}, \qquad z \leq 0.$$

At the interface $r_1 = r_2$ the tangential component of $\bar{E}$ must be continuous. Hence the potential must be continuous and

$$q + q^r = q^t(\epsilon_0/\epsilon). \qquad \text{(2.61)}$$

The normal component of $\bar{D}$ must also be continuous. First we find

$$D_z = \frac{q \cos \theta_1}{4\pi r_1^2} + \frac{q^r \cos \theta_2}{4\pi r_2^2}, \qquad z \geq 0$$

$$= \frac{q^t \cos \theta_1}{4\pi r_1^2}, \qquad z \leq 0.$$

At the interface $r_1 = r_2$ and $\theta_2 = \pi - \theta_1$, so that the continuity of D_z yields

$$q - q^r = q^t. \tag{2.62}$$

From equations (2.61) and (2.62) we find

$$q^r = \frac{\epsilon_0 - \epsilon}{\epsilon_0 + \epsilon} q, \qquad q^t = \frac{2\epsilon}{\epsilon_0 + \epsilon} q. \tag{2.63}$$

Note that as $\epsilon \to \infty$, $q^r \to -q$ and $q^t \to 2q$.

Still another case is that of a direct current source in a conducting medium, sea water for example, with a nonconducting medium above as shown in Figure 2.22. Here the boundary condition is: the normal component J_z of the conduction current density must vanish at the interface. For a source I at point A this condition will be satisfied by the addition of an image source I at point A' at the same distance above the interface. Thus

$$V = \frac{I}{4\pi\sigma r_1} + \frac{I}{4\pi\sigma r_2}, \qquad z \leq 0. \tag{2.64}$$

On the interface

$$V = \frac{I}{2\pi\sigma r_1}, \qquad z = 0.$$

This is twice the potential of current I emerging from A. The potential is continuous across the interface. Hence, for the electric field above the interface we have

$$V = \frac{I}{2\pi\sigma r_1}, \qquad E_{r_1} = \frac{I}{2\pi\sigma r_1^2}, \qquad z > 0. \tag{2.65}$$

At the interface the tangential component of $\bar{E}$ maintains the current in the sea water just below. In sea water the normal component of $\bar{E}$ vanishes since the normal component of the conduction current density vanishes. The discontinuity in the normal component of $\bar{E}$ is due to a surface layer of charge of density

$$q_s = D_n = \frac{\epsilon_0 I \cos \theta_1}{2 \pi \sigma r_1^2}.$$

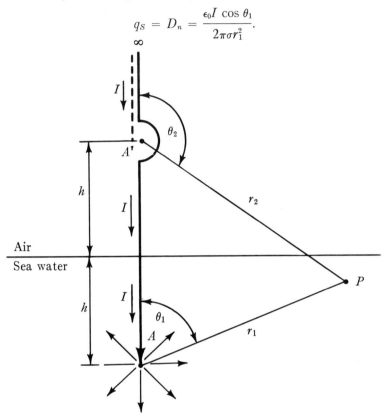

FIGURE 2.22 *A point source of direct current I in a conducting medium (such as sea water) at point A and its image at A' in a nonconducting medium, such as air.*

The magnetic intensity below the interface is obtained by adding two magnetic intensities. One is due to the current I which runs through the wire to point A and then spreads radially from A. The other is due to the reflection of this radial current from the interface which appears to emanate radially from the image source at A'. Thus

$$H_\varphi = -\frac{I(1 + \cos \theta_1)}{4 \pi \rho} - \frac{I(1 + \cos \theta_2)}{4 \pi \rho}$$

$$\hspace{6cm} (2.66)$$

$$= -\frac{I(2 + \cos \theta_1 + \cos \theta_2)}{4 \pi \rho}, \quad z \leq 0.$$

Above the interface the magnetomotive force round a circle of radius ρ, coaxial with the wire, equals $-I$ since this is the only current crossing the area of the circle. Therefore

$$H_\varphi = -\frac{I}{2\pi\rho}, \qquad z \geq 0. \tag{2.67}$$

Note that H_φ is continuous at the interface.

2.13 Tubes of flow and equipotential surfaces

Examples in this section illustrate the manner in which boundary conditions affect fields in mixed media and explain why such fields are usually complicated and hard to evaluate. In the first series of related examples we consider electric fields between two infinite perfectly conducting coaxial cylinders, either equally and oppositely charged or carrying equal and opposite currents. Two different media, conducting in one case and dielectric in the other, are separated either by radial planes, Figure 2.23(a), or by a coaxial cylindrical surface, Figure 2.23(b).

Let us consider in detail the radial current flow in case (a). When the media are separated by radial planes, $\vec{E}$ is continuous across them; $\vec{E}$ is at right angles to the cylinders because they are perfectly conducting. These conditions are satisfied if we assume that $\vec{E}$ is radial

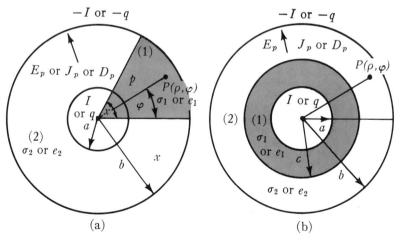

(a)   (b)

FIGURE 2.23 *A cross section of two coaxial metal cylinders, either equally but oppositely charged, or carrying equal but opposite currents: (a) when two different, conducting or dielectric media are separated by radial planes; (b) when the media are separated by a coaxial cylindrical boundary.*

in both media

$$E_\rho = \frac{A}{\rho}, \qquad 0 \le \varphi \le 2\pi.$$

Hence

$$J_\rho = \frac{\sigma_1 A}{\rho}, \qquad 0 < \varphi < \alpha$$

$$= \frac{\sigma_2 A}{\rho}, \qquad \alpha < \varphi < 2\pi.$$

Let K be the total radial current per unit length of the coaxial pair

$$K = \int_0^{2\pi} J_\rho \rho \, d\varphi = \sigma_1 A \alpha + \sigma_2 A (2\pi - \alpha).$$

Thus we can express A in terms of K and obtain

$$E_\rho = \frac{K}{[\sigma_1 \alpha + \sigma_2 (2\pi - \alpha)]\rho}, \qquad 0 \le \varphi \le 2\pi$$

$$J_\rho = \frac{\sigma_1 K}{[\sigma_1 \alpha + \sigma_2 (2\pi - \alpha)]\rho}, \qquad 0 < \varphi < \alpha \qquad (2.68)$$

$$= \frac{\sigma_2 K}{[\sigma_1 \alpha + \sigma_2 (2\pi - \alpha)]\rho}, \qquad \alpha < \varphi < 2\pi.$$

If $\sigma_2 = 0$, so that the medium is a dielectric (air, for instance), the radial current vanishes in the region but the electric intensity does not. Hence

$$J_\rho = 0, \qquad E_\rho = \frac{K}{\sigma_1 \alpha \rho}, \qquad \alpha < \varphi < 2\pi.$$

Therefore

$$D_\rho = \frac{\epsilon_0 K}{\sigma_1 \alpha \rho}, \qquad \alpha < \varphi < 2\pi.$$

Thus in this region the charge density on the inner cylinder is $\epsilon_0 K / \sigma_1 \alpha a$ and on the outer cylinder $-\epsilon_0 K / \sigma_1 \alpha b$.

When the boundary between media is cylindrical as shown in Figure 2.23(b), it is the radial current density or displacement density, as the case may be, which is continuous. Thus, for dielectric media,

$$D_\rho = \frac{q}{2\pi\rho}, \qquad a \le \rho \le b$$

$$E_\rho = \frac{q}{2\pi\epsilon_1\rho}, \qquad a \le \rho < c \tag{2.69}$$

$$= \frac{q}{2\pi\epsilon_2\rho}, \qquad c < \rho \le b.$$

Two analogous situations exist in the case of magnetostatic fields between coaxial cylinders carrying equal and opposite currents. See Figure 2.24. The fields are confined to the space between the cylinders. Magnetic lines are circles when the permeabilities μ_1 and μ_2 are equal. It appears that they can still be circles when $\mu_1 \ne \mu_2$, provided B_φ is continuous across the radial boundaries and H_φ across the cylindrical boundary. Thus in case (a) we set

$$B_\varphi = \frac{A}{\rho}, \qquad 0 \le \varphi \le 2\pi$$

$$H_\varphi = \frac{A}{\mu_1\rho}, \qquad 0 < \varphi < \alpha \tag{2.70}$$

$$= \frac{A}{\mu_2\rho}, \qquad \alpha < \varphi < 2\pi.$$

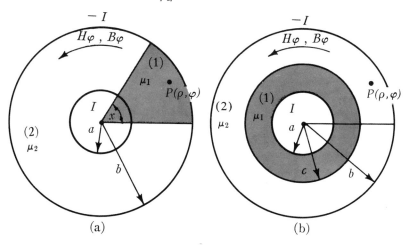

(a)   (b)

FIGURE 2.24   *A cross section of two coaxial cylinders carrying equal but opposite currents: (a) when two homogeneous media with different permeabilities are separated by radial planes; (b) when the media are separated by a coaxial cylindrical boundary.*

The magnetomotive force round a magnetic line should equal the enclosed current

$$\int_0^{2\pi} H_\varphi \rho \, d\varphi = I$$

or

$$\mu_1^{-1} A \alpha + \mu_2^{-1} A (2\pi - \alpha) = I. \qquad (2.71)$$

Hence

$$A = \frac{\mu_1 \mu_2 I}{\mu_2 \alpha + \mu_1 (2\pi - \alpha)} \qquad (2.72)$$

and we have the magnetic field, equation (2.70), in terms of the current in the cylinders.

The current is not distributed uniformly round the cylinders. There is no magnetic field outside the coaxial pair or in the interior of the inner cylinder. By the Ampere-Maxwell law the current is always equal to the magnetomotive force round a closed path encircling the current. Hence if we take a path along a magnetic line in region (1) between the interfaces with region (2) and complete the path with radial lines along the interfaces, piercing the inner cylinder and joined together in its interior, we find that current I_1 in the enclosed portion of the cylinder is

$$I_1 = \mu_1^{-1} A \alpha = \frac{\mu_2 \alpha I}{\mu_2 \alpha + \mu_1 (2\pi - \alpha)}.$$

The current in the remaining portion of the cylinder is

$$I_2 = \mu_2^{-1} A (2\pi - \alpha) = \frac{\mu_1 (2\pi - \alpha) I}{\mu_2 \alpha + \mu_1 (2\pi - \alpha)}.$$

We can take a section of the coaxial pair and form a toroid (see Figure 2.25) with a perfectly conducting boundary. A coaxial pair and two parallel planes form a link between the toroid and a generator. The field inside the toroid is the same as in the preceding case and the circulating currents in the two portions of the toroid are as given above.

The field inside a closely and uniformly wound solenoid of the same shape and dimensions as the toroid is also given by equations (2.70) and (2.72) in which $I = nI_w$, where n is the number of turns and I_w the current in the winding. The major difference is that the discontinuity in H_φ across the winding is now the same round the solenoid. Since H_φ in the interior is different in the regions with different permeabilities, we must have a magnetic field outside the

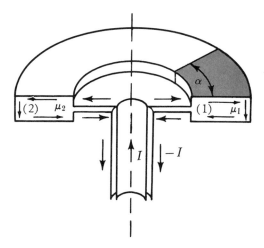

FIGURE 2.25   *A toroidal conductor carrying a circulating current with two sectors of different permeabilities.*

solenoid. The sources of this field are at the interfaces of the two media. If one medium is iron and the other air, the iron becomes a magnet. The magnetic lines emerging from one pole of this magnet and converging to the other leak out of the solenoid between the adjacent turns of the winding.

The difference between a toroid with perfectly conducting walls and a solenoid may be summarized as follows: In the toroid the field cannot escape from the interior but the current can and does redistribute itself; in the solenoid the circulating current cannot redistribute itself but the field can and does escape the interior through the gaps in the winding.

In the case of cylindrical layers with different permeabilities as illustrated in Figure 2.24(b), we have

$$H_\varphi = \frac{I}{2\pi\rho}, \qquad 0 \le \varphi \le 2\pi$$

$$B_\varphi = \frac{\mu_1 I}{2\pi\rho}, \qquad a \le \rho < c \qquad\qquad (2.73)$$

$$= \frac{\mu_2 I}{2\pi\rho}, \qquad c < \rho \le b.$$

Let us examine the reasons why the solutions in the foregoing examples turned out to be simple. Suppose we start with a homogenous isotropic medium and calculate the field. We can represent it graphically by drawing lines of flow tangential to $\bar{E}$, and equipotential surfaces perpendicular to the lines of flow. The field may thus

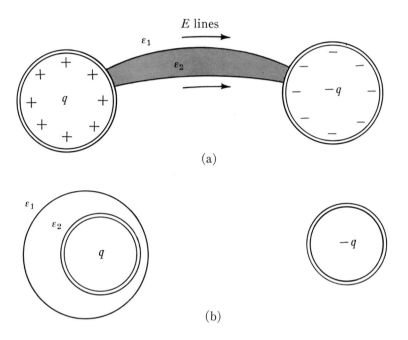

(a)

(b)

FIGURE 2.26 (a) A tube of flow between two charged conductors; (b) an equipotential layer surrounding one of them.

be divided either into tubes of flow, bounded by lines of flow, or into *equipotential layers*, bounded by equipotential surfaces. In the preceding examples tubes of flow are radial sectors in the case of electric fields and toroids in the case of magnetic fields. Equipotential layers are cylindrical shells in the case of electric fields and radial sectors in the case of magnetic fields.

By definition there is no flow of current, electric displacement, or magnetic flux, as the case may be, across the lateral boundary of a tube of flow. The flow takes place from one source to the other through the ends of the tube. If the medium within a complete tube of flow [see Figure 2.26(a)] is replaced with some other isotropic medium, the boundary conditions along the lateral boundary are satisfied by the same type of field configuration. The tangential component is continuous and produces either more flow or less, depending on the parameters of the new medium but does not produce any flow across the boundary. Thus the normal components of flow remain equal to zero and their continuity is preserved.

Similarly the medium within a complete equipotential layer surrounding a source, Figure 2.26(b), may be replaced with some other medium without upsetting the boundary conditions.

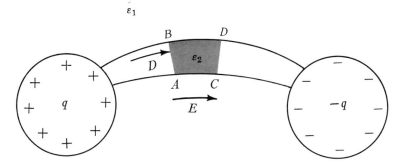

FIGURE 2.27   *An intersection ABCD of a tube of flow and an equipotential layer.*

The boundary conditions *will be upset if a portion of a tube of flow* (or of an equipotential layer) is replaced with some other medium. See Figure 2.27. The voltage from AB to CD would produce more flow between these surfaces if $\epsilon_2 > \epsilon_1$, and yet the amount of flow should have been preserved. Alternatively the same flow would lower the voltage between AB and CD and thus detach this volume from the equipotential layer. The field configuration has to change and the knowledge of the field for the homogeneous case does not help us solve the more general case.

2.14 Properties of fields in the large

Certain quantities may be associated with fields *in the large*. For a given field these quantities depend on its geometry, on the physical characteristics of the media and on the details of field distribution. However, the same quantities may be associated with many quite different fields. For example, current I in a tube of flow is proportional to the voltage V across it. The ratio

$$G = I/V$$

is a property of this tube. The quantity G may be either calculated or measured. Usually the voltage which produces the current is given. The resulting current can then be calculated if G, called the *conductance* of the tube, is known. The reciprocal of the conductance

$$R = 1/G = V/I$$

is called the *resistance* of the tube.

Tubes of flow are *in parallel*. Currents in the individual tubes are added to obtain the total current. The conductances of these tubes are also added to obtain the total conductance.

Equipotential layers are *in series*. The voltages across the individual layers are added to obtain the total voltage across them all. Hence the resistance of several equipotential layers is the sum of the resistances of the individual layers.

Analogous quantities may be associated with electrostatic and magnetostatic fields. In the next three sections we shall consider such quantities for more general fields.

2.15   Resistance and conductance coefficients

Let I_1 and I_2 be electric currents emerging from two perfectly conducting bodies K_1 and K_2, imbedded in a conducting medium, Figure 2.28. Each body is connected, of course, with an insulated wire to one terminal of a generator whose other terminal is connected to a wire conveying current from infinity (or ground). The potentials of K_1 and K_2 with reference to infinity (or ground) are linear functions of the currents

$$V_1 = r_{11}I_1 + r_{12}I_2,$$

$$V_2 = r_{21}I_1 + r_{22}I_2.$$

$$(2.74)$$

Analogous equations are true for any number of conductors. Co-

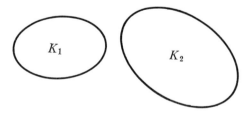

FIGURE 2.28   *Two perfect conductors K_1 and K_2 serving as sources of direct current in a dissipative medium.*

efficients r_{mn} are called the *mutual resistance coefficients* when $m \neq n$, and *self-resistance coefficients* when $m = n$.

To calculate these quantities we have to solve an appropriate field problem. For example, if K_1 and K_2 are spheres of radii a and b, small compared with the distance l between their centers, then approximately

$$V_1 = \frac{I_1}{4\pi\sigma a} + \frac{I_2}{4\pi\sigma l},$$

(2.75)

$$V_2 = \frac{I_1}{4\pi\sigma l} + \frac{I_2}{4\pi\sigma b}.$$

It is not just a coincidence that $r_{21} = r_{12}$. It is always true that

$$r_{mn} = r_{nm},$$

(2.76)

as we shall presently show.

To obtain the resistance coefficients experimentally we should disconnect one body, K_2 for instance, from the source of current and measure the ratios

$$r_{11} = V_1/I_1, \qquad r_{21} = V_2/I_1.$$

(2.77)

A mutual resistance coefficient is seen to be equal to the potential of one body due to a unit current emerging from another. The *reciprocity relation*, equation (2.76), means therefore that the *potential of K_m due to a unit current emerging from K_n equals the potential of K_n due to a unit current emerging from K_m.*

If $I_2 = -I_1$, the entire current emerging from K_1 flows into K_2. In accordance with the definition in Section 2.14, the resistance between K_1 and K_2 is

$$R = (V_1 - V_2)/I_1 = r_{11} - 2r_{12} + r_{22}.$$

(2.78)

Solving equation (2.74) for I_1 and I_2, we have

$$I_1 = g_{11}V_1 + g_{12}V_2,$$

$$I_2 = g_{21}V_1 + g_{22}V_2,$$

(2.79)

where

$$g_{11} = r_{22}/D, \qquad g_{22} = r_{11}/D,$$

$$g_{21} = g_{12} = -r_{12}/D, \qquad D = r_{11}r_{22} - r_{12}^2.$$

The g_{mn} are called the conductance coefficients. With a little thought given to the method of solving a field problem, such as that leading to equation (2.75), we conclude that the *resistance coefficients are essentially positive*. The self-conductances must also be positive: If V_2 is equal to zero, then the current must flow out of K_1 if V_1 is positive. Therefore D must be positive, and we conclude that the *mutual conductance coefficients are essentially negative*.

Some current emerging from K_1 goes directly to K_2; the rest goes to infinity (or ground). Likewise, some current from K_2 goes to K_1 and the rest goes to infinity (or ground). Hence, there is a net current between K_1 and K_2. This current, in the direction from K_1 to K_2, is proportional to the potential drop $V_1 - V_2$. The coefficient of proportionality, G_{12}, is called the *direct conductance* between K_1 and K_2. Thus that part of I_1 which goes directly to K_2 is $G_{12}(V_1 - V_2)$. The remainder, going to infinity, is $G_{1\infty}V_1$, where $G_{1\infty}$ is the direct conductance to infinity. Similarly, that part of I_2 which goes to K_1 is $G_{12}(V_2 - V_1) = -G_{12}(V_1 - V_2)$. Thus

$$I_1 = G_{1\infty}V_1 + G_{12}(V_1 - V_2),$$

$$I_2 = G_{12}(V_2 - V_1) + G_{2\infty}V_2. \tag{2.80}$$

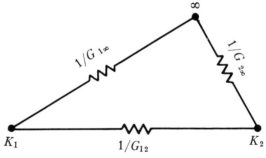

FIGURE 2.29 *An equivalent network representing properties in the large of the field of two sources of current, such as K_1 and K_2 in Figure 2.28.*

Comparing with equations (2.79), we have

$$g_{11} = G_{1\infty} + G_{12}, \qquad g_{12} = -G_{12},$$

$$g_{22} = G_{2\infty} + G_{12}, \qquad g_{21} = -G_{12}. \tag{2.81}$$

Thus we have proven the reciprocity theorem and have shown once more that the mutual conductance coefficients are negative (since the direct conductance G_{12} is essentially positive).

We have also shown that *in the large* the current flow in the medium may be represented by a network of resistors. See Figure 2.29. The resistances in this network are the reciprocals of the following conductances

$$G_{1\infty} = g_{11} + g_{12}, \qquad G_{12} = -g_{12},$$

$$G_{2\infty} = g_{22} + g_{12}.$$

2.16 Potential and capacitance coefficients

If the medium surrounding the conducting bodies in Figure 2.28 is dielectric, and if q_1 and q_2 are the charges on K_1 and K_2, then

$$V_1 = p_{11}q_1 + p_{12}q_2,$$
$$\tag{2.82}$$
$$V_2 = p_{21}q_1 + p_{22}q_2,$$

where the p are the *potential coefficients*. All equations are analogous to those in the preceding section (except that the conductivity σ, wherever it appears, should be replaced by the dielectric constant ϵ; only the names of various quantities are different.

If charges are expressed in terms of potentials,

$$q_1 = c_{11}V_1 + c_{12}V_2,$$
$$\tag{2.83}$$
$$q_2 = c_{21}V_1 + c_{22}V_2.$$

The coefficients are called the *capacitance coefficients*.

If $q_2 = -q_1$ and all other conductors, if any, are uncharged, the ratio

$$C = q_1/(V_1 - V_2) \tag{2.84}$$

is called the *capacitance* between K_1 and K_2.

The equivalent network of capacitors is similar to that in Figure 2.29. The *direct capacitance* C_{12} will appear between the nodes K_1 and K_2. The remaining capacitances will be $C_{1\infty}$ and $C_{2\infty}$.

2.17 Inductance coefficients

With some understandable differences the properties of magnetic fields in the large are similar to those of electric fields. Let I_1 and I_2 be the currents in two conducting loops, Figure 2.30, Φ_1 be the magnetic flux linked with the first loop, and Φ_2 be the flux linked with the second loop. The magnetic field at each point of the field is in part proportional to I_1 and in part to I_2. The same will be true of Φ_1 and Φ_2,

$$\Phi_1 = L_{11}I_1 + L_{12}I_2,$$
$$\Phi_2 = L_{21}I_1 + L_{22}I_2. \tag{2.85}$$

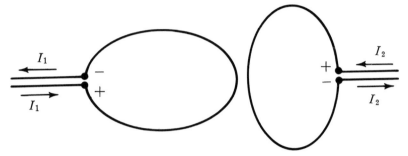

FIGURE 2.30   *Two current loops.*

Here L_{11} and L_{22} are the self-inductances of the loops and $L_{21} = L_{12}$ is the mutual inductance.

If I_1 and I_2 are varying with time and the loops are perfectly conducting, the voltages between the terminals are

$$V_1 = \dot{\Phi}_1 = L_{11}\dot{I}_1 + L_{12}\dot{I}_2,$$
$$V_2 = \dot{\Phi}_2 = L_{21}\dot{I}_1 + L_{22}\dot{I}_2. \tag{2.86}$$

If we have two closely-wound coils with n_1 and n_2 turns, we should replace in equations (2.85) I_1 by n_1I_1 and I_2 by n_2I_2. Thus

$$\Phi_1 = n_1L_{11}I_1 + n_2L_{12}I_2,$$
$$\Phi_2 = n_1L_{21}I_1 + n_2L_{22}I_2.$$

Then the voltages across the terminals of the coils are

$$V_1 = n_1\dot{\Phi}_1 = n_1^2L_{11}\dot{I}_1 + n_1n_2L_{12}\dot{I}_2,$$
$$V_2 = n_2\dot{\Phi}_2 = n_1n_2L_{21}\dot{I}_1 + n_2^2L_{22}\dot{I}_2. \tag{2.87}$$

The quantities $n_1^2L_{11}$ and $n_2^2L_{22}$ are the inductances of the coils and $n_1n_2L_{12}$ is the mutual inductance. Actually the "transformer ratios" n_1^2, n_2^2, and n_1n_2 will be reduced by the flux leakage between the turns of the coils.

2.18   Transmission lines

Electric charge in a wire PQ, as shown in Figure 2.31(a), moving slowly back and forth in a uniform magnetic field is subject to a force

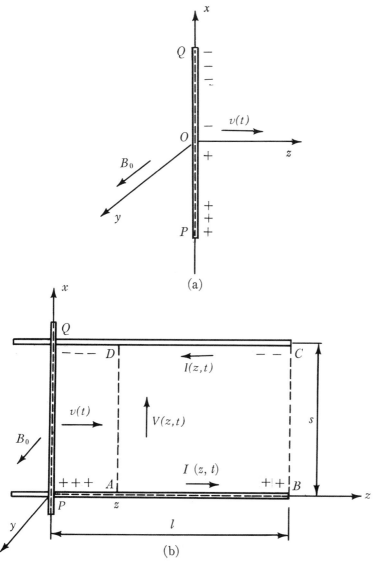

FIGURE 2.31 (a) *A wire moving in a magnetic field; (b) a wire sliding on parallel wires in a magnetic field.*

(Sections 1.17 and 1.18). This *motional* or *induced* force per unit charge is

$$E_x^i = -B_0 v(t), \qquad (2.88)$$

where B_0 is the magnitude of the magnetic flux density and $v(t)$ is the speed of the wire. The density (per unit length) of the displaced charge $Q(x, t)$ may be obtained from equation (2.18) where we use $A(x)$ as the function defined in equation (2.16), since this is a better approximation then $A_1(x)$. Thus

$$Q(x, t) = -\frac{B_0 v(t) x}{A(x)}. \tag{2.89}$$

The electric field around the wire can now be calculated as in Section 2.2.

At distances large compared with the length s of the wire, the electric field is essentially that of a dipole. Two elements of charge, $Q(x, t)\, dx$ and $Q(-x, t)\, dx$, form a dipole of moment $2xQ(x, t)\, dx$ and the moment of the entire charge distribution is

$$p = 2 \int_0^{\frac{1}{2}s} xQ(x, t)\, dx.$$

Replacing $A(x)$ in equation (2.89) by its average value [equation (2.17)] we have approximately

$$p = -\tfrac{1}{12} C_0 B_0 s^3 v(t), \tag{2.90}$$

where

$$C_0 = \frac{\pi\epsilon}{\ln (s/2a) - 1},$$

and a is the radius of the wire. The electric field is concentrated around the wire since the field of a dipole decreases as the cube of the reciprocal of the distance.

Suppose now that the wire is sliding back and forth on a pair of parallel wires of length l, Figure 2.31(b). The field voltage between the ends of the wire is

$$V_{PQ} = -sE_x^i = B_0 s v(t), \tag{2.91}$$

where s is the distance between the axes of the wires. The motional voltage will displace electric charge from the upper wire to the lower. Let $q(z, t)$ be the charge per unit length on the lower wire. Except near ends, the field around the wire due to this charge is given by equation (2.56). Hence the transverse voltage from the lower wire to the upper, due to this charge, is

$$V_1 = \int_a^s E_\rho\, d\rho = \frac{q(z, t) \ln (s/a)}{2\pi\epsilon},$$

where a is the radius of the wire. The charge on the upper wire is $-q(z, t)$ and it produces an equal voltage. Thus the total transverse voltage is

$$V(z, t) = \frac{q(z, t)}{C}, \tag{2.92}$$

where C is the *capacitance per unit length of the parallel pair*

$$C = \frac{\pi \epsilon}{\ln (s/a)}. \tag{2.93}$$

The current $I(z, t)$ in the lower wire equals the time rate of increase of the charge on AB, Figure 2.31 (b),

$$I(z, t) = \frac{\partial}{\partial t} \int_z^l q(z, t) \, dz = \int_z^l C \frac{\partial}{\partial t} V(z, t) \, dz. \tag{2.94}$$

According to Faraday-Maxwell law the electromotive force round the closed circuit $ABCDA$ is

$$V_{AB} + V_{BC} + V_{CD} + V_{DA} = -\frac{\partial \Phi}{\partial t}, \tag{2.95}$$

where Φ is the magnetic flux (out of the paper) through the rectangle. The magnetic intensity of the field produced by the current in the lower wire is [equation (2.57)]

$$H_\varphi = \frac{I(z, t)}{2 \pi \rho}, \qquad \rho \geq a.$$

The contribution of this to Φ is

$$\Phi_1 = \int_z^l \int_a^s \mu H_\varphi \, d\rho \, dz = \int_z^l \frac{\mu}{2\pi} \ln \frac{s}{a} I(z, t) \, dz.$$

There is an equal contribution from the field produced by the current in the upper wire. Hence

$$\Phi = \int_z^l L I(z, t) \, dz, \tag{2.96}$$

where L is the *inductance per unit length of the parallel pair*

$$L = \frac{\mu}{\pi} \ln \frac{s}{a}. \tag{2.97}$$

If R_1 and R_2 are the resistances of the lower and upper wires, per unit length, then

$$V_{AB} = \int_z^l R_1 I(z, t) \, dz,$$

$$V_{DC} = -\int_z^l R_2 I(z, t) \, dz. \tag{2.98}$$

These equations are approximate. To understand the nature of approximations consider a wire (Figure 2.32) carrying current. There is a magnetic field inside the wire [see equation (2.57)]. As long as the current is steady, the magnetic field is constant and does not affect the distribution of current. But when it is varying with time, the time derivative of magnetic flux linked with a closed circuit (in a

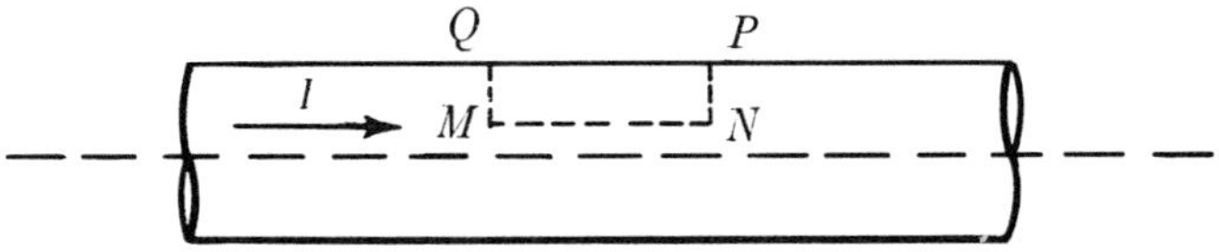

FIGURE 2.32   *A closed circuit MNPQM in a radial plane of a conducting wire carrying current I.*

radial plane) will make V_{MN} and V_{QP} unequal. The current distribution will no longer be uniform. This will affect the resistances and the inductance. If variations with time are "slow enough," the effect will be small. If the wire is very thin, the flux linked with the rectangle $MNPQ$ is small, and the effect will be small even for more rapidly varying fields. Later we shall demonstrate that the effect of the time-variable magnetic field is to drive the current toward the surface of the wire (the "skin effect") and thus increase the resistance.

The remaining voltages in equation (2.95) are

$$V_{BC} = V(l, t), \qquad V_{DA} = -V(z, t).$$

Taking all these results into consideration, we transform equation (2.95) into

$$V(z, t) = V(l, t) + \int_z^l (R_1 + R_2) I(z, t) \, dz + \int_z^l L \frac{\partial}{\partial t} I(z, t) \, dz. \tag{2.99}$$

Equations (2.99) and (2.94) determine the relation between the transverse voltage from one wire to the other and the current in the wires. The transverse voltage at the sliding wire [see equation (2.91)] is

$$V(0, t) = B_0 s v(t). \tag{2.100}$$

Neglecting the time derivatives, we have initial approximations

$$V^{(0)}(z, t) = V(l, t), \qquad I^{(0)}(z, t) = 0.$$

Thus the voltage, generated in the moving wire may be "transmitted" to large distances from it. Substituting the first of these equations in equation (2.94), we obtain the next approximation to the current

$$I^{(1)}(z, t) = \int_z^l C \frac{\partial}{\partial t} V(l, t) \, dz = C(l - z) \frac{\partial}{\partial t} V(l, t). \tag{2.101}$$

Even though C is small, for long wires the current in the sliding wire and near it may be substantial. Substituting in equation (2.99), we obtain the next approximation for the transverse voltage

$$V^{(1)}(z, t) = V(l, t) + \tfrac{1}{2}(R_1 + R_2)C(l - z)^2 \frac{\partial}{\partial t} V(l, t)$$
$$+ \tfrac{1}{2}LC(l - z)^2 \frac{\partial^2}{\partial t^2} V(l, t).$$

These successive approximations can be continued indefinitely. Simpler results are obtained if the dependence on time is sinusoidal, $V(l, t) = V(l) \sin \omega t$, since the time derivatives can be easily calculated and the end voltage $V(l)$ can be related to the "generator" voltage given by equation (2.100) in the present example. Of course, equations connecting $V(z, t)$ and $I(z, t)$ do not depend on the kind of generator we happen to connect to the wires.

If the parallel wires are shorted at the far end BC (see Figure 2.33) the equations connecting $V(z, t)$ and $I(z, t)$ are essentially the same as in the preceding case except that $V(l, t)$ is equal to zero in equation (2.99), and current $I(l, t)$ through the shorting rod should be included on the right-hand side of equation (2.94) so that it becomes

$$I(z, t) = I(l, t) + \int_z^l C \frac{\partial}{\partial t} V(z, t) \, dz. \tag{2.102}$$

For the shorted pair the initial approximation is

$$I^{(0)}(z, t) = I(l, t).$$

Substituting this in equation (2.99), we have

$$V^{(0)}(z, t) = (R_1 + R_2)(l - z)I(l, t) + L(l - z) \frac{\partial}{\partial t} I(l, t). \tag{2.103}$$

This may be substituted in equation (2.102) and the iterative process may be continued indefinitely.

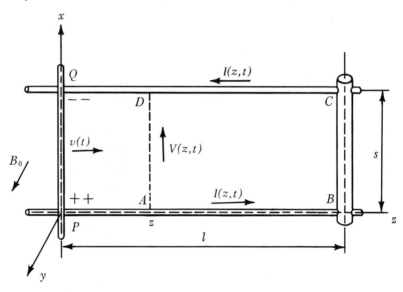

FIGURE 2.33   *A wire PQ sliding on parallel wires PB and QC, terminated by a resistive rod BC, in the presence of a magnetic field.*

More generally we may have some resistance R_L ("load" resistance) at the far end BC. In this case neither $V(l, t)$ nor $I(l, t)$ vanishes. Instead we have

$$V(l, t) = RI(l, t).$$

Again, there is only one unknown quantity which can ultimately be related to the generator voltage or the "input voltage" at $z = 0$.

Thus a pair of parallel conductors may be used for transmitting electric and magnetic effects to large distances from their source. The name for such a pair is *transmission line*.

In equations (2.99) and (2.102) the quantity l does not have to refer to the end of the line. If l is equal to $z + \Delta z$, where Δz is infinitesimal, we may express the increments ΔV and ΔI in terms of I and V and obtain $\partial V/\partial z$ and $\partial I/\partial z$ in the limit. Alternatively we can differentiate equations (2.99) and (2.102) with respect to z.

2.19   Coaxial transmission lines

A pair of coaxial cylindrical conductors as shown in Figure 2.34 constitutes a *coaxial transmission line*. Transmission equations are

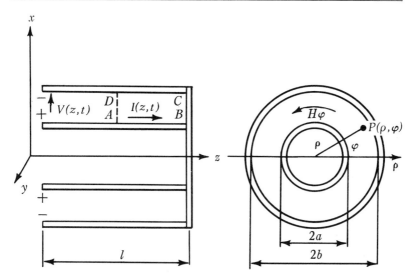

FIGURE 2.34 *Axial and transverse cross sections of coaxial cylinders, shorted with a conducting disk.*

of the same form as in the case of parallel wires, with the only difference in the expressions for the inductance and capacitance per unit length. For the coaxial line

$$L = \frac{\mu}{2\pi} \ln \frac{b}{a}, \qquad C = \frac{2\pi\epsilon}{\ln (b/a)}, \tag{2.104}$$

where a is the *outer* radius of the inner cylinder and b is the *inner* radius of the outer cylinder. The cylinders are assumed to be so thin that the current is uniformly distributed throughout their cross sections. In Chapter 4 we shall remove this restriction by evaluating V_{AB} and V_{CD} in terms of $I(z, t)$ for rapidly varying fields.

The major difference between a parallel pair and a coaxial pair is in the character of field distributions. In the former case the field extends to fairly large distances in the radial direction. In the latter it is confined almost entirely to the region occupied by the coaxial line. In the time-invariable case there is no magnetic field outside the outer cylinder. There is a weak electric field depending on the resistance of the outer cylinder. In the time-variable case this field will generate a magnetic field which will react back, etc. If the coaxial pair is close to the earth, the outer conductor will make a transmission line with ground return. As the frequency increases, however, the external field will start decreasing very rapidly. This will be shown in Chapter 4 where we consider propagation of fields in highly dissipative media.

2.20 Limitations of the step-by-step method of calculating self-consistent fields

In Section 2.18 the step-by-step method of calculating self-consistent fields (Section 1.29) was applied successfully to transmission lines. Starting with the conditions imposed on the voltage and current at the far end, we worked back to the generator. Equally well, we could have started from the generator if the input voltage $V(0, t)$ had been given. The input current, however, depends on the conditions at the far end. In step-by-step calculations we need $I(0, t)$ as well as $V(0, t)$. In the preceding examples it is possible to express the electric and magnetic fields in terms of these two quantities, one known and the other unknown, as accurately as we wish and then to determine the unknown quantity from the conditions at $z = l$.

The situation is quite different in the case of an electric dipole. Starting with the electric field, we obtained the first approximation to the magnetic field. The success depended on the circular symmetry. In Section 2.8 we tried to obtain from this field the second approximation to the electric field and found it impossible to allocate the contributions to E_z and E_ρ (or to E_r and E_θ). This can be remedied by applying Maxwell's integral equations to differential circuits. But another difficulty will remain. The field of an electric dipole is not unique. If the dipole is surrounded by a concentric conducting sphere of radius $r = r_0$, or by a concentric dielectric shell, its field will certainly be affected. It can be shown that the field of an electrostatic dipole is affected less and less as the radius of the sphere or the shell increases, so that in an infinite space it is determined uniquely by local conditions. It is impossible to show that this is also true for a time-variable dipole for the simple reason that it is not true. To obtain a sufficiently general field for a time-variable dipole in order to satisfy the conditions which might exist at large distances from it, we should start not only with a local electric field but also with a local magnetic field, independent of the electric field [in the same sense that $I(0, t)$, is independent of $V(0, t)$]. Unfortunately, all we know about this local magnetic field is that it must be time-variable to begin with, since no appropriate magnetostatic field can exist besides the one associated with direct current element.

One way out of the difficulty is to start with assumed fields at $r = r_0$ and work backwards to the dipole. There are simpler methods of analysis, however, which will be explained in Chapter 5.

3

Energy Storage, Dissipation, and Transfer

3.0 Introduction

All physical phenomena are accompanied by transformations of one form of energy into another. Electromagnetic phenomena are no exception. In Section 1.8 we calculated the work done by electric intensity when maintaining electric current. Experience shows that the spent energy appears as heat. The heat *is distributed* throughout the volume occupied by the field and the energy is delivered somehow from the generator to different regions of the field. The amount of generated heat depends on the local conditions and only indirectly on the generator.

When electric particles of opposite sign are separated against the force of attraction, work is done. The corresponding amount of energy, "electric energy," must then be associated with the separated charges. Similarly, "magnetic energy" is associated with moving charges (in addition to the kinetic energy). There is evidence that electric and magnetic energies are associated with electric and magnetic fields rather than with electric particles themselves. If we raise a body so that it acquires potential energy and then let it fall, we can account for all its potential energy when it is transformed into kinetic energy or into heat. If we separate electric charges of opposite signs and let them recombine, there is some residual energy for which we cannot account unless we assume that the energy is in electromagnetic fields. After the process of separation and recombination of charges has been finished, the field does not disappear entirely. The residual field, the "radiation field," is a shell of $\bar{E}$ and $\bar{H}$ traveling and expanding outwards. Radar echoes bear witness.

In this chapter we shall develop the idea of storage of electric and magnetic energy in various regions of a field and the idea of *flow* of energy from one region to another. These ideas are useful in studying electric oscillations in which electric energy is transformed periodically into magnetic energy and vice versa, and in calculating idealized

127

equivalent circuits for fields in actual physical structures. On the basis of energy considerations, it is possible to assign definite meanings to the following expressions: a "primarily electric" field, a "primarily magnetic" field, and a "slowly varying" field. Throughout this book the student should pay special attention to energy storage, dissipation, and flow.

3.1 Energy conversion and flow

Consider the concrete situation shown in Figure 2.33. A wire PQ can slide along a pair of wires terminated with a rod BC whose resistance is R_l. Assume that the resistance of the wires is negligible in comparison with R_l. In the absence of a magnetic field, a force is needed to set the wire PQ in motion. To maintain a constant speed v_0 a force is needed to overcome friction. In the presence of a magnetic field, an additional force F is needed to push the wire through the field. This comes about in the following way. The charge moving *with* the wire is acted upon by a downward force. As the charge moves downward, it becomes subject to another force acting to the left. Hence an equal force F is required to push the wire to the right through the field.

The work done by the latter force per second is $F(dz/dt) = Fv_0$. This work W must equal the work done, per second, by the motional or induced voltage V_{QP}^i when driving the downward current I_0 against the field voltage V_{PQ}; that is

$$W = Fv_0 = V_{QP}^i I_0.$$

From equation (2.88) we find $V_{QP}^i = -E_x^i s = B_0 v_0 s$. Therefore

$$F = B_0 I_0 s.$$

Since we have assumed that the resistance of the wires is negligible, $V_{BC} = V_{PQ} = V_{QP}^i$, the work W is also the work done, per second, in maintaining the current through the resistive rod BC. An equivalent amount of heat appears in the rod.

Thus mechanical energy is converted into electrical energy, transferred to a distant resistor BC, and there converted into heat. To trace the transfer of energy in greater detail we shall consider a simple field configuration as illustrated in Figure 3.1. The figure shows a longitudinal section of width w of a pair of coaxial cylinders of nearly equal radii, which locally are almost parallel planes. The field is substantially uniform in every transverse cross section. When the

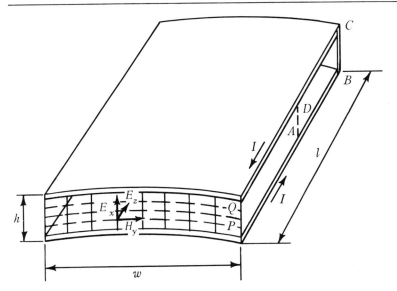

FIGURE 3.1   *A strip of width w of a pair of coaxial cylinders of large and nearly equal radii.*

current I_0 is steady, the Faraday-Maxwell law yields

$$V_{PQ} = V_{PB} + V_{BC} + V_{CQ}. \tag{3.1}$$

Multiplying by I_0, we have

$$V_{PQ}I_0 = V_{PB}I_0 + V_{BC}I_0 + V_{CQ}I_0. \tag{3.2}$$

The first term on the right is work done per second by V_{PB} driving current I_0, that is, the power dissipated in the lower strip. The second term is the power dissipated in the terminating strip, and the third term is the power dissipated in the upper strip. The left side equals the work done per second by the impressed voltage, driving current I_0, against the field voltage V_{PQ}; that is, the power leaving the generator.

In the present case the magnetic intensity H_y is constant throughout the field. The longitudinal electric intensity $E_{z,1}$ at and in the lower strip is also constant. Also $E_{z,2}$ is constant at and in the upper strip. If the strips are identical $E_{z,2}$ is equal to $-E_{z,1}$. The transverse voltage $V(z)$ and transverse electric intensity $E_x(z)$ vary with z. Since

$$V_{PQ} = hE_x(0), \qquad I_0 = wH_y,$$

$$V_{PB} = lE_{z,1} \qquad V_{QC} = lE_{z,2} \qquad V_{BC} = hE_x(l),$$

equation (3.2) becomes

$$hw E_x(0) H_y = lw E_{z,1} H_y - lw E_{z,2} H_y + hw E_x(l) H_y.$$

The left side suggests that power enters the field uniformly throughout its cross section, and that *power flow per unit area in the z direction
is*

$$E_x(0) H_y.$$

The flow is in the direction of the advance of a right-handed corkscrew whose handle is turned from E_x to H_y. The right side suggests
that power is *leaving* the space between the strips in accordance with
the same rule. Thus the first term represents the downward flow into
the lower strip; the second, the upward flow into the upper strip;
and the third, the forward flow into the resistor BC. Thus, the power
flow per unit area may be represented by a vector, called the *Poynting
vector*,

$$\vec{P} = \vec{E} \times \vec{H}. \tag{3.3}$$

3.2   Distribution of magnetic energy

Uniform speed can not be attained instantaneously. An infinite force
would be required. As the speed $v(t)$ of the sliding wire in Figure 2.33
increases from zero to v_0, the current $I(t)$ increases from zero to I_0.
Similarly the current in Figure 3.1 must increase gradually from zero
to I_0. Equation (3.1) does not describe this transition period. The
equation that does describe this period contains the term $\partial\Phi/\partial t$
representing the magnetic current linked with the closed path
$PBCQP$. In accordance with the Faraday-Maxwell law, we add the
voltage $\partial\Phi/\partial t$ to the right side of equation (3.2). The corresponding
increase in the input voltage is

$$V'_{PQ} = \frac{\partial\Phi}{\partial t} = \mu hl \frac{\partial H_y(t)}{\partial t}. \tag{3.4}$$

In equation (3.2) direct current I_0 should be replaced by $I(t)$ and
there will be additional power entering the field,

$$V'_{PQ} I(t) = \mu hl \frac{\partial H_y(t)}{\partial t} \, w H_y(t).$$

Additional energy entering the field during the transition interval
$(0, \tau)$ is

$$\int_0^\tau V'_{PQ} I(t) \, dt = \mu hlw \int_0^\tau H_y(t) \frac{\partial H_y(t)}{\partial t} \, dt = \tfrac{1}{2}\mu hlw H_y^2(\tau) \tag{3.5}$$

since $H_y(0) = 0$. Thereafter energy enters at the rate given by equation (3.2) and we already know what happens to it. The preceding equation suggests that the extra energy that entered the field remains there and is associated with the magnetic field. If the current were permitted to decrease back to zero, the magnetic field would disappear. During this period, the decreasing magnetic flux would give rise to an input voltage in a direction opposite to that of V'_{PQ} and energy would flow back to the generator.

Equation (3.5) indicates that energy is distributed throughout the magnetic field and that the amount stored per unit volume is

$$\tfrac{1}{2}\mu H^2. \tag{3.6}$$

In terms of electric current, equation (3.4) becomes

$$V'_{PQ} = \frac{\mu h l}{w}\frac{\partial I(t)}{\partial t} = Ll\frac{\partial I(t)}{\partial t},$$

where L is the inductance per unit length of the strip transmission line and Ll is the total inductance of the loop $PBCQ$. Magnetic energy of the entire field, equation (3.5), can then be expressed as

$$\mathcal{E}_m = \tfrac{1}{2}Ll I_0^2. \tag{3.7}$$

3.3 Distribution of electric energy

In the preceding section we assumed that during the transition period the current is independent of z as it actually is thereafter. But during this period the transverse voltage is rising and there is a transverse displacement current between the strips and the corresponding charging currents in the strips [see equation (2.102)]. The input current equals $I(t)$, as assumed in the preceding section, plus the total charging current. The energy entering the field will be greater than that calculated in the preceding section. The extra amount will be stored in the electric field between the strips.

To remove unnecessary complications, let us assume that at the far end BC in Figure 3.1 there is no connection between the strips, so that only the charging current exists. The density of charge on the lower strip is $D_x = \epsilon E_x$, and the total charge $\epsilon w l E_x$. Hence the charging current is

$$I(t) = \epsilon w l \frac{\partial E_x}{\partial t},$$

and the energy entering the space between the strips

$$\int_0^\tau VI(t)\ dt = \int_0^\tau \epsilon wlh E_x \frac{\partial E_x}{\partial t}\ dt = \tfrac{1}{2}\epsilon wlh E_x^2(\tau) \qquad (3.8)$$

since $E_x = 0$ at $t = 0$. Thus, the energy stored per unit volume of the electric field is

$$\tfrac{1}{2}\epsilon E^2. \qquad (3.9)$$

In terms of the voltage V between the strips, the stored electric energy after completion of the transition period is

$$\mathcal{E}_e = \frac{1}{2}\frac{\epsilon wl}{h} V^2 = \tfrac{1}{2}ClV^2, \qquad (3.10)$$

where C is the capacitance per unit length of the strip transmission line and Cl is the total capacitance.

We have considered simple fields in order to focus attention on essential factors. Expressions (3.3), (3.6), and (3.9) are general and can be deduced from the analysis of fields which are either between coaxial cylinders of arbitrary radii or outside parallel wires. In most situations there are complicating factors which are best ignored until the essentials are understood.

3.4   Oscillations in a cavity

Figure 3.2(a) represents an axial section of a metal cylinder with a coaxial plunger. Suppose that we somehow displace a charge q from the lower face of the cavity to the bottom of the plunger and then let the charge go. Alternatively suppose that the cavity consists of the two sections, one of which is a circular plate capacitor as shown in Figure 3.2(b). The capacitor can be charged and then the rest of the cavity can be slipped over it. The opposite charges will tend to unite and current $I = -\dot{q}$ will flow in the walls of the cavity. At the moment the positive charge q has left completely the bottom face of the plunger and neutralized the negative charge on the bottom of the cavity, the current continues to flow and the positive charge starts accumulating on the bottom of the cavity. The negative charge will be accumulating on the bottom face of the plunger. This accumulation stops when the electric field of the displaced charge stops the current and then reverses its direction. Oscillations continue until the energy of the electromagnetic field inside the cavity is dissipated as heat in the walls. The equation for such *free* or *natural* oscillations can be obtained as follows.

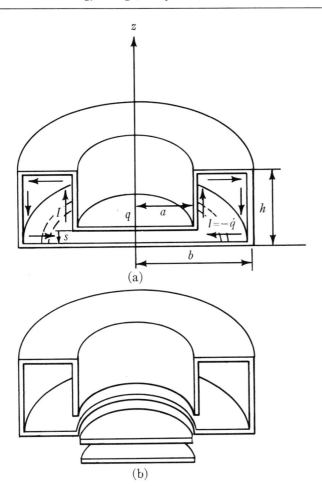

FIGURE 3.2 *A cylindrical cavity: (a) with a coaxial cylindrical plunger: (b) the same with the bottom of the plunger and the opposite section of the cavity shown separately to demonstrate that they constitute a circular plate capacitor.*

To begin with there is an electric field between the bottom of the cavity and the bottom face of the plunger. If we assume that the charge is distributed uniformly, displacement density is $D_z = -q/\pi a^2$ and the electric intensity is $E_z = -q/\epsilon \pi a^2$. The stored electric energy is

$$\mathcal{E}_e = \frac{1}{2} \int_0^s \int_0^{2\pi} \int_0^a \epsilon E_z^2 \rho \, d\rho \, d\varphi \, dz = \frac{q^2}{2C_t}, \qquad (3.11)$$

where

$$C_t = \frac{\epsilon \pi a^2}{s} \tag{3.12}$$

is the total capacitance of the field.

In reality the field is distributed nonuniformly. From the nature of the above calculations, however, it is clear that there is *stored electric energy proportional to the square of the charge*. Only the value of the coefficient C_t may be somewhat different.

As the charge starts moving, a magnetic field is created. If we assume that I is constant in the torus, that is, if the displacement currents from the lateral surface of the plunger to the bottom of the cavity (indicated by dotted lines in Figure 3.2) are neglected,

$$H_\varphi = \frac{I}{2\pi\rho} = \frac{-\dot{q}}{2\pi\rho}. \tag{3.13}$$

Then the stored magnetic energy will be

$$\mathcal{E}_m = \frac{1}{2} \int_0^h \int_0^{2\pi} \int_a^b \mu H_\varphi^2 \rho \, d\rho \, d\varphi \, dz = \tfrac{1}{2} L_t \dot{q}^2, \tag{3.14}$$

where

$$L_t = \frac{\mu h}{2\pi} \ln (b/a) \tag{3.15}$$

is the total inductance of the torus. Again it should be noted that equation (3.14) is exact for some value of the coefficient L_t even though we may not be able to compute L_t exactly.

As the current flows through resistive walls, some energy will be dissipated in heat. The dissipated power is proportional to the square of the current

$$W = R_t \dot{q}^2, \tag{3.16}$$

where R_t is the total resistance.

Equation (3.16) represents the time rate of decrease in the total energy of the cavity

$$\frac{d}{dt} \left(\tfrac{1}{2} L_t \dot{q}^2 + \frac{q^2}{2C_t} \right) = -R_t \dot{q}^2. \tag{3.17}$$

After differentiation and cancellation of $\dot{q}$, we obtain

$$L_t \ddot{q} + R_t \dot{q} + \frac{q}{C_t} = 0. \tag{3.18}$$

This is a second-order linear differential equation with constant coefficients which possesses exponential solutions of the form

$$q = Ae^{pt}. \tag{3.19}$$

Substituting in equation (3.18) and cancelling $A \exp (pt)$, we have

$$L_t C_t p^2 + R_t C_t p + 1 = 0.$$

Solving, we obtain

$$p_{1,2} = -\frac{R_t}{2L_t} \pm \sqrt{\frac{R_t^2}{4L_t^2} - \frac{1}{L_t C_t}}. \tag{3.20}$$

Hence the general solution is

$$q = A \exp (p_1 t) + B \exp (p_2 t). \tag{3.21}$$

The square root is real if

$$R_t > 2\sqrt{L_t/C_t}$$

in which case the discharge is nonoscillatory. In metal cavities, however, we have

$$R_t \ll 2\sqrt{L_t/C_t} \tag{3.22}$$

and equation (3.20) becomes

$$p_{1,2} = -\xi \pm j\omega, \tag{3.23}$$

where

$$\xi = \frac{R_t}{2L_t}, \qquad \omega = \frac{1}{\sqrt{L_t C_t}}. \tag{3.24}$$

Thus

$$q = e^{-\xi t}(Ae^{j\omega t} + Be^{-j\omega t}).$$

Since q is essentially real, B must be the complex conjugate of A. Let $A = \frac{1}{2}(M + jN)$; then $B = \frac{1}{2}(M - jN)$ and

$$q = e^{-\xi t}(M \cos \omega t - N \sin \omega t). \tag{3.25}$$

This equation represents exponentially decaying oscillations of frequency $f = \omega/2\pi$. From equations (3.12), (3.15), and (3.24) we find

$$\omega = \frac{1}{a\sqrt{\mu\epsilon}\sqrt{(h/2s)} \ln (b/a)}. \tag{3.26}$$

In free space

$$\frac{1}{\sqrt{\mu_0\epsilon_0}} = 2.998 \times 10^8 \simeq 3 \times 10^8 \text{ m/sec.} \tag{3.27}$$

Assuming

$$a = 2 \text{ cm}, \qquad b = 4 \text{ cm}, \qquad h = 4 \text{ cm}, \qquad s = 1 \text{ mm},$$

we have approximately

$$\omega = 4 \times 10^9, \qquad f = 640 \text{ mc/sec}.$$

3.5 Damping constant

The quantity ξ defined in equations (3.24) and (3.25) is called the *damping constant* and the ratio ξ/f the *logarithmic decrement*. Both quantities are measures of the rapidity with which the fields in the cavity decrease and the rapidity with which their energy is dissipated. When the cavity walls are good conductors, the *natural frequency* of oscillations, $\omega/2\pi$, depends little on the dissipation of energy and can thus be determined on the assumption that the walls are perfectly conducting. This often makes it easier to calculate the frequency and the field distribution within the cavity. From the field distribution it is possible to obtain the power dissipated in the walls of the cavity since the tangential component of $\bar{H}$ gives the current per unit length at right angles to itself. The damping constant is then determined from the ratio of energy dissipated per second to the total energy content.

Thus we rewrite equation (3.17) as follows:

$$\frac{d\mathcal{E}}{dt} = -W_{av} = -k\mathcal{E}, \tag{3.28}$$

where W_{av} is the *average* dissipated power and

$$k = W_{av}/\mathcal{E}$$

is the fraction of total energy it represents. Solving equation (3.28) we have

$$\mathcal{E} = \mathcal{E}_0 e^{-kt},$$

where $\mathcal{E}_0$ is the energy content at $t = 0$. At some instant $\mathcal{E}$ is entirely electric and is proportional to the square of the amplitude of charge, q_a^2. At other instants it is entirely magnetic and is proportional to $\dot{q}_a^2$. Therefore, the damping constant for the field intensities is

$$\xi = \tfrac{1}{2}k = \frac{W_{av}}{2\mathcal{E}}. \tag{3.29}$$

Let us apply this equation to the problem in Section 3.4. Neglecting dissipation in equation (3.18), we solve the equation and obtain

$$\dot{q} = \dot{q}_a \sin \omega t,$$

where ω is given in equations (3.24). The cosine term, appearing in equation (3.25), need not be included since it would merely shift the origin of time (irrelevant in the present case). The average dissipated power is

$$W_{av} = t^{-1} R_t \dot{q}_a^2 \int_0^t \sin^2 \omega t \, dt$$

$$= \tfrac{1}{2} t^{-1} R_t \dot{q}_a^2 \int_0^t (1 - \cos 2\omega t) \, dt \qquad (3.30)$$

$$= \tfrac{1}{2} R_t \dot{q}_a^2 \quad \text{as} \quad t \to \infty.$$

At some instants the entire energy of the field is magnetic (when $\sin \omega t = 1$ and $\cos \omega t = 0$). Hence

$$\mathcal{E} = \tfrac{1}{2} L_t \dot{q}_a^2. \qquad (3.31)$$

On the average, half of the energy is electric and half is magnetic. From equations (3.29), (3.30), and (3.31) we obtain

$$\xi = R_t / 2 L_t$$

which agrees with equation (3.24).

3.6 Equivalent circuit for parallel wires shorted at the far end

Consider Figure 3.3(a) which shows a pair of parallel wires connected to a generator at one end and shorted at the other. Suppose that the internal generator voltage is varying slowly. As a first approximation, the current in the loop will be the same at all points and the input voltage may be obtained from equation (2.103) if we let $z = 0$

$$V(0, t) = RlI_0 + Ll \frac{\partial I_0}{\partial t}.$$

In this equation R and L are the resistance and the inductance per unit length of the pair and Rl and Ll are the equivalent "lumped" resistance and inductance of the loop.

As the voltage varies faster, the transverse displacement currents become significant and the input current will be larger than I_0 by an amount equal to the total displacement current (or the charging current), equation (2.102). The input voltage will also be affected. In the equivalent lumped circuit in Figure 3.3(b) we include a capacitor in parallel with the equivalent resistor and inductor. The value of the equivalent capacitance may be obtained from improved

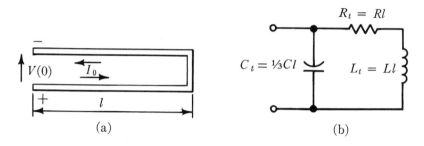

FIGURE 3.3   (a) *A pair of parallel wires shorted at the right end; (b) its equivalent circuit when the voltage impressed at the left end is varying slowly.*

voltage and current distributions; but the quickest and most effective method is to calculate the energy of the electric field. Referring again to equation (2.103), we observe that in the present notation,

$$V(z, t) = \left(RI_0 + L\frac{\partial I_0}{\partial t} \right) (l - z) = V(0, t)\left(1 - \frac{z}{l} \right).$$

The voltage is distributed linearly with z. From equation (3.10) we can obtain the stored electric energy per unit length. Therefore the total energy in the present case is

$$\mathcal{E}_e = \tfrac{1}{2}C[V(0, t)]^2 \int_0^l \left(1 - \frac{z}{l} \right)^2 dz.$$

Hence

$$\mathcal{E}_e = \tfrac{1}{6}Cl[V(0, t)]^2 = \tfrac{1}{2}C_t[V(0, t)]^2,$$

where C_t is the equivalent *lumped* capacitance (total capacitance). This capacitance is smaller than Cl because the voltage is not distributed uniformly along the wires.

  If the loop is suddenly disconnected from the generator, the current *away* from the open ends will continue to flow until the charges accumulated near the ends stop its flow and then reverse its direction of flow. Oscillations will ensue. The natural frequency of oscillations may be obtained from equations (3.24), (2.93), (2.97), and (3.27)

$$\omega = \frac{\sqrt{3}}{l\sqrt{LC}} = \frac{\sqrt{3}}{l\sqrt{\mu_0\epsilon_0}} = \frac{\sqrt{3} \times 3 \times 10^8}{l}. \qquad (3.32)$$

This frequency is so high that the application of the equivalent lumped circuit idea might be seriously questioned. In the next chapter the exact value

$$\omega = \frac{\pi}{2l\sqrt{\mu_0\epsilon_0}}$$

will be obtained. On comparison, we find that the approximate value is only 10 per cent higher than the exact value. This is very encouraging since exact solutions are available only for simple geometric configurations. No exact solution is available for the cylindrical cavity with a coaxial plunger (see Figure 3.2); but with some relatively simple improvement in the method described in Section 3.4 the natural frequency can be calculated with an error of only a fraction of one per cent.

3.7   Equivalent circuit for parallel wires open at the far end

Another configuration is shown in Figure 3.4. First there is a capacitance Cl between the two wires. The charging current is a linear

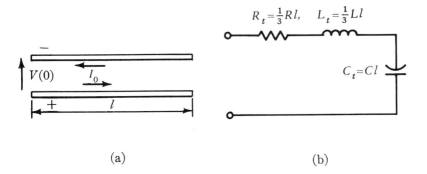

(a)   (b)

FIGURE 3.4   (a) A pair of parallel wires open at the right end; (b) its equivalent circuit when the voltage impressed at the left end is varying slowly.

function of the distance z from the generator (assuming that the capacitance per unit length is constant, that is, the wires are of constant radius)

$$I(z) = I_0 \left(1 - \frac{z}{l} \right).$$

Both the magnetic energy and dissipated power are proportional to the square of the current and the results indicated in Figure 3.4(b) follow.

3.8 Equivalent circuit for a parallel plate capacitor

Suppose that a voltage V_0 is applied uniformly between the edges of two parallel circular plates of radius a, Figure 3.5. If q is the total

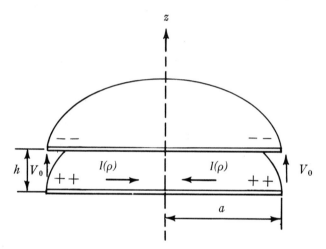

FIGURE 3.5 *One half of a circular plate capacitor with a voltage V_0 impressed uniformly round the edges of the capacitor.*

charge on the lower plate, the charge density is $q/\pi a^2$. This is equal to the displacement density D_z. Hence $V_0 = hE_z = qh/\epsilon\pi a^2$ and the equivalent lumped capacitance is

$$C_t = \frac{q}{V_0} = \frac{\epsilon\pi a^2}{h}. \tag{3.33}$$

The charge on the lower plate within the circle of radius ρ is $q\rho^2/a^2$ and the charging current at distance ρ from the axis is

$$I(\rho) = \dot{q}\rho^2/a^2.$$

This is also the upward displacement current enclosed by the cylinder of radius ρ. Hence

$$H_\varphi = \frac{I(\rho)}{2\pi\rho} = \frac{\dot{q}\rho}{2\pi a^2}. \tag{3.34}$$

The stored magnetic energy is

$$\mathcal{E}_m = \frac{1}{2} \int_0^h \int_0^{2\pi} \int_0^a \mu H_{\varphi\rho}^2 \, d\rho \, d\varphi \, dz = \frac{\mu h}{16\pi} \dot{q}^2 = \tfrac{1}{2} L_t \dot{q}^2. \tag{3.35}$$

Thus the equivalent lumped inductance in series with the circular plate capacitor is

$$L_t = \mu h / 8\pi. \tag{3.36}$$

3.9 Equivalent circuit for a slotted toroidal conductor

Let a toroidal conductor be open at $\rho = a$ and so connected to a generator that current I_0 enters uniformly round the lower edge

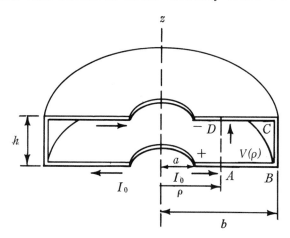

FIGURE 3.6   One half of a toroidal conductor.

$\rho = a$ and leaves round the upper edge as shown in Figure 3.6. Here

$$H_\varphi = -\frac{I_0}{2\pi\rho}, \qquad a \le \rho \le b \tag{3.37}$$

and

$$\mathcal{E}_m = \tfrac{1}{2} L_t I_0^2,$$

where

$$L_t = \frac{\mu_0 h}{2\pi} \ln (b/a) \qquad (3.38)$$

is the total inductance of the toroid.

Applying the Faraday-Maxwell law to a rectangle $ABCD$ in a typical radial plane and neglecting the resistance, we have

$$V(\rho) = V_{AD} = -\int_0^h \int_\rho^b \frac{\partial B_\varphi}{\partial t} \, d\rho \, dz = \frac{\mu_0 \dot{I}_0 h}{2\pi} \ln \frac{b}{\rho}. \qquad (3.39)$$

Hence

$$E_z = \frac{\mu_0 \dot{I}_0}{2\pi} \ln \frac{b}{\rho},$$

and the stored electric energy is

$$\mathcal{E}_e = \tfrac{1}{2}\epsilon_0 \int_0^h \int_0^{2\pi} \int_a^b E_z^2 \rho \, d\rho \, d\varphi \, dz = \frac{\epsilon_0 h}{4\pi} (\mu_0 \dot{I}_0)^2 P, \qquad (3.40)$$

where the integral P may be evaluated by parts

$$P = \int_a^b \rho \left(\ln \frac{b}{\rho} \right)^2 d\rho = \frac{1}{2} \int_a^b \left(\ln \frac{b}{\rho} \right)^2 d(\rho^2)$$

$$= \tfrac{1}{2}\rho^2 \left(\ln \frac{b}{\rho} \right)^2 \bigg|_a^b + \int_a^b \rho \ln \frac{b}{\rho} \, d\rho.$$

After another integration by parts, we obtain

$$P = \tfrac{1}{4}(b^2 - a^2) - \tfrac{1}{2}a^2 \ln \frac{b}{a} - \tfrac{1}{2}a^2 \left(\ln \frac{b}{a} \right)^2. \qquad (3.41)$$

Substituting this in equation (3.40) and equating to

$$\mathcal{E}_e = \tfrac{1}{2}C_t[V(a)]^2 \qquad (3.42)$$

which defines the equivalent lumped capacitance, we find

$$C_t = \frac{2\pi\epsilon_0 P}{h \, [\ln (b/a)]^2}. \qquad (3.43)$$

3.10   Use of equivalent circuits

In Section 3.6 we found the frequency of free oscillations on a pair of wires shorted at one end from energy considerations. The magnetic energy was calculated on the assumption that the magnetic field was uniformly distributed as it is when the current is time-invariant. From this field distribution we then obtained the distribution of the electric field and the corresponding electric energy.

Charge density on the lower wire, being proportional to transverse voltage, varies as $(l - z)$. Hence the charging current varies as $(l - z)^2$. The magnetic field produced by this current was neglected. The approximate frequency was found to differ from the exact by 10 per cent.

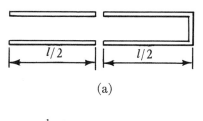

(a)

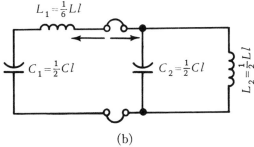

(b)

FIGURE 3.7   (a) A transmission line of length l, open at one end and shorted at the other; (b) the calculation its equivalent circuit for obtaining an improved value of the line's lowest natural frequency.

We now obtain an improved value for the natural frequency. Note Figure 3.7(a) which shows a pair of wires of length l divided into two sections, each of length $l/2$. In Figure 3.7(b) each section is represented by an appropriate equivalent circuit. The natural frequencies of the combined network are obtained by equating the sum of the admittances (or the impedances) in each direction to zero. Thus

$$\frac{j\omega C_1}{1 - \omega^2 L_1 C_1} + \frac{1 - \omega^2 L_2 C_2}{j\omega L_2} = 0 \qquad (3.44)$$

and finally

$$(\omega^2 LCl^2)^2 - 60(\omega^2 LCl^2) + 144 = 0.$$

Solving, we obtain

$$\omega_1 = \frac{1.58}{l\sqrt{\mu_0\epsilon_0}}, \qquad \omega_2 = \frac{7.58}{l\sqrt{\mu_0\epsilon_0}}. \qquad (3.45)$$

In equation (3.32) the factor $\sqrt{3} = 1.732$ was compared with the exact value $\pi/2 \simeq 1.57$. The error in the new value, 1.58, is smaller than one per cent.

The new equivalent network also has a higher natural frequency, the significance of which will be discussed in the next section.

3.11 Higher modes of oscillation

In Section 3.6 it was found that slowly varying current in parallel wires connected to a generator at one end and shorted at the other is distributed nearly uniformly along the wires. Hence, the magnetic energy is also distributed nearly uniformly along the entire length. On the other hand, the transverse voltage vanishes at the shorted end and increases linearly with the distance from the shorted end. Therefore, the electric energy increases with the square of the distance from the shorted end. Similarly in Section 3.7 it was shown that when wires are open at the far end, electric energy is distributed nearly uniformly along the wires while magnetic energy increases as the square of the distance from the open end. In the analysis of electric oscillations on a pair of parallel wires shorted at one end, it was natural to subdivide the distributed field into two regions; one, near the open end, where the electric field is relatively strong and the magnetic field is weak, and the other near the shorted end where the magnetic field is strong and the electric field relatively weak. During the oscillations, energy fluctuates between these regions and is converted from one type to another.

If the fields are varying rapidly, all that can be said is: in the *immediate* vicinity of the open end the magnetic field is weak and in the *immediate* vicinity of the shorted end the electric field is weak. Nothing can be said about the intermediate region. In fact, we know that electric and magnetic energies are continuously distributed along the wires and a possibility exists that oscillations may take place between adjacent sections of the parallel pair. Starting with oscillations on a shorted pair as shown in Figure 3.8(a) and assuming that two such pairs are placed back to back, one arrives at a mode of oscillation in a pair open at both ends, as shown in Figure 3.8(b). Since for the assumed directions of currents in the wire there is no

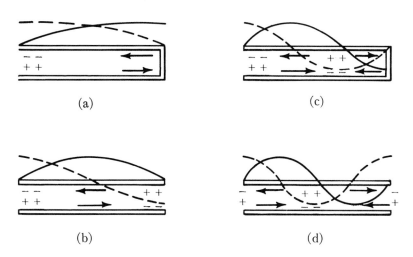

(a)   (c)

(b)   (d)

FIGURE 3.8   *Higher modes of oscillation in sections of transmission lines.*

current in the shorting bar, the bar can be removed without disturbing the fields. For the same length of wires the frequency of oscillations in this mode is twice as high as in the shorted pair.

This argument leads to a sequence of other possible modes of oscillation with increasingly higher frequencies such as those illustrated in Figures 3.8(c, d). It is now clear that the methods described in the preceding sections for calculating natural frequencies of electric oscillations *are restricted, in their present form, to the modes with the lowest frequencies. From the start, we assumed* that the entire field could be divided into only *two* regions, one with a strong electric field and the other with a strong magnetic field. Although the equivalent circuit in Figure 3.7 has a mode of oscillation with a higher frequency, we cannot expect this frequency to be a good approximation to the next mode of oscillation in the shorted pair shown in Figure 3.8(c), since the actual field distribution for this mode does not at all resemble the assumed distribution. In fact, the frequency of this mode is three times as large as that of the lowest mode while in equation (3.45) we have $\omega_2 \simeq 4.8\omega_1$.

This does not mean that our method cannot be modified so that it will become applicable to higher modes. We would only need to find a way of calculating proper values of equivalent lumped inductances and capacitances.

3.12   Comparison of strengths of electric and magnetic fields

Maxwell's equations imply that time-variable fields are never purely electric or purely magnetic. Where they are "varying slowly," such fields may be only "primarily" electric or "primarily" magnetic. We have already considered a number of examples. We now give a more precise meaning to the words "primarily electric," "primarily magnetic," and "slowly varying."

The physical dimensions of the $\bar{E}$ and $\bar{H}$ are different. Hence we cannot compare the magnitudes of $\bar{E}$ and $\bar{H}$ directly in order to decide which is the larger. But we can compare stored energy densities and total stored energies. If $\mathcal{E}_e$ is the electric energy stored in a given region of an electromagnetic field and $\mathcal{E}_m$ is the stored magnetic energy, then *in this region the filed is primarily electric or primarily magnetic* depending on whether

$$\mathcal{E}_e \gg \mathcal{E}_m \quad \text{or} \quad \mathcal{E}_m \gg \mathcal{E}_e.$$

Similarly at a given point the *magnitude E of electric intensity is greater than, equal to, or smaller than the magnitude H of magnetic intensity* depending upon whether

$$\tfrac{1}{2}\epsilon E^2 > \tfrac{1}{2}\mu H^2, \qquad \tfrac{1}{2}\epsilon E^2 = \tfrac{1}{2}\mu H^2, \qquad \tfrac{1}{2}\epsilon E^2 < \tfrac{1}{2}\mu H^2.$$

Thus one may consider electric and magnetic fields *equally strong if*

$$E = \eta H, \qquad \eta = \sqrt{\mu/\epsilon}. \tag{3.46}$$

Since the magnetic flux density B equals μH, this equation may also be written as

$$E = cB, \qquad c = 1/\sqrt{\mu\epsilon}. \tag{3.47}$$

The quantity η has the physical dimensions of resistance and is called the *intrinsic impedance of the medium*. In free space

$$\eta_0 = \sqrt{\mu_0/\epsilon_0} = 376.7 \simeq 120\pi \text{ ohms}.$$

The quantity c has the dimensions of velocity and is called the *intrinsic velocity of the medium*. In free space

$$c_0 = 1/\sqrt{\mu_0\epsilon_0} = 2.998 \times 10^8 \simeq 3 \times 10^8 \text{ m/sec}.$$

These two quantities play a very important role in the propagation of electromagnetic waves.

In free space a magnetic field of intensity equal to one ampere per meter is comparable in strength to an electric field of 377 volts per meter. Similarly a magnetic field in which the flux density is one gauss (10^{-4} weber/m²) is comparable in strength to an electric field of 30 000 volts/meter.

3.13 The meaning of "slowly varying field"

It is now possible to define more precisely a "slowly varying field." Consider the example of two parallel wires of length l shorted at the far end (Section 3.6). The stored magnetic energy is

$$\mathcal{E}_m = \tfrac{1}{2}LlI^2.$$

In terms of the voltage at the near end, the stored electric energy is

$$\mathcal{E}_e = \tfrac{1}{6}ClV^2.$$

If $I = I_a \sin \omega t$, then $V = Ll\dot{I} = \omega LlI_a \cos \omega t$. Therefore

$$\mathcal{E}_m = \tfrac{1}{2}LlI_a^2 \sin^2 \omega t = \tfrac{1}{4}LlI_a^2(1 - \cos 2\omega t),$$

$$\mathcal{E}_e = \tfrac{1}{6}\omega^2 C L^2 l^3 I_a^2 \cos^2 \omega t = \tfrac{1}{12}\omega^2 C L^2 l^3 I_a^2(1 + \cos 2\omega t).$$

The ratio of the average electric energy to the average magnetic energy is

$$\frac{\text{av }(\mathcal{E}_e)}{\text{av }(\mathcal{E}_m)} = \tfrac{1}{3}\omega^2 LCl^2. \tag{3.48}$$

As long as this ratio is considerably smaller than unity, the field is primarily magnetic and is "varying slowly." In terms of the equivalent lumped parameters this condition is

$$\omega^2 L_t C_t \ll 1 \qquad \text{or} \qquad \omega \ll 1/\sqrt{L_t C_t}.$$

Similarly from equations (3.33) and (3.36) we find that if

$$\omega \ll 1/\sqrt{C_t L_t} = 2\sqrt{2}/a\sqrt{\mu\epsilon}, \tag{3.49}$$

the field between parallel metal plates of radius a is primarily electric and is varying slowly.

The smaller is the region occupied by a field, the greater is the range of frequencies in which the field can be either primarily electric or primarily magnetic. As the dimensions of physical capacitors and coils become smaller, the structures become more nearly ideal circuit elements.

3.14   Electric networks

A system of physical resistors, inductors, and capacitors connected together constitute a physical electric network. If the network elements are well designed, they may be approximated over a large frequency range by ideal resistors, inductors, and capacitors. The

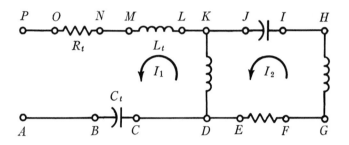

FIGURE 3.9   *An electric network with two independent meshes.*

voltages between the terminals of ideal elements are related to the currents through the elements as follows (see Figure 3.9):

$$V_{ON} = R_t I_{ON}, \qquad V_{ML} = L_t \frac{dI_{ML}}{dt}, \qquad I_{BC} = C_t \frac{dV_{BC}}{dt}, \qquad (3.50)$$

where R_t, L_t, and C_t are the lumped resistance, inductance, and capacitance of the respective elements. It is understood that at sufficiently high frequencies it will be necessary to replace a physical resistor by an equivalent network consisting of an ideal inductor in series with an ideal resistor, shunted by an ideal capacitor as shown in Figure 3.10(a). The equivalent circuits for physical inductors and capacitors are shown in Figure 3.10(b, c).

Applying the Faraday-Maxwell law to a closed circuit in Figure 3.9, we have

$$V_{AB} + V_{BC} + V_{CD} + V_{DK} + V_{KL} + V_{LM} + V_{MN}$$
$$+ V_{NO} + V_{OP} + V_{PA} = -\frac{d\Phi_1}{dt}.$$

The connecting leads are usually good conductors and their resistances may be neglected. Then

$$V_{BC} + V_{DK} + V_{LM} + V_{NO} + V_{PA} = -\frac{d\Phi_1}{dt}. \qquad (3.51)$$

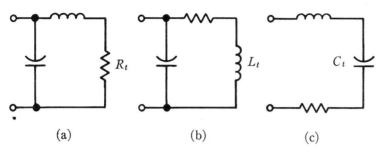

FIGURE 3.10 (a) The equivalent network for a physical resistor contains an ideal inductor in series with an ideal resistor and an ideal capacitor in shunt with both. (b) The equivalent network for a physical inductor is analogous to the resistor network but has different orders of magnitude of the constituent resistances and inductances. (c) The equivalent network for a physical capacitor consists of an ideal capacitor in series with an ideal inductor and an ideal resistor.

The magnetic flux is a linear function of the *mesh currents* I_1 and I_2 [see equation (2.85)]. The coefficient L_{11} is the self inductance of the first circuit and L_{12} is the mutual inductance of the two circuits. In practical circuits L_{11} and L_{12} are usually negligible in comparison with other inductances in the network. Equating the right-hand side of equation (3.51) to zero, we obtain the *first Kirchhoff equation.*

The mesh currents in the network have a meaning only to the extent to which the displacement currents between the various leads may be neglected. At sufficiently high frequencies it may be necessary to include the effect of these displacement currents by introducing ideal capacitors between every pair of leads. Even these approximations may be inadequate when the frequency is high enough.

4

Waves

4.0 Introduction

In this chapter we shall develop basic concepts associated with simple types of time-harmonic electromagnetic waves: characteristic impedance (or, more generally, wave impedance), propagation constant, phase constant, phase velocity, wavelength, attenuation constant, and reflection coefficient for impedance discontinuities. The chapter is concluded with sections on nonuniform transmission lines, image parameters, and a qualitative analysis of waves in hollow tubes.

4.1 Maxwell's laws of interaction between time-harmonic electric and magnetic fields

Quantities varying sinusoidally with time, called *time-harmonic* quantities, may be represented by complex quantities in the sense that the actual quantities are real parts of the complex quantities. If the real quantities are replaced by their complex representations in any *linear* set of equations, then the real parts of the solutions of the resulting equations are solutions of the original equations. Let

$$\bar{E}(u, v, w)e^{j\omega t}, \qquad \bar{H}(u, v, w)e^{j\omega t} \tag{4.1}$$

be complex vectors representing time-harmonic electric and magnetic fields of frequency $f = \omega/2\pi$. The coordinates (u, v, w) may be any set of coordinates, usually orthogonal, such as the Cartesian set (x, y, z), the cylindrical set (ρ, ϕ, z), or the spherical set (r, θ, φ). Each component of $\bar{E}$ and $\bar{H}$ is a complex quantity whose amplitude equals the amplitude of the corresponding sinusoidal quantity and whose phase is the initial phase (the phase at $t = 0$) of that quantity.

Let us substitute expressions (4.1) into Maxwell's equations (1.76) and (1.77) for source-free regions. In the present case the differentiation with respect to t is equivalent to multiplication by $j\omega$ and

$$e^{j\omega t} \oint E_s(u, v, w) \, ds = -j\omega\mu \, e^{j\omega t} \int H_n(u, v, w) \, dS,$$

$$e^{j\omega t} \oint H_s(u, v, w) \, ds = (\sigma + j\omega\epsilon) \, e^{j\omega t} \int E_n(u, v, w) \, dS.$$

$$(4.2)$$

If two complex quantities are equal, their real and imaginary parts are separately equal. Thus

$$\bar{E}(u, v, w; t) = \mathrm{re} \; \bar{E}(u, v, w) \, e^{j\omega t},$$

$$\bar{H}(u, v, w; t) = \mathrm{re} \; \bar{H}(u, v, w) \, e^{j\omega t},$$

$$(4.3)$$

are solutions of Maxwell's equations.

In equations (4.2) the exponential time factor may be canceled. Dropping specific reference to coordinates, we have

$$\oint E_s \, ds = -j\omega\mu \int H_n \, dS,$$

$$(4.4)$$

$$\oint H_s \, ds = (\sigma + j\omega\epsilon) \int E_n \, dS.$$

4.2   Equations for time-harmonic fields in transmission lines

In Sections 2.18 and 2.19 we derived equations for transmission lines consisting of two thin parallel wires and two thin coaxial cylindrical conductors. The "thinness" was assumed to ensure uniform distribution of current in the conductors. The word "thin" was left vague except in a qualitative sense: if the fields were varying more rapidly, the conductors would have to be thinner for the equations to remain valid. We shall now remove the restriction of "thinness" and in deriving the equations study more carefully all the assumptions we make.

Figure 4.1 shows radial and transverse cross-sections of two coaxial metal cylinders. On the left they are connected to a generator which creates a radial voltage distributed uniformly around the cylinders. Let $V(z)$ be the transverse voltage at distance z from the left end, and $I(z)$ the current in the inner cylinder, which can be

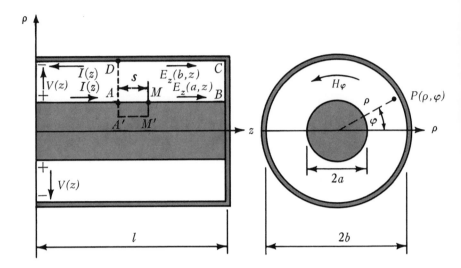

either a solid or a hollow shell. At $z = l$ the cylinders are terminated by a plug which can be either a good conductor, so that the transmission line is effectively shorted, or a thin resistive film deposited uniformly on glass or some other nonconducting material. Let us assume therefore that neither $V(l)$ nor $I(l)$ vanishes. Their ratio will be determined by the impedance of the plug. Applying the first of Maxwell's equations (4.4), to the closed path $ABCDA$, we have

$$V_{AB} + V_{BC} + V_{CD} + V_{DA} = -j\omega\mu \int_z^l \int_a^b H_\varphi \, d\rho \, dz,$$

where

$$V_{AB} = \int_z^l E_z(a, z) \, dz, \qquad V_{BC} = V(l),$$

$$V_{CD} = -V_{DC} = -\int_z^l E_z(b, z) \, dz, \qquad V_{DA} = -V(z).$$

In these equations a is the outer radius of the inner cylinder and $E_z(a, z)$ is the longitudinal electric intensity on its outer surface. Similarly $E_z(b, z)$ is the electric intensity on the inner surface $\rho = b$

of the outer conductor. Rearranging the terms, we obtain

$$V(z) = V(l) + \int_z^l [E_z(a, z) - E_z(b, z)] \, dz + j\omega\mu \int_z^l \int_a^b H_\varphi \, d\rho \, dz.$$

$$(4.5)$$

If the dielectric between the cylinders is not perfect, there is a radial conduction current as well as displacement current. If σ and ϵ are the conductivity and dielectric constant, the radial densities of these currents will be σE_ρ and $j\omega\epsilon E_\rho$. Hence

$$I(z) = I(l) + \int_z^l \int_0^{2\pi} (\sigma + j\omega\epsilon) E_\rho(\rho, z) \, \rho \, d\varphi \, dz, \qquad (4.6)$$

where the integral represents the total radial current through a cylindrical surface of radius ρ, coaxial with the cylinders. This equation is always correct if ρ is equal to a. As written, it is correct only when the function

$$\rho E_\rho(\rho, z) = A(z) \qquad (4.7)$$

is independent of ρ. This condition implies that radial current flows straight from one cylinder to the other, and that none of it is diverted in the longitudinal direction between the cylinders.

If the cylinders are not perfectly conducting, there is always a longitudinal electric field of intensity E_z and longitudinal currents of density $(\sigma + j\omega\epsilon) E_z$ exist in the medium between the cylinders. Currents in the two cylinders are in opposite directions; therefore $E_z(a, z)$ and $E_z(b, z)$ are in opposite directions. Hence, $E_z(\rho, z)$ is smaller between the cylinders than on their surfaces. How large are these longitudinal currents in the dielectric in comparison with the currents in the cylinders? In metals the conductivity σ_m is very large. In copper, for example, $\sigma_m = 5.8 \times 10^7$. In dielectrics the conductivity is very small. In pyrex glass, for instance, $\sigma = 10^{-12}$. Even in such poor dielectrics as sand in which $\sigma = 0.002$ the longitudinal conduction currents are negligibly small. The radial currents cannot be neglected as readily because they increase with the length of the line. Similarly the ratio of the longitudinal displacement current density between the cylinders to the conduction density in the cylinders is $j\omega\epsilon/\sigma_m$. For glass, $\epsilon = 4 \times 10^{-11}$. The frequency must be very high indeed for this ratio to be comparable to unity. True, the cross-section of the dielectric between the cylinders is larger than the cross-section of the conductors; but not large enough to permit significant total longitudinal displacement currents at frequencies which are not exceedingly high. Thus we are justified in neglecting these currents for the present. What happens when the longitudinal currents become substantial will be considered later.

We are now in a position to express the various terms on the right in equations (4.5) and (4.6) in terms of $V(z)$ and $I(z)$. The quantity $E_z(a, z)$ is doubled if $I(z)$ is doubled; that is, whatever its value is, $E_z(a, z)$ is proportional to $I(z)$. Similarly $E_z(b, z)$ is proportional to $-I(z)$. Thus we set

$$E_z(a, z) = Z_1 I(z), \qquad E_z(b, z) = -Z_2 I(z), \qquad (4.8)$$

where Z_1 and Z_2 are called the *internal impedances*, or the *surface impedances, per unit length* of the corresponding conductors. At low frequencies they are simply the resistances per unit length. In the next section we shall derive the equations from which these quantities may be determined.

Since we decided to neglect the longitudinal displacement currents, the magnetomotive force around a magnetic line of radius ρ, $2\pi\rho H_\varphi$, equals the current in the inner cylinder and

$$H_\varphi = \frac{I(z)}{2\pi\rho}. \qquad (4.9)$$

Referring to equation (4.7), we have

$$V(z) = \int_a^b E_\rho \, d\rho = A(z) \ln (b/a),$$

that is,

$$\rho E_\rho = \frac{V(z)}{\ln (b/a)}. \qquad (4.10)$$

Taking these results into consideration, we transform equations (4.5) and (4.6) into

$$V(z) = V(l) + \int_z^l ZI(z) \, dz,$$

$$\qquad (4.11)$$

$$I(z) = I(l) + \int_z^l YV(z) \, dz,$$

where
$$Z = Z_1 + Z_2 + j\omega L, \qquad L = \frac{\mu}{2\pi} \ln \frac{b}{a},$$

(4.12)

$$Y = G + j\omega C = \frac{2\pi(\sigma + j\omega\epsilon)}{\ln(b/a)}.$$

In these equations Z and Y are called, respectively, the *series impedance* per unit length of the transmission line and the *shunt admittance* per unit length. In the present case they are independent of z and may be taken outside the integral signs. We deliberately left them under the integral signs since the derivation of equations (4.11) remains valid *to the extent that longitudinal displacement currents are negligible*, even when a, b, and the thicknesses of the cylinders are functions of z.

One should note that equations (4.11) are equations *in the large* for fields between the cylinders, from which $\bar{E}$ and $\bar{H}$ at various points may be obtained with the aid of equations (4.9) and (4.10).

Equations for parallel wires and other transmission lines are also of the form of equations (4.11). Only the parameters Z and Y are different. The real part of Z is called the *resistance per unit length* and the imaginary part the *reactance per unit length*. The real and imaginary parts of Y are, respectively, the *conductance* and the *susceptance* per unit length.

4.3   Field in the interior of a metal cylinder

When $\omega = 0$, the longitudinal current in a metal cylinder, such as the inner cylinder of the coaxial line in Figure 4.1, is distributed uniformly. If ω is not equal to zero, the magnetic current linked with a closed path, such as $A'M'MAA'$, will generate a circulatory electromotive force which will make $V_{A'M'}$ unequal to V_{AM} and will upset the uniform distribution. The radial current density must be continuous across the outer surface of the conductor. Just outside, this density is $(\sigma + j\omega\epsilon)E_\rho(a + 0, z)$, where "$a + 0$" indicates "just outside." Just inside it is $\sigma_m E_\rho(a - 0, z)$. Therefore, $E_\rho(a - 0, z)$ is an exceedingly small fraction of $E_\rho(a + 0, z)$. Thus *in the metal cylinder* we may neglect the radial electric field.

Let $E_z(\rho, z)$ be the longitudinal electric intensity at distance ρ from the axis, and $I(\rho, z)$ be the longitudinal current enclosed by the cylindrical surface of radius ρ. Applying the Faraday-Maxwell law to rectangular path $A'M'MAA'$ in a radial plane as shown in Figure 4.1, we have

$$\int_z^{z+s} E_z(\rho, z)\ dz - \int_z^{z+s} E_z(a, z)\ dz = -\frac{j\omega\mu}{2\pi} \int_z^{z+s} \int_\rho^a \rho^{-1} I(\rho, z)\ d\rho\ dz.$$

The current $I(\rho, z)$ is a slowly varying function of z since its variation depends on the weak radial current in the dielectric medium between the cylinders. Thus, even when s is large compared with $2a$, the above equation yields

$$s E_z(\rho, z) - s E_z(a, z) = -\frac{j\omega\mu}{2\pi}\, s \int_\rho^a \rho^{-1} I(\rho, z)\ d\rho$$

or

$$E_z(\rho, z) = E_z(a, z) - \frac{j\omega\mu}{2\pi} \int_\rho^a \rho^{-1} I(\rho, z)\ d\rho. \tag{4.13}$$

Also

$$I(\rho, z) = \int_0^{2\pi} \int_0^\rho \sigma_m E_z(\rho, z) \rho\ d\rho\ d\varphi$$

$$= 2\pi\sigma_m \int_0^\rho \rho E_z(\rho, z)\ d\rho. \tag{4.14}$$

Note the similarity between these equations and the transmission line equations (4.11). In fact, equations (4.13) and (4.14) *are* field transmission equations in the radial direction. In the next section we shall obtain the solution of these equations for low frequencies, and later in this chapter for high frequencies.

4.4 Step-by-step solution of transmission equations

Let us now apply the step-by-step method of dealing with Maxwell's equations for interaction between electric and magnetic fields to the special case represented by equation (4.11). We let

$$V(z) = V_0(z) + V_1(z) + V_2(z) + \cdots,$$

$$I(z) = I_0(z) + I_1(z) + I_2(z) + \cdots, \tag{4.15}$$

where

$$V_0(z) = V(l), \qquad I_0(z) = I(l),$$

$$V_n(z) = \int_z^l Z\, I_{n-1}(z)\ dz, \qquad I_n(z) = \int_z^l Y\, V_{n-1}(z)\ dz.$$

If Z and Y are independent of z

$$V_1(z) = Z(l - z) I(l), \qquad I_1(z) = Y(l - z) V(l)$$

$$V_2(z) = \tfrac{1}{2}ZY(l - z)^2 V(l), \qquad I_2(z) = \tfrac{1}{2}YZ(l - z)^2 I(l)$$

$$V_3(z) = \frac{1}{2 \cdot 3} Z^2 Y(l - z)^3 I(l) \qquad (4.16)$$

$$I_3(z) = \frac{1}{2 \cdot 3} ZY^2(l - z)^3 V(l).$$

Successive terms appear more symmetrical if we let

$$\sqrt{ZY} = \Gamma, \qquad \sqrt{Z/Y} = K \qquad (4.17)$$

so that

$$Z = K\Gamma, \qquad Y = K^{-1}\Gamma. \qquad (4.18)$$

In equations (4.16) we substitute Γ^2 for each product ZY, and use equations (4.18) for the remaining Z or Y. Then

$$V(z) = V(l) \left[1 + \frac{1}{2!} \Gamma^2(l - z)^2 + \frac{1}{4!} \Gamma^4(l - z)^4 + \cdots \right]$$

$$+ KI(l) \left[\Gamma(l - z) + \frac{1}{3!} \Gamma^3(l - z)^3 + \frac{1}{5!} \Gamma^5(l - z)^5 + \cdots \right]$$

or

$$V(z) = V(l) \cosh \Gamma(l - z) + KI(l) \sinh \Gamma(l - z).$$

Similarly

$$I(z) = I(l) \cosh \Gamma(l - z) + K^{-1}V(l) \sinh \Gamma(l - z).$$

$V(z)$ and $I(z)$ may be expressed in terms of the input voltage $V(0)$ and the terminal impedance

$$Z_t = V(l)/I(l) \qquad (4.19)$$

and in many other ways suitable for each particular occasion.

In the interior of a metal cylinder the parameters Z and Y depend on the variable of integration. Nevertheless the successive integrations can be carried out and the solutions may be expressed as infinite series which can be recognized as those for certain Bessel functions. We now evaluate a few terms in order to obtain some idea of what happens to the resistance of a wire at low frequencies. From equation (4.13) we have the initial approximation

$$E_z(\rho, z) = E_z(a, z)$$

which gives the uniform current distribution. Substituting in equation (4.14), we obtain

$$I(\rho, z) = \pi\sigma_m\rho^2 E_z(a, z).$$

Returning to equation (4.13), we find

$$E_z(\rho, z) = [1 - \tfrac{1}{4}j\omega\mu\sigma_m(a^2 - \rho^2)]E_z(a, z).$$

Continuing, one obtains

$$I(\rho, z) = [\pi\sigma_m\rho^2 - \tfrac{1}{4}\pi j\omega\mu\sigma_m^2\rho^2(a^2 - \tfrac{1}{2}\rho^2)]E_z(a, z).$$

If we stop with these approximations, the internal impedance per unit length, equation (4.8) becomes

$$Z_1 = \frac{E_z(a, z)}{I(a, z)} = \frac{1}{\pi\sigma_m a^2(1 - \tfrac{1}{8}j\omega\mu\sigma_m a^2)}.$$

If the frequency is such that $\omega\mu\sigma_m a^2 \ll 8$, we have

$$Z_1 = \frac{1}{\pi\sigma_m a^2}(1 + \tfrac{1}{8}j\omega\mu\sigma_m a^2) = \frac{1}{\pi\sigma_m a^2} + \frac{j\omega\mu}{8\pi}. \qquad (4.20)$$

The first term is the dc resistance per unit length of the cylinder. The second term indicates that the conductor has internal inductance, $\mu/8\pi$. This can be found from energy considerations as readily as the internal inductance of a capacitor, equation (3.36), was found. At low frequencies they are the same, since it does not matter whether the magnetic field is produced by displacement current or conduction current. In both instances we start with uniform current distributions.

To this order of approximation in equation (4.20) the resistance is not affected by the frequency. From the next approximation to the current we have

$$Z_1^{-1} = \pi\sigma_m a^2(1 - \tfrac{1}{8}j\omega\mu\sigma_m a^2 - \tfrac{1}{48}\omega^2\mu^2\sigma_m^2 a^4).$$

Inverting and calculating the resistive component to the order of this approximation, we obtain

$$R_1 = \frac{1}{\pi\sigma_m a^2}(1 + \tfrac{1}{192}\omega^2\mu^2\sigma_m^2 a^4).$$

For copper

$$R_1 \simeq R_0(1 + 1100f^2a^4).$$

If $a = 1$ cm $= 10^{-2}$ m and $f = 100$ cps, the increase in resistance is 11 per cent. For higher frequencies, one could hardly use the formula since the correction term would be too large and higher order corrections would be needed. If $a = 1$ mm, the same relative increase in resistance would occur when $f = 10\,000$.

4.5 Equivalent circuits

To focus our attention on a section (z_1, z_2) of the transmission line, let $z = z_1$ and $l = z_2$ in equations (4.11). In the integrals we replace $I(z)$ and $V(z)$ by their mean values in the interval (z_1, z_2). We then have

$$V(z_1) - V(z_2) = Z(z_2 - z_1)I_{\text{mean}},$$

$$I(z_1) - I(z_2) = Y(z_2 - z_1)V_{\text{mean}}. \tag{4.21}$$

Let us assume that $z_2 - z_1$ is so small that the voltage difference on the right side of the first equation is small compared to V_{mean}, and the current difference on the right side of the second equation is small compared to I_{mean}. This automatically excludes sections which are

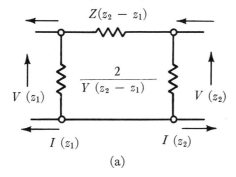

(a)

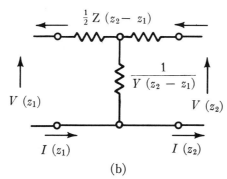

(b)

FIGURE 4.2 *Equivalent networks for short sections of transmission lines: (a) a Π network; (b) a T network.*

either shorted or open at $z = z_2$. With this restriction the difference in transverse voltages across the ends of the section equals the voltage drop across a lumped impedance $Z(z_2 - z_1)$. The difference in currents equals the current through a lumped shunt impedance $1/Y(z_2 - z_1)$. These lumped impedances can be divided symmetrically as in Figure 4.2(a, b). In case (a) we have a "Π network" and in case (b) a "T network." Thus, transmission lines may be represented by a sequence of either Π or T networks.

Equations (4.21) are not good enough for obtaining equivalent circuits of shorted or open sections, unless, of course, we subdivide them into still shorter sections and therefore have many Π or T networks in cascade. For a shorted section we use equations (4.16) and, setting, $V(l) = 0$, we take

$$V(z) = V_1(z) + V_3(z) = Z(l - z)[1 + \tfrac{1}{6}ZY(l - z)^2]I(l)$$

$$I(z) = I_0(z) + I_2(z) = [1 + \tfrac{1}{2}ZY(l - z)^2]I(l).$$

That is, we take the first two *effective* approximations for $V(z)$ and $I(z)$. The input admittance of a shorted section of length $l - z$ is

$$\frac{I(z)}{V(z)} = \frac{1 + \tfrac{1}{2}ZY(l - z)^2}{Z(l - z)[1 + \tfrac{1}{6}ZY(l - z)^2]}$$

$$= \frac{1}{Z(l - z)}[1 + \tfrac{1}{2}ZY(l - z)^2][1 - \tfrac{1}{6}ZY(l - z)^2]$$

$$= \frac{1}{Z(l - z)}[1 + \tfrac{1}{3}ZY(l - z)^2]$$

$$= \frac{1}{Z(l - z)} + \tfrac{1}{3}Y(l - z)$$

as far as the quantities of the order of $(l - z)$ are concerned. We have already obtained this result by the energy method (which is simpler) when Z is equal to $j\omega L$ and Y is equal to $j\omega C$. The factor one-third enters because the voltage vanishes at $z = l$ and hence there is little electric energy stored in the vicinity of $z = l$.

The case of an open section is similar.

4.6 Differential equations

Differentiating equations (4.11) with respect to z and noting that *under* the integral signs z is a "dummy variable," which can be replaced by u, let us say, we obtain

$$\frac{dV}{dz} = -ZI, \qquad \frac{dI}{dz} = -YV, \qquad (4.22)$$

where Z and Y may, in general, be functions of z.

The conditions at the terminal end of the line have disappeared and must be included in the calculation of the arbitrary constants which appear in the general solutions of these differential equations.

4.7 Characteristic impedance

If Z and Y are independent of z, equations (4.22) may be solved by the usual methods. There is a certain important property, however, which can best be highlighted by posing the following question: Is there a terminal impedance such that the ratio of $V(z)$ to $I(z)$ is independent of z, thus causing the input impedance to be equal to the terminal impedance independently of the length of the line? One way to answer this question is to assume

$$V(z) = KI(z) \qquad (4.23)$$

and see what happens. Since the K we seek does not depend on z

$$dV(z) = K\, dI(z).$$

Equations (4.22) become

$$K\frac{dI(z)}{dz} = -Z\, I(z),$$

$$\qquad (4.24)$$

$$\frac{dI(z)}{dz} = -KY\, I(z).$$

Dividing

$$K = Z/KY$$

or

$$K = \sqrt{Z/Y}, \qquad (4.25)$$

we have our answer: It is "yes" and we have the value of such a terminal impedance. This impedance is called the *characteristic impedance* of the transmission line. Later this concept will be generalized to apply to nonuniform transmission lines. In order that K

be physically realizable the algebraic sign of the square root should be chosen in accordance with the condition

$$\text{re } K > 0. \tag{4.26}$$

For nondissipative transmission lines

$$K = \sqrt{L/C}. \tag{4.27}$$

4.8 Propagation constant

Substituting from equation (4.25) in (4.24) we have

$$\frac{dI}{dz} = -\Gamma I, \tag{4.28}$$

where

$$\Gamma = Z/K = \sqrt{ZY}. \tag{4.29}$$

Therefore

$$I = Ae^{-\Gamma z}. \tag{4.30}$$

The normally complex quantity

$$\Gamma = \alpha + j\beta \tag{4.31}$$

is called the *propagation constant*. Its real part α is the *attenuation constant* and the imaginary part the *phase constant*. The names are self-explanatory if equation (4.30) is written in an expanded form,

$$I = Ae^{-\alpha z}e^{-j\beta z}. \tag{4.32}$$

Thus α is the relative rate of change in the amplitude per unit length, and β is the rate of change of the phase, also per unit length. For nondissipative line, $\alpha = 0$.

From equation (4.23) we find

$$V = KA\ e^{-\Gamma z}. \tag{4.33}$$

4.9 Phase velocity, wavelength

Assuming a nondissipative line and introducing the time factor in the expression (4.32) for the current, we have

$$Ie^{j\omega t} = Ae^{j(\omega t - \beta z)}.$$

The actual current, the real part of this expression, is a time-harmonic function for a fixed z. Also it is a sinusoidal function of z at a given instant t. The phase

$$\Phi = \omega t - \beta z$$

will appear constant to an observer moving in the z direction with a velocity

$$v = \frac{dz}{dt} = \frac{\omega}{\beta}. \tag{4.34}$$

This is the *phase velocity*.

The distance from crest to crest is called the *wavelength* λ. When z increases by λ, the phase decreases by 2π. Hence

$$\beta\lambda = 2\pi, \qquad \lambda = 2\pi/\beta, \qquad \beta = 2\pi/\lambda. \tag{4.35}$$

From equations in the preceding section we obtain

$$\beta = \omega\sqrt{LC}, \qquad v = \frac{1}{\sqrt{LC}}, \qquad \lambda = \frac{2\pi}{\omega\sqrt{LC}} = \frac{1}{f\sqrt{LC}} \tag{4.36}$$

and

$$f\lambda = v.$$

4.10 Transfer of power

The average power dissipated in the terminal resistance K (we are still assuming a nondissipative line terminated by its characteristic impedance) is

$$P = \tfrac{1}{2}KI_a^2, \tag{4.37}$$

where I_a is the amplitude of the current through K. Since I_a is independent of z, this is also the power entering the line at $z = 0$, and presumably carried by the wave to the terminal resistance.

4.11 Attenuation constant

When dealing with slightly dissipative transmission lines, considerable simplification may often be achieved by neglecting dissipation to begin with, solving the idealized problem, and obtaining the effect of dissipation from the idealized solution. The method is based on the assumption that slight dissipation does not affect the fields *locally* and is significant only when we compare the strengths of fields at two widely separated places in the line.

For instance, if R is the series resistance and G the shunt conductance, both per unit length of the line, the average power dissipated per unit length is

$$W = \tfrac{1}{2}RI_a^2 + \tfrac{1}{2}GV_a^2 = \tfrac{1}{2}(R + K^2G)I_a^2,$$

where I_a and V_a are the amplitudes of the current and voltage. The power P carried by the wave is given by equation (4.37). Hence the relative decrease in power, per unit length, is

$$\frac{W}{P} = \frac{R}{K} + KG.$$

Since power is proportional to the square of the amplitude of current (or voltage), the relative rate of change of the amplitude of either is half of this ratio

$$\alpha = \frac{W}{2P} = \frac{R}{2K} + \tfrac{1}{2}KG. \qquad (4.38)$$

4.12   Reflection

So far we have considered waves in a line terminated into its characteristic impedance K so that the ratio $V(z)/I(z)$ is independent of z. If the terminal impedance

$$V(l)/I(l) = Z_t \neq K,$$

the difference $Z_t - K$ gives rise to a backward or *reflected* wave. By analogy with equation (4.30) for the current wave traveling in the direction of increasing z (the distance from the origin of the wave), we obtain the following expression for the current wave traveling back from $z = l$ in the direction of increasing $l - z$ (or decreasing z)

$$I^r = Be^{-\Gamma(l-z)}. \qquad (4.39)$$

The voltage of the reflected wave is obtained from equation (4.22) by differentiation. Thus

$$V^r = -KBe^{-\Gamma(l-z)}. \qquad (4.40)$$

The sum of the incident wave given by equations (4.30) and (4.33) and the reflected wave is the total wave

$$I(z) = Ae^{-\Gamma z} + Be^{-\Gamma(l-z)},$$
$$V(z) = KAe^{-\Gamma z} - KBe^{-\Gamma(l-z)}.$$

The ratio B/A may be determined from the terminal condition

$$\frac{V(l)}{I(l)} = Z_t = K \frac{Ae^{-\Gamma l} - B}{Ae^{-\Gamma l} + B}.$$

Thus

$$B = Ae^{-\Gamma l} \frac{K - Z_t}{K + Z_t}.$$

Note that $A \exp(-\Gamma l)$ is the complex amplitude of the incident current wave at the *impedance discontinuity* at point $z = l$.

Summarizing

$$I(z) = A[e^{-\Gamma z} + ke^{-\Gamma l}e^{-\Gamma(l-z)}],$$

$$V(z) = KA[e^{-\Gamma z} - ke^{-\Gamma l}e^{-\Gamma(l-z)}],$$

$$(4.41)$$

where

$$k = \frac{K - Z_t}{K + Z_t} \tag{4.42}$$

is the *reflection coefficient* for the current wave, and $-k$ is the reflection coefficient for the voltage wave.

The constant A may be expressed either in terms of the input voltage or in terms of the input current.

4.13   Input impedance

From equation (4.41) we derive the *input impedance*

$$Z_i = \frac{V(0)}{I(0)} = K \frac{1 - ke^{-2\Gamma l}}{1 + ke^{-2\Gamma l}}. \tag{4.43}$$

4.14   Standing waves

Suppose that the line is nondissipative and shorted at $z = l$. Then $k = 1$ and equations (4.41) may be transformed into

$$I(z) = A' \cos \beta(l - z),$$

$$V(z) = jKA' \sin \beta(l - z),$$

$$(4.44)$$

where $A' = 2A \exp(-j\beta l)$ is a new constant. At all points the current is either in phase or 180° out of phase, the amplitude is sinusoidally distributed, and we have a *standing wave* pattern.

Similarly there are standing waves when the line is open at $z = l$.

4.15 Modes of oscillation

Suppose that the line is shorted at $z = l$ and open at $z = 0$. Then $I(0) = 0$ and $A' = 0$ *unless*

$$\cos \beta l = 0, \qquad \beta_n l = (n + \tfrac{1}{2}) \pi, \qquad (4.45)$$

where $n = 0, 1, 2, \cdots$. Since $\beta = \omega \sqrt{LC}$, this can happen only for the following frequencies and corresponding wavelengths

$$\omega_n = \frac{(2n + 1) \pi}{2l \sqrt{LC}}, \qquad \lambda_n = \frac{4l}{2n + 1}. \qquad (4.46)$$

The corresponding current and voltage distributions are

$$I(z) \propto \sin \beta_n z = \sin \frac{(2n + 1) \pi z}{2l},$$

$$\qquad (4.47)$$

$$V(z) \propto jK \cos \beta_n z = jK \cos \frac{(2n + 1) \pi z}{2l}.$$

These equations express possible *free* oscillations, that is, oscillations which do not require continuous excitation. They will arise if we momentarily connect the line to a generator and then disconnect it, or if we touch the line some place with a charged body, or if we merely move a charged body or a magnet past the line. In such a case all of the *modes* of *oscillation* corresponding to different integral values of n will usually be excited. To excite a pure mode it is necessary to obtain at some instant a charge or current distribution conforming to equations (4.47) for the particular n of the desired mode.

From equations (4.46) we find that the length of the section must equal an odd number of quarter-wavelengths,

$$l = (2n + 1) \frac{\lambda_n}{4}. \qquad (4.48)$$

Current and voltage distributions for $n = 0$, 1 are shown in Figure 3.8(a, c) with obvious forms for higher values of n.

4.16 Propagation in highly dissipative media and skin effect

Equations (4.13) and (4.14) express radial propagation of fields in the interior of a metal cylinder at a typical place along the line. E_z and H_φ are the only field components present and their relative directions are such that power is flowing into the cylinder from the dielectric medium between the cylinders. Thus their relative values are independent of z and if one is concerned only with these, the z coordinate may be ignored and a simpler notation, $E_z(\rho)$, $I(\rho)$, and $H_\varphi(\rho)$ may be used to express the dependence on ρ. Differentiating these equations, we obtain

$$\frac{dE_z(\rho)}{d\rho} = \frac{j\omega\mu}{2\pi\rho} I(\rho), \qquad \frac{dI(\rho)}{d\rho} = 2\pi\sigma_m\rho E_z(\rho). \qquad (4.49)$$

Suppose that our conductor is a thin cylindrical shell whose outer and inner radii are a and $a - h$, respectively. Let us introduce a new variable,

$$u = a - \rho,$$

which represents the distance from the outer surface of the shell, into our equations, thus obtaining

$$\frac{dE_z(u)}{du} = -\frac{j\omega\mu}{2\pi(a - u)} I(u),$$

$$\frac{dI(u)}{du} = -2\pi\sigma_m(a - u) E_z(u).$$

Neglecting u in comparison with a, we have

$$\frac{dE_z(u)}{du} = j\frac{\omega\mu}{2\pi a} I(u),$$

$$\frac{dI(u)}{du} = -2\pi a\sigma_m E_z(u). \qquad (4.50)$$

Equations (4.49) and (4.50) are of the same form as equations (4.22). In equations (4.50), however, Z and Y are constant and we can use the results already obtained

$$I(u) = Ae^{-\Gamma u} + Be^{-\Gamma(h-u)},$$

$$E_z(u) = KAe^{-\Gamma u} - KBe^{-\Gamma(h-u)},$$

where

$$K = \frac{1}{2\pi a}\sqrt{\frac{j\omega\mu}{\sigma_m}}, \qquad \Gamma = \sqrt{j\omega\mu\sigma_m}. \tag{4.51}$$

Since $I(h) = 0$,

$$B = -Ae^{-\Gamma h}$$

and

$$I(u) = A(e^{-\Gamma u} - e^{-2\Gamma h + \Gamma u})$$

$$E_z(u) = KA(e^{-\Gamma u} + e^{-2\Gamma h + \Gamma u}). \tag{4.52}$$

In particular, the internal impedance of the conductor is

$$Z_1 = \frac{E_z(0)}{I(0)} = K\frac{1 + e^{-2\Gamma h}}{1 - e^{-2\Gamma h}}. \tag{4.53}$$

For copper $\mu = 4\pi \times 10^{-7}$ and $\sigma_m = 5.8 \times 10^7$ so that

$$\Gamma = \sqrt{j\omega 4\pi \times 5.8} = (1 + j)2\pi\sqrt{5.8f}. \tag{4.54}$$

The attenuation constant is seen to be large even at moderate frequencies so that the field decays rapidly with increasing distance from the surface, as the frequency increases. The internal impedance approaches its ultimate value

$$Z_1 = K = \frac{1}{2\pi a}\sqrt{\frac{j\omega\mu}{\sigma_m}}. \tag{4.55}$$

Of course, the propagation constant is expressed in nepers per meter. It is more instructive to express it in nepers *per millimeter*

$$\Gamma = 0.0151\sqrt{f}(1 + j).$$

If $f = 10\,000$, then at the depth of one millimeter from the surface the magnitude of the exponential terms in equation (4.53) is

$$e^{-2\alpha h} = e^{-3.02} = 0.048.$$

Thus at high frequencies the field and the current in a conductor are confined to a thin layer exposed to the field in the dielectric medium. This phenomenon is called the *skin effect* and is a direct consequence of the high attenuation of waves in conducting media.

4.17 Nonuniform transmission lines

If the transmission line is nondissipative but the parameters L and C are functions of the distance along the line, the transmission equations (4.22) become

$$\frac{dV(z)}{dz} = -j\omega L(z)I(z),$$

$$\tag{4.56}$$

$$\frac{dI(z)}{dz} = -j\omega C(z)V(z).$$

Let us introduce a new independent variable, the *phase integral*,

$$\vartheta = \omega \int_0^z \sqrt{L(z)C(z)}\ dz \tag{4.57}$$

so that

$$d\vartheta = \omega\sqrt{L(z)C(z)}\ dz.$$

If V, I, L, and C are expressed in terms of ϑ, equations (4.56) become

$$\frac{dV(\vartheta)}{d\vartheta} = -jK(\vartheta)I(\vartheta),$$

$$\tag{4.58}$$

$$\frac{dI(\vartheta)}{d\vartheta} = -\frac{jV(\vartheta)}{K(\vartheta)},$$

where

$$K(\vartheta) = \sqrt{L(\vartheta)/C(\vartheta)}. \tag{4.59}$$

Introducing new dependent variables $\hat{V}(\vartheta)$ and $\hat{I}(\vartheta)$ such that

$$V(\vartheta) = [K(\vartheta)]^{\frac{1}{2}}\hat{V}(\vartheta), \qquad I(\vartheta) = [K(\vartheta)]^{-\frac{1}{2}}\hat{I}(\vartheta) \tag{4.60}$$

and substituting in equations (4.58), we find

$$\frac{d\hat{V}}{d\vartheta} = -j\hat{I} - \frac{K'}{2K}\hat{V}, \qquad \frac{d\hat{I}}{d\vartheta} = -j\hat{V} + \frac{K'}{2K}\hat{I}, \tag{4.61}$$

where

$$K' = K'(\vartheta) = \frac{dK(\vartheta)}{d\vartheta}.$$

If $K' \ll 2K$, approximate solutions are

$$\hat{I} = Ae^{-j\vartheta} + Be^{j\vartheta}, \qquad \hat{V} = Ae^{-j\vartheta} - Be^{j\vartheta}.$$

At $z = 0$, $\vartheta = 0$. Let $\vartheta = \Theta$ at $z = l$. We may express A and B in terms of $\hat{I}(\Theta)$, $\hat{V}(\Theta)$, and Θ. Thus

$$A = \tfrac{1}{2}[\hat{I}(\Theta) + \hat{V}(\Theta)]e^{j\Theta},$$

$$B = \tfrac{1}{2}[\hat{I}(\Theta) - \hat{V}(\Theta)]e^{-j\Theta}.$$

Substituting in the above equations and letting $\vartheta = 0$, we have expressions connecting $\hat{V}$ and $\hat{I}$ at one end of the line with $\hat{V}$ and $\hat{I}$ at the other end. Thus

$$\hat{I}(0) = \hat{I}(\Theta) \cos \Theta + j\hat{V}(\Theta) \sin \Theta,$$

$$\hat{V}(0) = \hat{V}(\Theta) \cos \Theta + j\hat{I}(\Theta) \sin \Theta.$$

From these and equations (4.60) we obtain the relations between the voltages and currents at two ends

$$I(0) = \sqrt{\frac{K(\Theta)}{K(0)}} \left[I(\Theta) \cos \Theta + j \frac{V(\Theta)}{K(\Theta)} \sin \Theta\right],$$

$$\tag{4.62}$$

$$V(0) = \sqrt{\frac{K(0)}{K(\Theta)}} [V(\Theta) \cos \Theta + jK(\Theta)I(\Theta) \sin \Theta].$$

4.18 Image parameters

Equations (4.62) are identical with equations for a two-pair transducer in terms of its *image parameters*

$$V_1 = \sqrt{\frac{K_1}{K_2}} (V_2 \cos \Theta + jK_2I_2 \sin \Theta);$$

$$\tag{4.63}$$

$$I_1 = \sqrt{\frac{K_2}{K_1}} (I_2 \cos \Theta + jK_2^{-1}V_2 \sin \Theta),$$

where K_1 and K_2 are *image impedances* and Θ is the *image transfer constant*. If the transducer or the transmission line is terminated at the second pair of terminals into its image impedance K_2, the impedance seen at the first pair of terminals is K_1. Also, if the transducer or the line is terminated at the first pair of terminals into its image impedance K_1, the impedance seen at the second pair of terminals is K_2.

If the transducer or the line is either shorted $(V_2 = 0)$ or open $(I_2 = 0)$ at the second pair of terminals, the corresponding impedances seen at the first pair are

$$Z_{1,sh} = jK_1 \tan \Theta, \qquad Z_{1,op} = -jK_1 \cot \Theta. \qquad (4.64)$$

Similarly

$$Z_{2,sh} = jK_2 \tan \Theta, \qquad Z_{2,op} = -jK_2 \cot \Theta. \qquad (4.65)$$

Hence

$$K_1 = \sqrt{Z_{1,sh}Z_{1,op}}, \qquad K_2 = \sqrt{Z_{2,sh}Z_{2,op}}$$

$$\tan \Theta = \frac{-jZ_{1,sh}}{K_1} = \frac{-jZ_{2,sh}}{K_2} = \sqrt{-\frac{Z_{1,sh}}{Z_{1,op}}} = \sqrt{-\frac{Z_{2,sh}}{Z_{2,op}}}. \qquad (4.66)$$

4.19 Waves in hollow tubes

At high frequencies two conductors are not essential for guiding electric waves. One may suffice. Figure 4.3 depicts a hollow metal

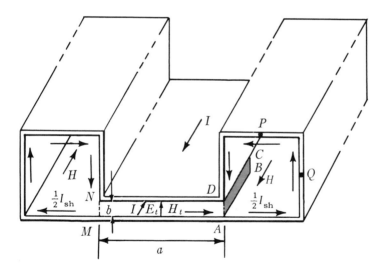

FIGURE 4.3 *A rectangular waveguide with a wide ridge.*

tube consisting of two parallel strips of width a, distance b apart, and two cylinders, each of rectangular cross-section S, connecting the edges of the strips. Let $V = bE_t$ be the transverse voltage between the strips and $I = aH_t$ the longitudinal current in the lower strip. In addition there will be lateral currents in the cylindrical walls and longitudinal magnetic flux produced by these currents. Applying the Faraday-Maxwell law to a rectangular path $ABCDA$, where $AB = dz$, we have

$$\frac{dV}{dz} = -\frac{j\omega\mu b}{a} I. \tag{4.67}$$

The longitudinal current I will decrease by an amount dI in distance dz due to a leakage in the form of the vertical displacement current $j\omega\epsilon a E_t \, dz = (j\omega\epsilon a/b) V \, dz$ and shunt leakage in the form of conduction currrent. To obtain the latter we note that the electromotive force round the closed path $AQPDA$ equals $-V$ (if we assume that the walls of the tube are perfectly conducting). On the other hand, this must equal the magnetic current $-j\omega\Phi$ linked with the path. Therefore, $\Phi = V/j\omega$, $B = V/j\omega S$, $H = V/j\omega\mu S$ and the shunt conduction current $H \, dz = V \, dz/j\omega\mu S$. There is an equal leakage current via the left cylinder. Hence

$$\frac{dI}{dz} = -\left(\frac{j\omega\epsilon a}{b} + \frac{2}{j\omega\mu S}\right)V. \tag{4.68}$$

These equations are approximate since we have assumed that the transverse magnetic field E_t, H_t is uniform and is confined to the region between the strips, that the longitudinal magnetic field is also

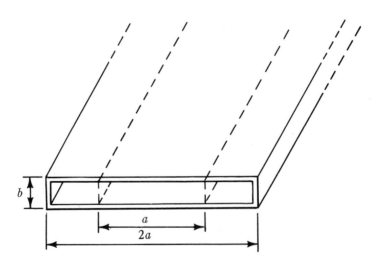

FIGURE 4.4 *A waveguide of rectangular cross section.*

uniform and confined to the cylindrical portions of the tube, and that there is no electric field there. These approximations are analogous to those we made in analyzing electric oscillations in cavities and can be improved. The approximations are particularly rough in the case of a tube of rectangular cross-section as shown in Figure 4.4 where the middle portions of the top and bottom may be thought of as "two parallel strips." In this case the exact solution is known and our intuitive thinking can be checked. Since, in this case, $S = \frac{1}{2}ab$, we have

$$\frac{dV}{dz} = -\frac{j\omega\mu b}{a} I, \qquad \frac{dI}{dz} = -\left(\frac{j\omega\epsilon a}{b} + \frac{4}{j\omega\mu ab}\right) V. \qquad (4.69)$$

The propagation constant is

$$\Gamma = \sqrt{\frac{4}{a^2} - \omega^2\mu\epsilon}. \qquad (4.70)$$

When $\omega\sqrt{\mu\epsilon} < 2/a$, Γ is real so that V, I, and the field decay exponentially with increasing z (assuming that they are excited at $z = 0$). When $\omega\sqrt{\mu\epsilon} > 2/a$, Γ is pure imaginary and waves may travel in the tube. The critical frequency and the corresponding wavelength are

$$\omega_c = \frac{2}{a\sqrt{\mu\epsilon}}, \qquad \lambda_c = \pi a. \qquad (4.71)$$

The exact value is $\lambda_c = 4a$. For the tube in Figure 4.3 where b is small compared with the total height, the results should be more accurate.

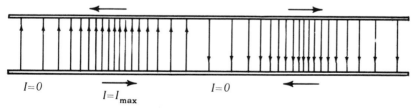

$I=0$ $I=I_{max}$ $I=0$

FIGURE 4.5 *The relative distribution of transverse displacement currents associated with waves along parallel wires.*

The case just considered is analogous to a two-conductor transmission line shown in Figure 4.5 in that two portions of the tube act as the forward and return conductors. In both instances we have transverse displacement currents. But at low frequencies in a hollow tube these displacement currents are negligible in comparison with the lateral conduction currents, and the "strip line" or center portion is effectively short-circuited at its edges. As the frequency increases, the shunt inductive reactance increases, the transverse conduction currents decrease, and parallel strips become in effect separate conductors.

There is another possibility of wave propagation in which the entire current in a hollow conductor *returns as a longitudinal dis-*

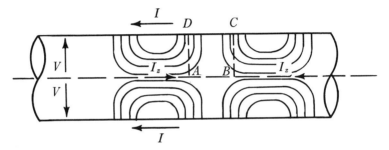

FIGURE 4.6   *Illustrating the nature of possible waves in the interior of a circular cylindrical conducting tube.*

placement current. See Figure 4.6. Since at low frequencies displacement currents are feeble, this possibility can occur only at high frequencies. In Chapter 6 we shall develop a method for solving such problems exactly, at least for simple shapes of tubes. It is instructive, however, to obtain at least qualitative results from direct physical considerations. Assuming a circularly symmetric field, we have radial and longitudinal components of electric field E_ρ and E_z. Magnetic lines of force are circles and we have only H_φ. If the tube is perfectly conducting E_z must vanish at its surface and so we *assume*

$$E_z = E_0 \left(1 - \frac{\rho^2}{a^2} \right). \tag{4.72}$$

The actual distribution of E_z is undoubtedly different. It would be a remarkable accident if we were to guess it exactly; but here we are concerned with qualitative aspects of a possible field. We now obtain in succession

$$J_z = j\omega\epsilon E_0 \left(1 - \frac{\rho^2}{a^2}\right),$$

$$I_z(\rho) = \int_0^{2\pi}\int_0^{\rho} J_z\rho \, d\rho \, d\varphi = j\omega\epsilon\pi E_0 \left(\rho^2 - \frac{\rho^4}{2a^2}\right),$$

$$I = I_z(a) = \tfrac{1}{2}j\omega\epsilon\pi a^2 E_0,$$

$$E_0 = \frac{2I}{j\omega\epsilon\pi a^2},$$

$$H_\varphi(\rho) = \frac{I_z(\rho)}{2\pi\rho} = \tfrac{1}{2}j\omega\epsilon E_0 \left(\rho - \frac{\rho^3}{2a^2}\right),$$

$$\int_0^a B_\varphi \, d\rho = \tfrac{3}{16}j\omega\mu a^2\epsilon E_0 = \frac{3\mu}{8\pi} I.$$

Hence, applying the Faraday-Maxwell law to a rectangle $ABCDA$ in a radial plane, where $AB = dz$, we have

$$\frac{dV}{dz} = -j\omega\int_0^a B_\varphi \, d\rho - E_0 = -\left(\frac{3j\omega\mu}{8\pi} + \frac{2}{j\omega\epsilon\pi a^2}\right) I. \qquad (4.73)$$

Here $V = V_{AD}$ is the transverse voltage from the axis to the periphery of the tube.

The rate of change in the longitudinal current depends on the radial displacement currents and must be proportional to the transverse voltage

$$\frac{dI}{dz} = -j\omega C V. \qquad (4.74)$$

There seems to be no simple way of estimating C without a better understanding of what happens inside the tube.

The propagation constant is

$$\Gamma = \sqrt{\frac{2C}{\epsilon\pi a^2} - \frac{3\omega^2\mu C}{8\pi}}. \qquad (4.75)$$

At low frequencies Γ is real and there are no traveling waves. The critical frequency, for which $\Gamma = 0$ and above which traveling waves are possible, is given by

$$\omega_c\sqrt{\mu\epsilon}a = \frac{4}{\sqrt{3}} = 2.31. \qquad (4.76)$$

The exact value (to three figures) is 2.40. The critical wavelength is comparable to the diameter of the tube.

Evidently, similar types of fields can exist between coaxial cylinders. Indeed they are required if the voltage distribution impressed at the input end of the coaxial line does not conform to the radial field we have been considering. Below a certain critical frequency these fields are attenuated with increasing distance from the end and represent just an "end-effect." The critical wavelength is of the order of the distance between the cylinders. Thus, regardless of the distribution of applied voltage, the propagation in coaxial pairs is governed by equations (4.11) until very high frequencies are reached when these equations apply only if we maintain a proper distribution of the input voltage.

5

Spherical Waves

5.0 Introduction

In this chapter we shall examine some simple types of *spherical waves*, that is, waves traveling in all directions from the center of their excitation. The simplest problem mathematically is to find the field associated with an electric current wave in a wire starting from some point and going to infinity. The solution of this problem may then be used for solving other problems, namely: problems concerning waves between coaxial cones, cylinders, or parallel planes; problems concerning waves guided by thin diverging cones or parallel wires; and finally the problem of waves excited in free space by an electric charge oscillating back and forth between two nearby points.

We have seen that electric generators do work when exciting waves guided by parallel wires and that therefore waves carry energy away from the generators to distant points. Similarly, spherical waves in free space carry away energy from their sources. From the law of conservation of energy we conclude that the density of this *radiant energy* varies inversely as the square of the distance from the source of these waves (the same energy must pass through every sphere concentric with the source).

As in the case of waves along wires, the phase of spherical waves is retarded with increasing distance from the source. Hence, the waves arriving at a given point in space from two or more sources will *interfere* either constructively or destructively. This interference produces *directive radiation*.

5.1 Maxwell's equations for circularly symmetric fields

In Chapter 1 we derived expressions for electric and magnetic fields generated by a semi-infinite direct current filament and a direct current element. Those expressions should be approximately correct in the case of slowly varying currents since there is no reason to expect any abrupt change in the nature of the fields. In Section 2.8

177

we attempted to obtain the effect of the time-variable magnetic field on the electric field of the element and failed because we were unable to apportion this effect between E_z and E_ρ. Integral equations (1.76) and (1.77) are too gross for analysis of the details of fields unless we know more about their general character from other physical considerations. In order to calculate the fine-grained effects, we need equations expressing local conditions in the vicinity of a typical point. Such conditions are obtained by applying equations (1.76) and (1.77) to infinitesimal mesh circuits formed by coordinate

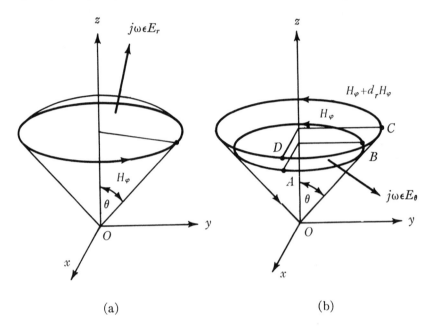

(a)   (b)

FIGURE 5.1 *Illustrating the derivation of Maxwell's differential equations for circularly symmetric fields from Maxwell's integral equations.*

lines. General partial differential equations may be obtained in this manner for any system of coordinates. We shall confine ourselves to fields in which magnetic lines are circles with centers on the z axis and electric lines are in planes passing through the z axis. Thus there are only three components to consider: H_φ, E_r, E_θ, each independent of φ.

Consider a typical magnetic line surmounted by a spherical cap of radius r, concentric with the origin, as shown in Figure 5.1(a). The magnetomotive force round this line should equal the total radial displacement current through the cap

$$2\pi r \sin\theta\, H_\varphi = \int_0^{2\pi}\int_0^\theta j\omega\epsilon E_r r^2 \sin\theta\, d\theta\, d\varphi$$

$$= 2\pi j\omega\epsilon r^2 \int_0^\theta E_r \sin\theta\, d\theta.$$

Canceling $2\pi r$ and differentiating with respect to θ, we have

$$\frac{\partial}{\partial\theta}(\sin\theta\, H_\varphi) = j\omega\epsilon r \sin\theta E_r. \tag{5.1}$$

Next we view Figure 5.1(b) which shows two magnetic lines on a typical cone coaxial with the z axis and separated by distance dr. The differential increment in the magnetomotive force should equal the displacement current in the direction of *decreasing* θ through the strip bounded by these lines

$$\frac{\partial}{\partial r}(2\pi r \sin\theta\, H_\varphi)\, dr = -j\omega\epsilon E_\theta(2\pi r \sin\theta)\, dr,$$

that is,

$$\frac{\partial}{\partial r}(rH_\varphi) = -j\omega\epsilon(rE_\theta). \tag{5.2}$$

Finally, consider Figure 5.2 which illustrates an infinitesimal

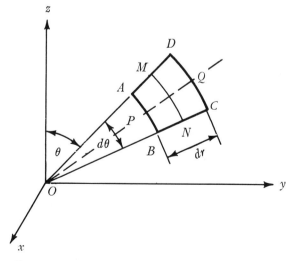

FIGURE 5.2 *A differential circuit in a radial plane.*

circuit $ABCD$ in a radial plane bounded by arcs of concentric circles whose radii are r and $r + dr$, and by radii θ and $\theta + d\theta$. The counter-clockwise electromotive force round the curvilinear rectangle should equal the magnetic current through the rectangle in the direction of *increasing φ*

$$V_{AB} + V_{BC} + V_{CD} + V_{DA} = j\omega\mu H_\varphi r \, d\theta \, dr.$$

Since

$$V_{DC} - V_{AB} = \frac{\partial}{\partial r} (V_{MN}) \, dr,$$

$$V_{BC} - V_{AD} = \frac{\partial}{\partial \theta} (V_{PQ}) \, d\theta,$$

$$V_{MN} = E_\theta r \, d\theta, \qquad V_{PQ} = E_r \, dr,$$

we have

$$-\frac{\partial}{\partial r} (rE_\theta) \, dr \, d\theta + \frac{\partial E_r}{\partial \theta} \, dr \, d\theta = j\omega\mu H_\varphi r \, d\theta \, dr.$$

Hence

$$\frac{\partial}{\partial r} (rE_\theta) = -j\omega\mu (rH_\varphi) + \frac{\partial E_r}{\partial \theta}. \tag{5.3}$$

Thus we have three partial differential equations connecting E_r, E_θ, and H_φ for *any* electromagnetic field with circular symmetry in which electric lines are in planes passing through the z axis. There is a similar set of equations for any field in which electric lines are circles coaxial with the z axis. This set includes fields generated by uniform circulating currents.

5.2 Waves on semi-infinite wire

In Chapter 1 we obtained the following expression for a semi-infinite direct current filament on the z axis [Figure 5.3(a)] issuing from the center O of a spherical frame of reference

$$H_\varphi = \frac{I(1 + \cos \theta)}{4\pi r \sin \theta}.$$

Let us now inquire whether there can exist a time-harmonic field with the same dependence on θ. To answer this question we assume

$$H_\varphi(r, \theta) = R(r) \frac{1 + \cos \theta}{\sin \theta}, \tag{5.4}$$

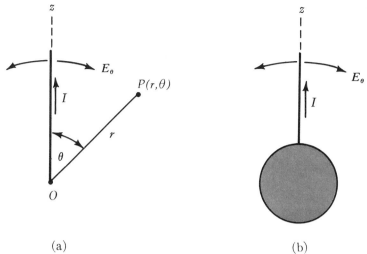

(a)   (b)

FIGURE 5.3   *Current filaments along the positive z axis: (a) with a point charge at the origin 0; (b) with a small charged sphere concentric with the origin.*

where $R(r)$ is an unknown function of r only. If no such field can exist, then equation (5.4) will be inconsistent with Maxwell's equations (5.1), (5.2), and (5.3). If it can exist we should be able to find proper expressions for H_φ, E_r, and E_θ.

Substituting from equation (5.4) into equation (5.1), we find

$$E_r = -\frac{R(r)}{j\omega\epsilon r}. \tag{5.5}$$

Substituting from equation (5.4) into equation (5.2) we have

$$rE_\theta = -\frac{1}{j\omega\epsilon}\frac{1 + \cos\theta}{\sin\theta}\frac{d(rR)}{dr}. \tag{5.6}$$

Substituting from equations (5.4), (5.5), and (5.6) into the remaining equation (5.3), we obtain

$$\frac{d^2(rR)}{dr^2} = -\beta^2(rR), \qquad \beta = \omega\sqrt{\mu\epsilon}. \tag{5.7}$$

Solving, we have

$$rR = Ae^{-j\beta r} + Be^{j\beta r}. \tag{5.8}$$

The first term of this solution represents waves traveling radially away from the center O. The second term represents waves converging to the center, for example, waves reflected from the inside of a conducting sphere concentric with O. Both types are known as *spherical waves*.

For waves traveling outward the current $I(r)$ in the wire is

$$I(r) = 2\pi r \sin \theta H_\varphi(r, \theta) \quad \text{as} \quad \theta \to 0$$

$$= 4\pi r R = 4\pi A e^{-j\beta r},$$

and

$$I(0) = I_0 = 4\pi A, \qquad A = I_0/4\pi.$$

Hence,

$$H_\varphi = \frac{I_0 e^{-j\beta r}(1 + \cos \theta)}{4\pi r \sin \theta}, \qquad E_\theta = \eta H_\varphi$$

$$\tag{5.9}$$

$$E_r = -\frac{I_0 e^{-j\beta r}}{4\pi j \omega \epsilon r^2}, \qquad \eta = \sqrt{\mu/\epsilon}.$$

The radial electric intensity decreases faster than the meridian intensity. The ratio of their magnitudes is

$$|E_r/E_\theta| = 1/\beta r = \lambda/2\pi r. \tag{5.10}$$

This ratio is less than one-sixth at a distance of one wavelength from the origin. Thus at larger distances $\bar{E}$ is nearly perpendicular to the wire as it should be if the wire is perfectly conducting and if there are no generators in series with it. Near the origin the component of $\bar{E}$ tangential to the wire is large. We need an equal and opposite electric intensity to maintain the current in the wire and to generate the field described by equations (5.9). At $r = 0$ this intensity is infinite. A more realistic physical situation is obtained by assuming a small metal sphere concentric with O, as shown in Figure 5.3(b). It is possible to modify the solution so that it would represent a wave generated by an impressed voltage, concentrated in the immediate vicinity of such a sphere. This modification is significant only in a restricted region around O.

5.3   Waves between coaxial cones

Imagine another semi-infinite wire along the negative z axis, carrying a progressive current wave $I_0 e^{-j\beta r}$. For this wave positive charge is accumulating at O, while an equal but negative charge is accumulating there due to the current which is flowing out of O along the positive z axis. There is no net charge accumulation at point O and for the combined field of two filaments $E_r = 0$. The contribution of this second current to the other field components may be obtained from equations (5.9) if we replace θ by $\pi - \theta$. Hence, *for two wires*

$$H_\varphi = \frac{I_0 e^{-j\beta r}}{2\pi r \sin \theta}, \qquad E_\theta = \eta H_\varphi. \qquad (5.11)$$

Since there is no radial electric field, we may insert two perfectly conducting cones, coaxial with the z axis without disturbing the field, as illustrated in Figures 5.4(a, b). Hence, equations (5.11) are proper expressions for the field between such coaxial cones. Electric lines are strictly along meridians. The voltage along a typical line is

$$V(r) = \int_{\theta_1}^{\theta_2} E_\theta r \, d\theta = \frac{\eta I_0}{2\pi} e^{-j\beta r} \int_{\theta_1}^{\theta_2} \frac{d\theta}{\sin \theta}$$

$$= \frac{\eta I_0}{2\pi} e^{-j\beta r} \int_{\theta_1}^{\theta_2} \frac{d(\theta/2)}{\sin (\theta/2) \cos (\theta/2)}$$

$$= \frac{\eta I_0}{2\pi} e^{-j\beta r} \int_{\theta_1}^{\theta_2} \frac{d \tan (\theta/2)}{\tan (\theta/2)},$$

where θ_1 and θ_2 are the half-cone angles. Thus

$$V(r) = KI_0 e^{-j\beta r}, \qquad K = \frac{\eta}{2\pi} \ln \left[\frac{\tan (\theta_2/2)}{\tan (\theta_1/2)} \right], \qquad (5.12)$$

where K is the characteristic impedance of a biconical transmission line (see Section 4.7).

In the case of two equal cones, Figure 5.4(a), of internal half-angle ψ, $\theta_2 = \pi - \psi$ and

$$K = \frac{\eta}{\pi} \ln \cot \left(\frac{\psi}{2} \right). \qquad (5.13)$$

When $\psi/2 \ll 1$

$$K = \frac{\eta}{\pi} \ln \frac{2}{\psi}. \qquad (5.14)$$

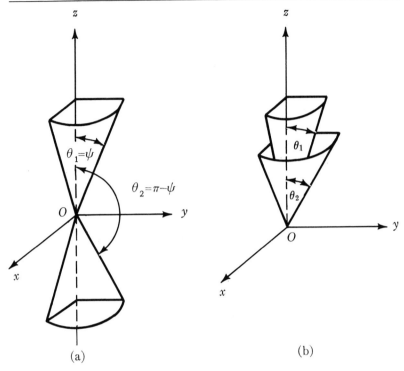

FIGURE 5.4   *Coaxial cones.*

5.4   Waves between coaxial cylinders

If we assume that in Figure 5.4(b) the cone angles approach zero in such a way that $r\theta_1$ and $r\theta_2$ remain constant, then the cones approach coaxial cylinders. Since $r \sin \theta = \rho$, equations (5.11) yield in the limit

$$H_\varphi = \frac{I_0 e^{-j\beta z}}{2\pi\rho}, \qquad E_\rho = \eta H_\varphi. \tag{5.15}$$

Equations (5.12) become

$$V(z) = K I_0 e^{-j\beta z}$$

$$K = \frac{\eta}{2\pi} \ln \frac{\theta_2}{\theta_1} = \frac{\eta}{2\pi} \ln \frac{r\theta_2}{r\theta_1} \tag{5.16}$$

$$= \frac{\eta}{2\pi} \ln \frac{b}{a},$$

where a and b are the radii of the cylinders.

5.5 Waves between parallel planes

As $(b - a)/(b + a)$ decreases, the coaxial cylinders in Figure 5.5 approach parallel planes. If

$$R = \tfrac{1}{2}(a + b) \tag{5.17}$$

is the mean radius, and if x is the radial distance from the mean

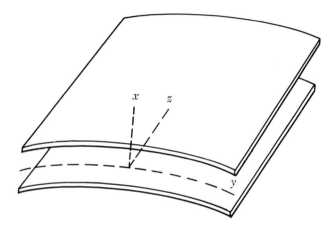

FIGURE 5.5 *A section of coaxial cylinders of large and nearly equal radii and bent cylindrical coordinates.*

cylinder, equations (5.15) may be expressed as

$$H_\varphi = H_y = \frac{I_0 e^{-j\beta z}}{2\pi(R + x)}, \qquad E_\rho = E_x = \eta H_y$$

$$= \frac{I_0 e^{-j\beta z}}{2\pi R}\left(1 - \frac{x}{R} + \frac{x^2}{R^2} \cdots\right).$$

The maximum value of x is $\tfrac{1}{2}(b - a)$. Hence to the extent to which $(b - a)/(b + a)$ is negligible in comparison with unity, we have a uniform field

$$H_y = \frac{I_0}{2\pi R}e^{-j\beta z}, \qquad E_x = \eta H_y. \tag{5.18}$$

Since $b = R + \tfrac{1}{2}h$ and $a = R - \tfrac{1}{2}h$ where $h = b - a$, the characteristic impedance may be expressed as

$$K = \frac{\eta}{2\pi} \ln \frac{1 + (h/2R)}{1 - (h/2R)}$$

$$= \frac{\eta}{2\pi} \left(\frac{h}{2R} - \frac{h^2}{8R^2} + \frac{h^3}{24R^3} - \cdots \right)$$

$$- \frac{\eta}{2\pi} \left(-\frac{h}{2R} - \frac{h^2}{8R^2} - \frac{h^3}{24R^3} - \cdots \right).$$

Hence

$$K = \frac{\eta h}{2\pi R} \left(1 + \frac{h^2}{12R^2} + \cdots \right). \tag{5.19}$$

5.6 Waves guided by thin diverging cones

The field of two diverging progressive current filaments, OA and OB as shown in Figure 5.6, may be obtained from equations (5.9). If the

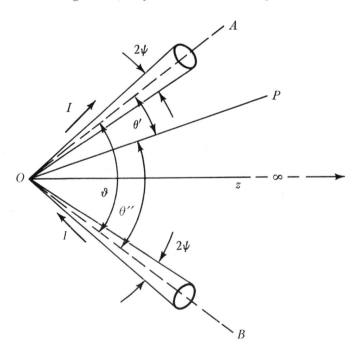

FIGURE 5.6   *Diverging thin conical conductors with a common apex.*

currents are equal and opposite at points equidistant from O, there is no accumulation of charge at O and the radial field vanishes. The transverse field may best be expressed in terms of mixed coordinates (r, θ', φ') and (r, θ'', φ'') where θ' and θ'' are the angles made by a typical radius OP with OA and OB, while φ' and φ'' are the angles fixing the position of P around OA and OB, respectively. The total field is the sum of two fields, one associated with the filament OA and the other with OB,

$$H_{\varphi'} = \frac{I_0 e^{-j\beta r}(1 + \cos \theta')}{4\pi r \sin \theta'}, \qquad E_{\theta'} = \eta H_{\varphi'}$$

$$\text{(5.20)}$$

$$H_{\varphi''} = \frac{I_0 e^{-j\beta r}(1 + \cos \theta'')}{4\pi r \sin \theta''}, \qquad E_{\theta''} = \eta H_{\varphi''}.$$

Electric lines run from one filament to the other on spherical surfaces concentric with 0. Without disturbing the field we can introduce perfectly conducting conical surfaces around each filament provided the electric lines cut these surfaces at right angles. This condition is fulfilled exactly by certain circular cones around OA and OB, whose axes, however, do not coincide with either OA or OB. But as the cone angles become smaller, their axes approach OA and OB.

The characteristic impedance of the transmission line formed by thin diverging cones is

$$K = \frac{\eta}{2\pi} \int_\psi^\vartheta \frac{1 + \cos \theta}{\sin \theta}\, d\theta = \frac{\eta}{2\pi} \int_\psi^\vartheta \frac{\cos (\theta/2)}{\sin (\theta/2)}\, d\theta$$

$$= \frac{\eta}{\pi} \ln \frac{\sin (\vartheta/2)}{\sin (\psi/2)}, \qquad\qquad \text{(5.21)}$$

where ϑ is the angle between the axes of the cones each of angle 2ψ.

5.7 Waves guided by parallel wires

Two diverging cones, as shown in Figure 5.6, approach a pair of parallel wires when ϑ and ψ approach zero in such a way that $r\vartheta$ and $r\psi$ remain constant. Point O recedes to infinity. Angles θ' and θ'' approach zero for all points in an increasingly large region around the wires: $\rho' = r \sin \theta'$ and $\rho'' = r\theta''$ are the distances from the axes of the wires, and $a = r \sin \psi$ is the radius of a wire.

5.8 Waves generated by an electric current element

The field of an electric current element AB of moment Il (an oscillating electric dipole), Figure 5.7, may be obtained by superposing the fields of two semi-infinite progressive current filaments. One of

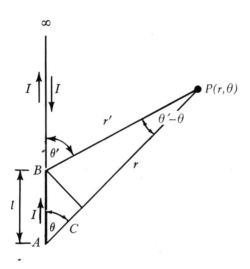

FIGURE 5.7 *Illustrating the calculation of the field of a current element AB from the fields of two semi-infinite current filaments.*

the filaments starts at A and the other starts at B. They are 180° out of phase so that beyond B there is no current. Using equation (5.9), we have

$$H_\varphi = \frac{Ie^{-j\beta r}(1 + \cos\theta)}{4\pi r \sin\theta} - \frac{Ie^{-j\beta l}e^{-j\beta r'}(1 + \cos\theta')}{4\pi r' \sin\theta'}.$$

The factor $\exp(-j\beta l)$ in the second term arises from the fact that the phase of the progressive current filament which starts at A is retarded by an amount βl on arrival at B. Noting that $r' \sin\theta' = r \sin\theta$, we obtain

$$H_\varphi = \frac{Ie^{-j\beta r}}{4\pi r \sin\theta} F, \tag{5.22}$$

where

$$F = 1 + \cos\theta - e^{-j\beta l - j\beta(r'-r)}(1 + \cos\theta').$$

As l approaches zero, AP and BP become more nearly parallel and

$$r - r' \rightarrow l \cos \theta$$

$$e^{-j\beta l - j\beta(r'-r)} \rightarrow 1 - j\beta l - j\beta(r' - r)$$

$$\rightarrow 1 - j\beta l(1 - \cos \theta).$$

Hence

$$F = 1 + \cos \theta - (1 + \cos \theta')[1 - j\beta l(1 - \cos \theta)]$$

$$= 1 + \cos \theta - 1 - \cos \theta' + j\beta l(1 + \cos \theta')(1 - \cos \theta).$$

Since the difference between θ' and θ is infinitesimal, the substitution of $\cos \theta$ for $\cos \theta'$ in the last term will alter F by an infinitesimal of the second order (note that βl is an infinitesimal). Thus

$$F = \cos \theta - \cos \theta' + j\beta l \sin^2 \theta.$$

As θ' approaches θ,

$$\cos \theta - \cos \theta' = 2 \sin \tfrac{1}{2}(\theta' + \theta) \sin \tfrac{1}{2}(\theta' - \theta)$$

$$\rightarrow (\theta' - \theta) \sin \theta.$$

Referring to Figure 5.7, we observe that $\theta' - \theta = BC/r = (l/r) \sin \theta$ except for infinitesimals of higher order. Therefore

$$F = (l/r) \sin^2 \theta + j\beta l \sin^2 \theta$$

and equation (5.22) becomes

$$H_\varphi = \frac{j\beta Il}{4\pi r}\left(1 + \frac{1}{j\beta r}\right) e^{-j\beta r} \sin \theta. \tag{5.23}$$

The remaining field components may be obtained by differentiation from equations (5.1) and (5.2)

$$E_r = \frac{\eta Il}{2\pi r^2}\left(1 + \frac{1}{j\beta r}\right) e^{-j\beta r} \cos \theta, \qquad \eta = \sqrt{\mu/\epsilon}$$

$$E_\theta = \frac{j\omega\mu Il}{4\pi r}\left(1 + \frac{1}{j\beta r} - \frac{1}{\beta^2 r^2}\right) e^{-j\beta r} \sin \theta. \tag{5.24}$$

At distances large compared with the wavelength, $(\beta r)^{-1} \ll 1$ and

$$H_\varphi = \frac{j\beta Il}{4\pi r} e^{-j\beta r} \sin \theta = \frac{jIl}{2\lambda r} e^{-j\beta r} \sin \theta,$$

$$\tag{5.25}$$

$$E_\theta = \eta H_\varphi, \qquad E_r = \frac{\eta Il}{2\pi r^2} e^{-j\beta r} \cos \theta.$$

As the distance from the current element increases, the radial electric intensity decreases much faster than the meridian intensity. Thus in a distant field $\bar{E}$ and $\bar{H}$ are perpendicular to the radial direction of wave propagation. The field is relatively strong in the equatorial plane of the element and vanishes on its axis.

Any linear distribution of current may be subdivided into current elements of moment $I(s)\,\overrightarrow{ds}$, where $\overrightarrow{ds}$ is an element of length and $I(s)$ is the current at a typical point of linear distribution. Any volume distribution of current may be subdivided into elements of moment $\bar{J}\,dv$, where $\bar{J}$ is the current density and dv is an element of volume. Thus the field of any current distribution may be obtained by integrating the field given by equations (5.23) and (5.24) over the region occupied by current.

5.9 Waves above perfectly conducting planes

In the equatorial plane of a current element, E_r vanishes and $\bar{E}$ is perpendicular to the plane. Hence the plane may be made a perfect conductor without perturbing the field. Thus equations (5.24) and (5.25) apply to a vertical current element of moment $Il/2$ just above a perfectly conducting plane.

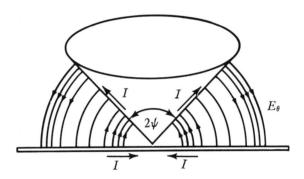

FIGURE 5.8 *Waves between an infinite conducting cone and a conducting plane (a cone of 180° angle).*

An instructive comparison can be made between waves in free space and waves in the half-space above a perfectly conducting plane, on the one hand, and waves beween coaxial cones or between a cone above a perfectly conducting plane, on the other hand. See Figure 5.8. In the case of cones, including the 180° cone which is a plane, the field varies inversely as the distance from the apex at which a voltage is applied [see equations (5.11)]. The variation with θ is relatively small if the cone angle 2ψ is equal to or larger than $120°$ since $\sin 60° = 0.866$. The same can be said of the field of the current element in the region $\pi/3 \le \theta \le 2\pi/3$ when $r \gg \lambda$. In fact, the difference becomes particularly significant only at distances smaller than λ. If $r = \lambda$, $\beta r = 2\pi = 6.28$ and the contributions of $1/\beta r$ and $1/(\beta r)^2$ to the field intensities are already relatively small.

   Both the differences and the similarities become understandable, if we note that conducting cones provide an easy path for radial electric current. On the other hand, in free space, for a given voltage drop the radial displacement current is small unless the area available for the flow is large. In other words, in the presence of cones, for a given radial current there is no radial voltage drop and the entire impressed voltage is transmitted, in a wave-like manner, to large distances. In the case of a current element in free space, on the other hand, most of the impressed voltage is consumed in driving radial displacement current in the vicinity of the element. Whatever is left at larger distances is then freely transmitted beyond.

5.10   Radiation

Let us examine the field in the vicinity of a current element. For this purpose we shall expand expressions (5.23) and (5.24) in power series in r. Thus

$$e^{-j\beta r} = 1 - j\beta r + \tfrac{1}{2}(j\beta r)^2 - \tfrac{1}{6}(j\beta r)^3 + \tfrac{1}{24}(j\beta r)^4 + \cdots,$$

$$\frac{e^{-j\beta r}}{j\beta r} = \frac{1}{j\beta r} - 1 + \tfrac{1}{2}(j\beta r) - \tfrac{1}{6}(j\beta r)^2 + \tfrac{1}{24}(j\beta r)^3 + \cdots,$$

$$\frac{e^{-j\beta r}}{(j\beta r)^2} = \frac{1}{(j\beta r)^2} - \frac{1}{j\beta r} + \tfrac{1}{2} - \tfrac{1}{6}j\beta r + \tfrac{1}{24}(j\beta r)^2 + \cdots.$$

Hence

$$H_\varphi = \left(\frac{Il}{4\pi r^2} + \frac{\beta^2 Il}{8\pi} - \frac{j\beta^3 r Il}{12\pi} + \cdots\right) \sin\theta,$$

$$E_r = \left(\frac{Il}{2\pi j\omega\epsilon r^3} - \frac{j\omega\mu Il}{4\pi r} - \frac{\eta\beta^2 Il}{6\pi} + \frac{j\eta\beta^3 r Il}{16\pi}\right) \cos\theta,$$

$$E_\theta = \left(\frac{Il}{4\pi j\omega\epsilon r^3} + \frac{j\omega\mu Il}{8\pi r} + \frac{\eta\beta^2 Il}{6\pi} - \frac{3j\eta\beta^3 r Il}{32\pi}\right) \sin\theta.$$

For slowly varying electric fields the first terms of these expressions were already obtained directly from Coulomb's law and from the Ampere-Maxwell law.

The components of $\vec{E}$ parallel to and perpendicular to the elements are

$$E_z = E_r \cos \theta - E_\theta \sin \theta$$

$$= \frac{Il(2 \cos^2 \theta - \sin^2 \theta)}{4\pi j\omega\epsilon r^3} - \frac{j\omega\mu Il}{4\pi r} + \frac{j\omega\mu Il \sin^2 \theta}{8\pi r} - \frac{\eta\beta^2 Il}{6\pi} + \cdots$$

and

$$E_\rho = E_r \sin \theta + E_\theta \cos \theta$$

$$= \frac{3Il \sin \theta \cos \theta}{4\pi j\omega\epsilon r^3} - \frac{j\omega\mu Il \sin \theta \cos \theta}{8\pi r}$$

$$- \frac{j\eta\beta^3 rIl \sin \theta \cos \theta}{16\pi} + \cdots.$$

Most of the terms are in time quadrature with current I (as signified by "$j\omega$") and represent the reactive field around the element. The last term in E_z is 180° out of phase with I. A voltage equal to $-E_z l$ is needed to drive current in the element against its field. The average work done by this voltage per second is

$$P = \tfrac{1}{2} \operatorname{re} \left[-(E_z l) I^* \right], \tag{5.26}$$

where the asterisk denotes the complex conjugate of I. Substituting the last term of E_z we have

$$P = \frac{\eta}{12\pi} (\beta l)^2 II^*, \tag{5.27}$$

where II^* is the square of the amplitude of the current.

In free space, $\eta \simeq 120\pi$ and

$$P = 40\pi^2 (l/\lambda)^2 II^*. \tag{5.28}$$

This is the average power contributed to the field by the electric generator driving current I. The medium is nondissipative. Since energy is consumed, we have to conclude that the wave carries it away radially at rate P. This is the *radiant energy*.

Figure 5.9 illustrates a thin resistive sheet of large radius r, concentric with the current element. Let there be a perfectly conducting sphere of radius $r + (\lambda/4)$. The wave which penetrates the first sphere will be totally reflected from the second and a standing wave will be formed between the two spheres. At the perfectly conducting sphere, E_θ vanishes and H_φ is maximum. Just outside the resistive sphere, E_θ is maximum and H_φ vanishes. Current will flow along the

Perfect conductor

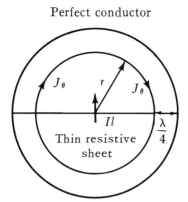

FIGURE 5.9   *Illustrating the concept of power carried by a spherical wave in free space.*

meridians of the resistive sphere in response to E_θ. Let J_θ be the current per unit length perpendicular to the lines of flow. Assume that the resistance per unit length is η so that $E_\theta = \eta J_\theta$. The Ampere-Maxwell law requires that $H_\varphi(r-0) - H_\varphi(r+0) = J_\theta$. Since $H_\varphi(r+0) = 0$, we have $H_\varphi(r-0) = J_\theta = \eta^{-1}E_\theta$. Hence both E_θ and H_φ of the dipole wave [see equation (5.25)] will be continuous at the resistive sphere and no reflected wave will be generated inside this sphere. The average power dissipated per unit area of the spherical sheet is

$$W = \tfrac{1}{2}E_\theta J_\theta^* = \tfrac{1}{2}E_\theta H_\varphi^* = \tfrac{1}{2}\eta H_\varphi H_\varphi^* \tag{5.29}$$

which is in agreement with equation (3.3) for power flow. The total power dissipated in the resistive sphere may be obtained by substituting for H_φ from equations (5.25) and integrating over the sphere

$$P = \tfrac{1}{2}\eta \int_0^{2\pi}\int_0^\pi H_\varphi H_\varphi^* r^2 \sin\theta \, d\theta \, d\varphi$$

$$= \frac{\eta\beta^2 l^2 II^*}{32\pi^2} \int_0^{2\pi}\int_0^\pi \sin^3\theta \, d\theta \, d\varphi$$

$$= \frac{\eta}{12\pi}(\beta l)^2 II^*.$$

This is equal to the power, equation (5.27), contributed to the field by the current element.

5.11   Interference and directive radiation

Consider Figure 5.10 which illustrates the distant field of two parallel
current elements, each of moment Is, a distance l apart. The combined field may be obtained from equations (5.25). If P is a distant
point in the direction at an angle ψ to the line AB joining the elements,

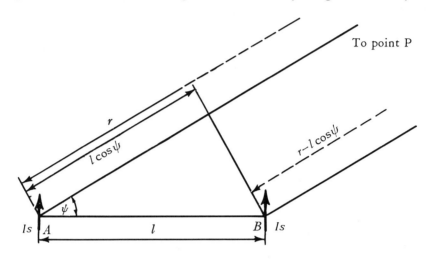

FIGURE 5.10   *Two current elements.*

then the difference between AP and BP is substantially the projection
of AB on AP

$$AP - BP = l \cos \psi.$$

The effect of this difference on the amplitudes of the individual
fields of the elements is of the second order; but the effect on the
phases is important unless l is a very small fraction of λ. Thus for the
total field, we obtain

$$H_\varphi = \frac{jIs}{2\lambda r} \{\exp(-j\beta r) + \exp[-j\beta(r - l \cos \psi)]\} \sin \theta$$

$$= \frac{jIs \exp(-j\beta r) \sin \theta}{2\lambda r} [1 + \exp(j\beta l \cos \psi)]$$

$$= \frac{jIse^{-j\beta r} \sin \theta}{2\lambda r} \exp(\tfrac{1}{2}j\beta l \cos \psi) \, 2 \cos(\tfrac{1}{2}\beta l \cos \psi).$$

Waves arriving at a distant point from different sources may be in
phase so that they will reinforce each other or they may partially, or

totally, destroy each other. If $l = \lambda/2$, they will destroy each other along the line joining the sources, $\psi = 0$ or π. The maximum reinforcement will take place in the plane perpendicular to the line joining them.

This phenomenon is called the *interference* of waves and is responsible for *directive radiation*. More and more of the total radiant energy can be thrown in certain directions by properly arranging more and more sources of radiation.

We can also control directivity by proper relative phasing of the individual sources. If the moment of the source at B is $Is \exp(-j\beta l)$ so that its phase lags by $\beta l = 2\pi l/\lambda$, the phase of the source at A, we have

$$H_\varphi = \frac{jIse^{-j\beta r} \sin \theta}{2\lambda r} \{1 + \exp[j\beta l (\cos \psi - 1)]\}.$$

The waves reinforce each other in the direction $\psi = 0$. In particular if $l = \lambda/4$, the bracketed term becomes

$$1 + \exp[j\pi (\cos \psi - 1)/2].$$

Its value is 2 in the direction AB, and zero in the opposite direction.

5.12   Current distribution in thin wires

"Electric current element" is a mathematical abstraction, a mathematical model of a hypothetical physical situation. It is useful for computing fields of known current distributions since such distributions can be subdivided into elements. Currents in conductors are determined by voltages impressed on them by other fields such as fields of electric generators. These calculations are rarely exact. In Section 5.3 we considered fields between infinite coaxial cones and found that the currents in the cones and the transverse voltage (along the meridians) are sinusoidal. Such waves can be excited by connecting the apexes of the cones to an electric generator. If the impressed voltage is V_0, the input current will be $I_0 = V_0/K$ and at any distance r the current will be $I_0 \exp(-j\beta r)$. If we introduce a metal sphere of radius $r = l$, the traveling wave will be reflected from the sphere and will converge to the center. The reflected current will be

$$I_0 \exp(-j\beta l) \exp[-j\beta(l - r)] = I_0 \exp(-2j\beta l) \exp(j\beta r).$$

The situation is more complex, however, if the cones are just terminated at distance $r = l$. The current at $r = l$ must vanish and there will be a reflected wave converging toward the center. The electric field of the forward and backward waves at $r = l$ will excite a field in free space beyond $r = l$. This field cannot conform to the field between the cones since the latter requires the presence of conducting cones. The field will be distorted both outside and inside the spherical surface $r = l$. All that we can say at this stage is that the total field will retain circular symmetry and that it will satisfy Maxwell's partial differential equations obtained in Section 5.1. The solution is very complicated since E_θ and H_φ have to be matched on the sphere $r = l$. The simple waves in Section 5.3 are called the *principal waves*.

Approximate solutions can be determined when the conical (or cylindrical) wires are thin. In Section 5.1 we obtained the exact field associated with an infinitely thin current filament along the positive z axis with the source at the origin O. This field is given by equations (5.9). Suppose that starting from $z = l$ we superimpose another semi-infinite current filament which cancels the original filament from there on. Its field may be obtained from equations (5.9) by making the following substitutions:

$$I_0 \rightarrow -I_0 \exp\ (-j\beta l),$$

$$r \rightarrow r_1, \qquad \theta \rightarrow \theta_1,$$

$$E_\theta \rightarrow E_{\theta_1}, \qquad H_\varphi \rightarrow H_{\varphi_1}, \qquad E_r \rightarrow E_{r_1},$$

where (r_1, θ_1) are spherical coordinates with reference to another origin at $z = l$. Thus we shall obtain the exact field of an infinitely thin progressive current filament of finite length, extending from $z = 0$ to $z = l$. At $z = l$ there is a point charge $(I_0/j\omega) \exp\ (-j\beta l)$. This charge can be removed by superimposing an equal and opposite charge with a progressive current wave traveling from $z = l$ in the negative z direction. This current wave can be canceled from $z = 0$ to $z = -\infty$ by another current wave along the negative z axis. In this manner we obtain the exact field of a standing current wave with a source at $z = 0$. At $z = l$ the current vanishes as it should at a free end of a wire. The field is the resultant of four fields of the type in equations (5.9).

The current distribution is sinusoidal just as it is in a pair of parallel wires. This we would expect from physical considerations. Figure 5.11 shows the transition from parallel wires to wires going in opposite directions. In case (a) when the separation between the wires is small in comparison with their length, the end effects are negligible at both ends A, B and C, D. As the wires are spread apart,

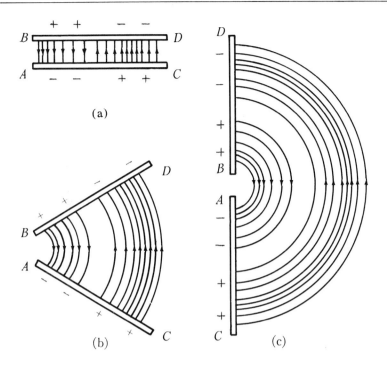

FIGURE 5.11   *Evolution of a linear antenna from a section of two parallel wires.*

the end effects remain negligible at A, B and become more pro-
nounced at C, D. The circular arcs from one wire to the other show
the electric lines along the meridians for the principal waves. For the
complete field the electric lines become increasingly distorted as the
distance from A, B increases. When the wires are thin, most of the
energy is near the wires. We recall that $E_\rho = q/2\pi\epsilon_0\rho$ and $H_\varphi = I/2\pi\rho$,
where ρ is the distance from the axis of the wire. Energy densities are
proportional to the squares of the absolute values of E_ρ and H_φ. If
the total energy is kept constant as the radius of the wire approaches
zero, the field will approach zero *except in the vicinity of the wires.*
It is this local field that determines primarily the nature of the
current distribution. Thus the spreading of the wires affects sig-
nificantly the distribution of the more distant field and relatively
little the distribution of current and charge on the wires.

Let us now determine the series inductance and shunt capacitance
per unit length for principal waves on thin diverging wires of constant
radius a. We subdivide them into infinitesimal sections and consider

each section as a section of a thin cone. That is, we think of a cylindrical wire as a "cone" with a gradually decreasing half-cone angle $\psi = a/z$, where a is the radius of the wire. The characteristic impedance, equation (5.14), will be

$$K = \frac{\eta}{\pi} \ln \frac{2z}{a}. \tag{5.30}$$

The velocity of propagation and the phase constant should remain essentially unaltered. If L and C are the inductance and capacitance per unit length, we have

$$\beta = \omega\sqrt{LC} = \omega\sqrt{\mu\epsilon}, \qquad K = \sqrt{L/C}.$$

Hence

$$LC = \mu\epsilon, \qquad K^2 = L/C$$

$$L = K\sqrt{\mu\epsilon}, \qquad C = \sqrt{\mu\epsilon}/K. \tag{5.31}$$

Using equation (5.30), we find

$$L = \frac{\mu}{\pi} \ln \frac{2z}{a}, \qquad C = \frac{\pi\epsilon}{\ln (2z/a)}. \tag{5.32}$$

Logarithmic functions are slowly varying functions and can be approximated by their average values

$$L_{av} = \frac{\mu}{\pi} \left(\ln \frac{2l}{a} - 1 \right), \qquad C_{av} = \frac{\pi\epsilon}{\ln (2l/a) - 1}. \tag{5.33}$$

The value of C_{av} is essentially equal to the one we can obtain from the electrostatic field considered in Section 2.3. There is an additional term $-\ln 2$ in the denominator which becomes less significant as $2l/a$ increases. Different methods of approximation are not expected to yield identical results unless higher order terms are all included. Equations (5.32) were obtained for infinitely long wires when electric lines are essentially the meridians. When the wires are terminated some electric field will exist outside the spherical surface of radius l, passing through the ends of the wires. This "end effect" is not included in equations (5.33). If it is included, the two approximations agree.

5.13   Short antenna

An antenna in Figure 5.12 is called "short" if $\beta l \ll 1$, where l is the length of each antenna arm. On such an antenna the charge dis-

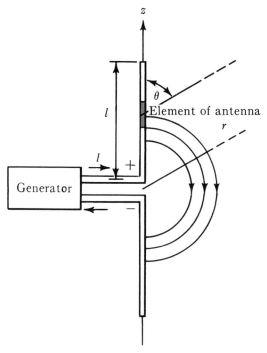

FIGURE 5.12   *A short antenna.*

tribution is substantially constant and the current distribution is linear.

$$I(z) = I_0 \left(1 - \frac{z}{l}\right), \qquad 0 < z < l$$

$$(5.34)$$

$$= I_0 \left(1 + \frac{z}{l}\right), \qquad -l < z < -0,$$

where I_0 is the input current. The generator "sees" the pair of wires as lumped circuit consisting of a total capacitance

$$C_t = Cl \qquad (5.35)$$

in series with a total inductance

$$L_t = \tfrac{1}{3}Ll. \qquad (5.36)$$

The distant field may be calculated from equations (5.25) by subdividing the current into elements of moment $I(z) \, dz$ and integrating their fields from $z = -l$ to $z = l$. In any direction θ the distance from a typical element is $r - z \cos \theta$. Since it was assumed that $\beta l \ll 1$, the effect of the expression

$$\beta z \cos \theta < \beta l \cos \theta \ll 1$$

on the phase of waves arriving from different elements to a distant point is negligible. Hence, the pair of wires acts as a current element of moment

$$p = \int_{-l}^{l} I(z) \, dz = 2I_0 \int_{0}^{l} \left(1 - \frac{z}{l}\right) dz = I_0 l, \qquad (5.37)$$

that is, the distant field of the current in two short wires of total length $2l$ is the same as that of a current element of length l. Hence the radiated power is given by equation (5.28). The generator sees a resistance, called the *radiation resistance* R_{rad} which can be determined from

$$P = \tfrac{1}{2} R_{\text{rad}} I_0 I_0^* = 40\pi^2 \, | \, l/\lambda \, |^2 I_0 I_0^*. \qquad (5.38)$$

Thus

$$R_{\text{rad}} = 80\pi^2 \, | \, l/\lambda \, |^2.$$

When (l/λ) is very small, the resistance of the wires may be considerably larger than R_{rad} and it should be included in the equiva-

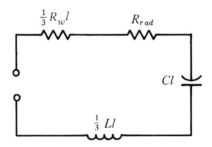

FIGURE 5.13 *The equivalent circuit for a short antenna.*

lent circuit for the short antenna (see Figure 5.13 where R_w is the resistance of the wire per unit length).

5.14 Half-wave antenna

The input impedance of a short antenna is capacitive and large. Additional inductance can be added in series to tune this capacitance out to make the delivery of power from the generator easier. Another way is to increase the length of the antenna until it becomes self-resonant. In Section 5.12 we found that the current in thin wires is essentially sinusoidal. At the ends it must vanish. Hence, at distance z from the center

$$I(z) = I_0 \sin \beta(l - z), \qquad 0 < z < l$$

$$= I_0 \sin \beta(l + z), \qquad -l < z < 0. \tag{5.39}$$

The voltage along the meridians from the upper to the lower wire is

$$V(z) = -\frac{1}{j\omega C_{av}} \frac{dI}{dz} = -jK_{av}I_0 \cos \beta(l - z). \tag{5.40}$$

These expressions are only for the principal wave and take no account of radiation. Thus when $l = \lambda/4$, the voltage and current distribution become

$$V(z) = -jK_{av}I_0 \sin \beta z,$$

$$I(z) = I_0 \cos \beta z. \tag{5.41}$$

The distant field is calculated again from equations (5.25), this time by including proper phase factor, Figure 5.14,

$$H_\varphi = \frac{j\beta I_0 e^{-j\beta r}}{4\pi r} \sin \theta \int_{-\lambda/4}^{\lambda/4} \cos \beta z \exp\left(j\beta z \cos \theta\right) dz \tag{5.42}$$

$$= \frac{I_0 e^{-j\beta r}}{2\pi r} \frac{\cos\left(\frac{1}{2}\pi \cos \theta\right)}{\sin \theta}.$$

To obtain the radiated power we substitute in equation (5.29) and integrate over a sphere of radius r

$$P = \tfrac{1}{2}\eta \int_0^{2\pi} \int_0^\pi H_\varphi H_\varphi^* r^2 \sin \theta \, d\theta \, d\varphi$$

$$= \frac{\eta}{2\pi} I_0 I_0^* \int_0^{\pi/2} \frac{\cos^2\left(\frac{1}{2}\pi \cos \theta\right)}{\sin \theta} \, d\theta.$$

By changing variables of integration and assuming that the antenna is in vacuum ($\eta \simeq 120\pi$), we can reduce this integral to

$$P = 15 I_0 I_0^* \int_0^{2\pi} \frac{1 - \cos u}{u} \, du = 15 \, Cin 2\pi \, I_0 I_0^* = 36.54 I_0 I_0^*. \tag{5.43}$$

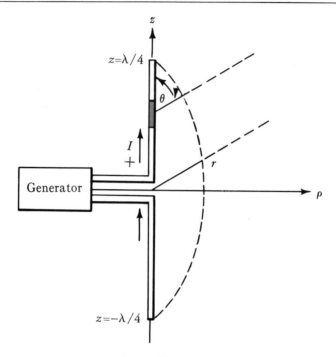

FIGURE 5.14   *A half-wave antenna.*

Hence, the input resistance of the half-wave antenna in free space is

$$R = 73.1 \text{ ohms.} \tag{5.44}$$

Incidentally, this result shows that in the vicinity of $z = 0$, the voltage distribution given by equation (5.41) is not good enough.

5.15   Retarded potentials

In Chapter 2 we introduced a potential function V such that

$$\vec{E} = -\text{grad } V. \tag{5.45}$$

This function is useful in calculations involving electrostatic fields. The definition was based on the assumption that there was no time-variable magnetic field. The above equation implies that the line integral of $\vec{E}$ round a closed curve vanishes. Hence, in a time-variable electromagnetic field $\vec{E}$ cannot be expressed as the gradient of any scalar function, no matter how it is defined. This does not mean, however, that a part of $\bar{E}$ could not be so expressed. Such a generalized potential function might still be useful in field calculations.

Since $\bar{E}$ and $\bar{H}$ for an oscillating dipole contain a phase retardation factor $\exp(-j\beta r)$, this factor should be expected in any function from which they might be obtained. Thus we assume a *retarded potential* of a point charge q

$$V_0 = \frac{qe^{-j\beta r}}{4\pi\epsilon r}. \tag{5.46}$$

As βr approaches zero, either because λ approaches infinity or r approaches zero, this potential approaches the electrostatic potential. For two point charges situated on the z axis, charge q at $z = l/2$ and $-q$ at $z = -l/2$, we have

$$V = \frac{qe^{-j\beta r_1}}{4\pi\epsilon r_1} - \frac{qe^{-j\beta r_2}}{4\pi\epsilon r_2}.$$

Assuming that l is infinitesimal, we retain only infinitesimals of the first order in

$$r_1 = r - \tfrac{1}{2}l\cos\theta, \qquad r_2 = r + \tfrac{1}{2}l\cos\theta$$

and in V itself. Hence

$$V = \frac{qe^{-j\beta r}}{4\pi r^2}\left[r_2\exp\left(\tfrac{1}{2}j\beta l\cos\theta\right) - r_1\exp\left(-\tfrac{1}{2}j\beta l\cos\theta\right)\right].$$

Replacing the exponentials by the first two terms in their power series, we find that the bracketed expression becomes

$$r_2 - r_1 + \tfrac{1}{2}(r_1 + r_2)j\beta l\cos\theta$$

which is equal to

$$l\cos\theta + j\beta rl\cos\theta.$$

Hence, for the dipole

$$V = \frac{qle^{-j\beta r}}{4\pi\epsilon r^2}(1 + j\beta r)\cos\theta.$$

Since $q = I/j\omega$,

$$V = \frac{Il}{4\pi j\omega\epsilon r^2}(1 + j\beta r)e^{-j\beta r}\cos\theta.$$

The negative of the gradient of V has the following spherical components

$$-\frac{\partial V}{\partial r} = \frac{\eta Il}{2\pi r^2}\left(1 + \frac{1}{j\beta r}\right)e^{-j\beta r}\cos\theta + \frac{j\omega\mu Il}{4\pi r}e^{-j\beta r}\cos\theta,$$

$$-\frac{\partial V}{r\partial\theta} = \frac{j\omega\mu Il}{4\pi r}\left(\frac{1}{j\beta r} - \frac{1}{\beta^2 r^2}\right)e^{-j\beta r}\sin\theta.$$

Subtracting these expressions from E_r and E_θ for the current element, we have

$$E_r + \frac{\partial V}{\partial r} = -\frac{j\omega\mu Il}{4\pi r}e^{-j\beta r}\cos\theta,$$

$$E_\theta + \frac{\partial V}{r\partial\theta} = \frac{j\omega\mu Il}{4\pi r}e^{-j\beta r}\sin\theta.$$

Expressions on the right are the r and θ components of a vector whose Cartesian components are

$$0,\ 0,\ -\frac{j\omega\mu Il}{4\pi r}e^{-j\beta r}.$$

The vector A whose components are

$$A_x = 0, \qquad A_y = 0, \qquad A_z = \frac{\mu Il e^{-j\beta r}}{4\pi r} \tag{5.47}$$

is called the retarded vector potential of the current element (situated at the origin along the z axis). Thus we have

$$\bar{E} = -j\omega\bar{A} - \operatorname{grad} V \tag{5.48}$$

for a typical current element, and therefore, by the principle of superposition, for any number of discrete elements or for any continuous distribution of elements. Thus if $\rho\,dv$ is an element of charge and $\bar{J}\,dv$ an element of current, we have from equations (5.46) and (5.47)

$$V = \int \frac{\rho e^{-j\beta r}\,dv}{4\pi\epsilon r}, \qquad \bar{A} = \int \frac{\mu\bar{J}e^{-j\beta r}\,dv}{4\pi r}, \tag{5.49}$$

where the integrations extend over the entire volume occupied by charge and current.

6

Normal Modes

6.0 Introduction

Little imagination is needed in order to calculate the field of any given source distribution in an infinite homogeneous isotropic medium. Thus, Coulomb's law gives the field of a single stationary electric particle. The field of any number of such particles is obtained by superposition of the fields of separate particles. If the number of particles in an element of volume is large, the summation may be approximated by integration (the charge is "smoothed" over a volume). To obtain the magnetic field of a given direct current distribution, the latter is subdivided into current elements. The field of a single element is obtained directly from physical laws; then the superposition principle is applied. The field of a time-varying current distribution is obtained in the same manner; only the field of a typical current element is somewhat more complicated.

In the case of two or more homogeneous media, boundary conditions must be satisfied at the interfaces between the media. Some imagination is needed for solving such problems. In Sections 2.4 and 2.5 solutions were synthesized for conducting and dielectric spheres imbedded in a uniform electric field in an infinite homogeneous dielectric. In Section 2.12 the field of a point charge in a semi-infinite medium above a conducting plane was constructed by superposing an "image field" on the field of the point charge in an infinite medium.

There are no simple rules for solving field problems under all conditions. Someone with imagination discovers a method for solving a specific problem or a class of problems and passes it on to posterity. One might think that the larger is the class of problems, the more powerful is the method. So it is, in a sense. Not infrequently it happens, however, that the "more powerful" method yields a form of solution more difficult to interpret than another form obtained by a "less powerful" method. Various methods often complement each other.

In this chapter we shall illustrate by examples a method of calculating fields which "works" for homogeneous media bounded by coordinate surfaces in Cartesian, cylindrical, and spherical systems.

It consists of solving problems piecemeal. First, one looks for certain special types of solutions of Laplace's or Maxwell's partial differential equations. Then one selects those solutions which satisfy the required conditions on *some* boundaries. Finally, one combines these solutions to satisfy the remaining boundary conditions as well as the conditions at the source of the field.

The examples in this chapter have been selected to illustrate the various phases in the application of the method. To present a broad view of the method, all phases are considered in the first example. Subsequent examples stress either one particular phase of the method or some feature of a particular physical situation. Most problems involve only plane boundaries and Cartesian coordinates. Problems involving cylindrical, spherical, and conical boundaries present no new features except for a greater complexity of some mathematical functions.

6.1   Direct current in conducting plates

Figure 6.1 shows a direct current I in a conducting plate of width w. Assume that the thickness of the plate is suddenly increased at

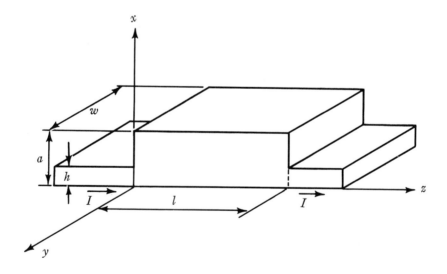

FIGURE 6.1   *Conducting plates of equal width w, but of different thickness, joined together and carrying direct current I.*

$z = 0$ and is decreased to its former thickness at $z = l$. Assume also that the flow is uniform in the y direction.

In Section 2.1 it was shown that if the magnetic field is time-invariable, the electric intensity can be expressed as the negative of the gradient of a potential function V. Thus

$$\vec{E} = -\text{grad } V. \tag{6.1}$$

We also know that the total current passing outward (or inward) through a closed surface is zero. This implies that the divergence of the current density $\vec{J}$ vanishes (see Appendix I); thus

$$\text{div } \vec{J} = 0. \tag{6.2}$$

If the conductivity σ of the plate is constant, we also have

$$\text{div } \vec{E} = 0. \tag{6.3}$$

Substituting from equation (6.1) into (6.3), we obtain Laplace's equation

$$\text{div grad } V = \Delta V = 0. \tag{6.4}$$

In Cartesian coordinates this becomes (see Appendix III)

$$\frac{\partial^2 V}{\partial x^2} + \frac{\partial^2 V}{\partial y^2} + \frac{\partial^2 V}{\partial z^2} = 0. \tag{6.5}$$

In our problem we have assumed that the flow is uniform in the y direction. Hence

$$\frac{\partial^2 V}{\partial x^2} + \frac{\partial^2 V}{\partial z^2} = 0. \tag{6.6}$$

There are several methods for solving such equations, one of which is the *method of separation of variables*. One assumes solutions in the form of a product of two functions, each depending on one variable only

$$V(x, z) = X(x)Z(z). \tag{6.7}$$

Substituting in equation (6.6) and dividing by the product XZ, we obtain

$$\frac{1}{X}\frac{d^2 X}{dx^2} + \frac{1}{Z}\frac{d^2 Z}{dz^2} = 0.$$

The first term is a function of x only and the second of z only. Their sum can vanish only if both terms are independent of both variables. Thus we set

$$\frac{1}{X}\frac{d^2X}{dx^2} = k, \qquad \frac{1}{Z}\frac{d^2Z}{dz^2} = -k, \tag{6.8}$$

where k is a *separation constant* which may be either real or complex.

The values of this constant are restricted, however, by the boundary conditions. The current density in the region $0 < z < l$, for example, must be parallel to the z axis at the boundaries $x = 0$ and $x = a$. That is, the normal component J_x of $\bar{J}$ and therefore E_x must vanish at $x = +0$ and $x = a - 0$. From equations (6.1) and (6.7) we have

$$E_x = -\frac{\partial V}{\partial x} = -X'(x)Z(z),$$

$$\tag{6.9}$$

$$E_z = -\frac{\partial V}{\partial z} = -X(x)Z'(z).$$

The boundary conditions require that

$$X'(+0) = 0, \qquad X'(a - 0) = 0. \tag{6.10}$$

Since the general solution for X is

$$X(x) = Ae^{-\sqrt{k}x} + Be^{\sqrt{k}x}, \tag{6.11}$$

we have

$$X'(x) = \sqrt{k}(-Ae^{-\sqrt{k}x} + Be^{\sqrt{k}x})$$

so that

$$\sqrt{k}(-A + B) = 0,$$

$$\sqrt{k}(-Ae^{-\sqrt{k}a} + Be^{\sqrt{k}a}) = 0.$$

The first equation will be satisfied if

$$k = 0 \quad \text{or} \quad B = A. \tag{6.12}$$

In the first eventuality the second equation is satisfied automatically. In the second case we must have

$$e^{-\sqrt{k}a} = e^{\sqrt{k}a} \quad \text{or} \quad e^{2\sqrt{k}a} = 1.$$

Let

$$\sqrt{k} = p + jq \tag{6.13}$$

where p and q are real quantities. Then

$$e^{2pa+2jqa} = e^{2pa}e^{2jqa} = 1.$$

Since the absolute value of the quantity on the left must equal unity, we must have $p = 0$. The remaining factor equals unity when

$$qa = n\pi, \qquad q = n\pi/a, \qquad n = 1, 2, 3, \cdots. \tag{6.14}$$

Substituting in equation (6.13), we have

$$k = -(n\pi/a)^2. \tag{6.15}$$

These values of the separation constant k are called the *proper values* or *eigenvalues* or *characteristic values* of the boundary value problem and the corresponding functions

$$X(x) = 2A \cos (n\pi x/a) \tag{6.16}$$

are the *proper functions* or *eigenfunctions* or *characteristic functions*. Note that the first possibility in equation (6.12) is included if $n = 0$ is included in the sequence of integers in equation (6.14).

Substituting from equation (6.15) into the right-hand equation of the set (6.8) and solving, we obtain

$$Z(z) = C_n e^{-n\pi z/a} + D_n e^{n\pi z/a}, \quad \text{if} \quad n \neq 0,$$
$$= C_0 + D_0 z, \quad \text{if} \quad n = 0. \tag{6.17}$$

Thus there is an infinite set of solutions for equation (6.6), all of which satisfy the boundary conditions at $x = 0, a$. The most general solution may be expressed as an infinite series,

$$V(x, z) = C_0 + D_0 z + \sum_{n=1}^{\infty} (C_n e^{-n\pi z/a} + D_n e^{n\pi z/a}) \cos (n\pi x/a), \tag{6.18}$$

where the arbitrary constants associated with $X(x)$ have been absorbed into C_n and D_n. Substituting in equation (6.9), we have

$$E_x = \sum_{n=1}^{\infty} (n\pi/a)(C_n e^{-n\pi z/a} + D_n e^{n\pi z/a}) \sin (n\pi x/a)$$

$$E_z = -D_0 + \sum_{n=1}^{\infty} (n\pi/a)(C_n e^{-n\pi z/a} - D_n e^{n\pi z/a}) \cos (n\pi x/a) \tag{6.19}$$

$$\text{for} \quad 0 \leq z \leq l.$$

The still unknown constants C_n, D_n can be determined from the boundary conditions at $z = 0$ and at $z = l$ which can be imposed either on V or on one or the other components of $\bar{E}$ or $\bar{J}$ depending on a particular problem. In the present case, current I flows in the z direction, on the average, and the coefficients may be expressed in terms of $J_z(x, 0)$ and $J_z(x, l)$. Multiplying E_z in equation (6.19) by σ to obtain J_z, and integrating over the area $0 \leq x \leq a, 0 \leq y \leq w$, when $z = 0$ or $z = l$, we have

$$-D_0 \sigma a w = \int_0^w \int_0^a J_z(x, 0) \, dx \, dy = \int_0^w \int_0^a J_z(x, l) \, dx \, dy = I,$$

that is,

$$D_0 = -I/\sigma a w. \tag{6.20}$$

The remaining coefficients are found if we multiply both sides of the expression for E_z by $\sigma \cos (m\pi x/a)$ to obtain $J_z \cos (m\pi x/a)$, integrate over the same areas, and use the fact that

$$\int_0^a \cos (n\pi x/a) \cos (m\pi x/a) \, dx = 0, \qquad n \neq m,$$

$$\tag{6.21}$$

$$= \tfrac{1}{2}a, \qquad n = m.$$

Thus, we find

$$\frac{m\pi}{2} \sigma w (C_m - D_m) = \int_0^w \int_0^a J_z(x, 0) \cos \frac{m\pi x}{a} \, dx \, dy,$$

$$\frac{m\pi}{2} \sigma w (C_m e^{-m\pi l/a} - D_m e^{m\pi l/a}) = \int_0^w \int_0^a J_z(x, l) \cos \frac{m\pi x}{a} \, dx \, dy.$$

The current enters the middle plate and leaves it only when $0 \leq x \leq h$ (see Figure 6.1). Therefore

$$C_m - D_m = F_{1,m}$$

$$\tag{6.22}$$

$$C_m e^{-m\pi l/a} - D_m e^{m\pi l/a} = F_{2,m},$$

where

$$F_{1,m} = \frac{2}{m\pi\sigma} \int_0^a J_z(x, 0) \cos \frac{m\pi x}{a} \, dx$$

$$\tag{6.23}$$

$$F_{2,m} = \frac{2}{m\pi\sigma} \int_0^a J_z(x, l) \cos \frac{m\pi x}{a} \, dx.$$

Solving equations (6.22), we have

$$C_m = \frac{F_{1,m} - F_{2,m} e^{-m\pi l/a}}{1 - e^{-2m\pi l/a}},$$

$$\tag{6.24}$$

$$D_m = \frac{-F_{2,m} e^{-m\pi l/a} + F_{1,m} e^{-2m\pi l/a}}{1 - e^{-2m\pi l/a}}.$$

If l/a is large, we have approximately

$$C_m = F_{1,m}, \qquad D_m = -F_{2,m}e^{-m\pi l/a}. \qquad (6.25)$$

In fact even if $l = a$, these equations are good approximations since $\exp(-\pi) = 0.043$. For larger values of m the approximations are good even when l is smaller than a. In other words the coefficients C_m are determined largely by the conditions at the face of the middle plate where the current enters and the coefficients D_m are determined by the conditions at the face where the current leaves.

Changing the subscript m back to n, we find J_z from equations (6.19), (6.20), and (6.25)

$$J_z = \frac{I}{aw} + \sum_{n=1}^{\infty} \sigma \frac{n\pi}{a} F_{1,n} e^{-n\pi z/a} \cos \frac{n\pi x}{a}$$

$$+ \sum_{n=1}^{\infty} \sigma \frac{n\pi}{a} F_{2,n} e^{-n\pi(l-z)/a} \cos \frac{n\pi x}{a}. \qquad (6.26)$$

Except in the vicinities of $z = 0$ and $z = l$, J_z is substantially constant over the cross section of the plate. The "end effects" *are confined to distances from the junctions smaller than the thickness of the plate.*

Integrals given in equation (6.23) can be calculated exactly if J_z is given at each face. In the problem formulated at the beginning of the section only the total current I is specified. The boundary conditions at $z = 0$ and $z = l$ are as follows:

$$J_z(x, 0) = 0, \qquad J_z(x, l) = 0, \qquad h < x \leq a,$$

$$J_z(x, -0) = J_z(x, +0), \qquad 0 \leq x < h, \qquad (6.27)$$

$$J_z(x, l-0) = J_z(x, l+0), \qquad 0 \leq x < h,$$

$$E_x(x, -0) = E_x(x, +0), \qquad 0 \leq x \leq h,$$

$$E_x(x, l-0) = E_x(x, l+0), \qquad 0 \leq x \leq h.$$

The last four equations represent the continuity of the normal component of current density and tangential component of electric intensity. For this particular problem there exists a method for satisfying all of these conditions exactly.

In most problems, however, one has to rely on methods of successive approximations. In the present case, for example, we can start by satisfying the conditions which seem to be the most important from the physical point of view. The current enters the thick plate from the thin plate through the junctions between them.

Hence the first equation in the set (6.27) must always be satisfied. From the results already obtained we know that the current distribution in the thin plate is uniform except within a distance h from the junction. This nonuniformity is a secondary effect. Uniform current enters the junction and spreads. As it spreads, the flow lines in the thin plate will become curved but the perturbation will not be as great as in the thick plate where the current spreads to the upper boundary. Thus we start with the assumption

$$J_z(x, 0) = \frac{I}{wh}, \qquad 0 \le x < h,$$

$$= 0, \qquad h < x \le a. \tag{6.28}$$

Hence from equations (6.23) and (6.25) in which we let m equal n, we find

$$C_n = F_{1,n} = \frac{2I}{n\pi\sigma hw} \int_0^h \cos\frac{n\pi x}{a} \, dx = \frac{2Ia}{n^2\pi^2\sigma hw} \sin\frac{n\pi h}{a}. \tag{6.29}$$

Confining ourselves to a single junction, we let $l = \infty$. From equations (6.19) and (6.29), we then obtain

$$E_x = \sum_{n=1}^{\infty} \frac{2I}{n\pi\sigma hw} \sin\frac{n\pi h}{a} \sin\frac{n\pi x}{a} e^{-n\pi z/a}, \qquad z \ge 0. \tag{6.30}$$

Thus although we started with an assumption, implied in equation (6.28), that $E_x = 0$, when $z = 0$, we find that once the current has entered the middle plate the lines of flow become curved. Even at $z = 0$ when $x > h$, $E_x \ne 0$ and there is current spreading toward the upper boundary of the middle plate as it should.

Since E_x must be continuous when $z = 0$, E_x is different from zero when $z < 0$. There will be an end-effect in the thin plate which will be represented by exponential terms, decreasing in the negative z direction

$$E_x(x, z) = \sum_{\alpha=1}^{\infty} A_\alpha e^{\alpha\pi z/h} \sin\frac{\alpha\pi x}{h}, \qquad z \le 0. \tag{6.31}$$

Coefficients A_α are the coefficients of the sine series for $E_x(x, 0)$ in the interval $0 \le x < h$

$$A_\alpha = \frac{2}{h} \int_0^h E_x(x, 0) \sin\frac{\alpha\pi x}{h} \, dx. \tag{6.32}$$

Substituting from equation (6.30) and integrating, we have

$$A_\alpha = (-)^{\alpha+1} \frac{4I}{\pi^2\sigma hw} \sum_{n=1}^{\infty} \frac{\alpha \sin^2(n\pi h/a)}{n[\alpha^2 - (nh/a)^2]}. \qquad (6.33)$$

When h/a approaches zero, the numerator under the summation sign approaches zero as $(h/a)^2$ and A_α approaches zero as h/a. If h/a approaches unity, A_α also approaches zero. In any case the end-effect is wiped out within a distance from the junction comparable to h.

Comparing equation (6.31) with equation (6.19), we find $E_z(x, z)$ and the longitudinal current density in the thin plate

$$J_z(x, z) = \frac{I}{wh} - \sum_{\alpha=1}^{\infty} \sigma A_\alpha e^{\alpha \pi z/h} \cos \frac{\alpha\pi x}{h}, \qquad z \leq 0. \quad (6.34)$$

The first term is the one with which we started [see equation (6.28)]. This expression, at $z = 0$, instead of equation (6.28), can now be used for calculating coefficients C_n in the thick plate. From the first term the expressions given by equation (6.29) are obtained. From the summation we find the correction terms

$$C_n^1 = \frac{2(-)^\alpha h^2 \sin (n\pi h/a)}{\pi^3 a} \sum_{\alpha=1}^{\infty} \frac{A_\alpha}{\alpha^2 - (nh/a)^2}. \qquad (6.35)$$

If h/a is much less than one, these terms are of order $(h/a)^4$ in comparison with the coefficients C_n.

In principle, the sequence of successive approximations can be continued indefinitely. Calculations become more laborious but at each stage they are straightforward.

6.2   Direct current in stratified plates

The problem in the preceding section is representative of a wide class of problems involving direct-current fields, electrostatic fields, magnetostatic fields, and time-variable fields. The method of solution is quite general; but its implementation varies with different classes of problems. The problems in this and the following sections are deliberately simplified to illustrate different features of the method.

Figure 6.2 shows a plate made of two parallel plates with different conductivities σ_1 and σ_2. The plates are in contact so that current can pass from one to the other. We have seen that the first important step in our method of solving a concrete problem is to find solutions of Laplace's equation which satisfy the boundary conditions along the

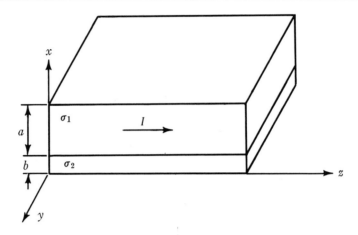

FIGURE 6.2   *A laminated conducting plate.*

plate. The next step was to satisfy the conditions at the ends of the plate. In the present problem we are concerned primarily with the first step.

Assume that the field is independent of the y coordinate so that one has to solve equation (6.6). The boundary conditions are

$$J_z(0, z) = 0, \quad J_z(a + b, z) = 0, \tag{6.36}$$

$$J_x(b - 0, z) = J_x(b + 0, z), \qquad E_z(b - 0, z) = E_z(b + 0, z). \tag{6.37}$$

The first two conditions are the same as in the preceding problem. The last two are needed because we have a discontinuity in the conductivity of the medium. The solutions that went into the series given by equations (6.18) and (6.19) are continuous functions of x and z. In the present problem J_x is continuous and therefore E_x *discontinuous* across the interface between two media. Hence, some modification of solution is needed.

We already know that our equations possess solutions varying exponentially in the general direction of current and sinusoidally at right angles. Thus let

$$E_z(x, z) = A \sin \Gamma x \, e^{-\Gamma z}, \qquad 0 \leq x < b$$
$$\tag{6.38}$$
$$= B \sin \Gamma(a + b - x)e^{-\Gamma z}, \qquad b < x \leq a + b,$$

where A, B, and Γ are unknown constants. The dependence on x

has been deliberately chosen to satisfy equations (6.36). The first boundary condition in equations (6.37) will be satisfied if

$$\sigma_2 A \sin \Gamma b = \sigma_1 B \sin \Gamma a. \tag{6.39}$$

Since

$$E_x = -\frac{\partial V}{\partial x},$$

we have

$$V(x, z) = -\int E_x \, dx$$

$$= A \Gamma^{-1} \cos \Gamma x \, e^{-\Gamma z}, \qquad 0 \le x < b, \tag{6.40}$$

$$= -B \Gamma^{-1} \cos \Gamma (a + b - x) \, e^{-\Gamma z}, \qquad b < x \le a + b$$

except for a function of z only, which we take as a separate solution,

$$V_0(z) = A_0 + A_1 z. \tag{6.41}$$

Therefore

$$E_z(x, z) = -\frac{\partial V}{\partial z} = A \cos \Gamma x \, e^{-\Gamma z}, \qquad 0 \le x < b,$$

$$\tag{6.42}$$

$$= -B \cos \Gamma (a + b - x) e^{-\Gamma z}, \qquad b < x \le a + b.$$

The second boundary condition in equation (6.37) will be satisfied if

$$A \cos \Gamma b = -B \cos \Gamma a. \tag{6.43}$$

Dividing equation (6.39) by equation (6.43), we have the *characteristic equation* for Γ

$$\sigma_2 \tan \Gamma b = -\sigma_1 \tan \Gamma a. \tag{6.44}$$

For each root Γ_n of this equation we have a set of solutions, given by equations (6.38), (6.40), and (6.42). The constants A and B are not independent but are related, as in equation (6.43). To satisfy the equation, let

$$A_n = P_n \cos \Gamma_n a, \qquad B_n = -P_n \cos \Gamma_n b, \tag{6.45}$$

where P_n is, so far, arbitrary.

Equation (6.44) may be solved numerically or graphically. Let

$$b/a = k, \qquad \Gamma a = u. \tag{6.46}$$

Then

$$\tan ku = -(\sigma_1/\sigma_2) \tan u. \tag{6.47}$$

The left side can be plotted versus ku and the right side versus u. We pick the values of ku and u which correspond to equal ordinates. From these values we plot u versus $k = (ku)/u$. Since the tangent function is periodic and is composed of an infinite number of branches, we can obtain $u = f(k)$. If a and b are given, we find k, the corresponding values of u, and finally the corresponding values of $\Gamma = u/a$.

The general solution, consistent with the boundary conditions given by equations (6.36) and (6.37), is the sum of solutions for different roots of the characteristic equation (6.44). Thus from equations (6.41), (6.42), and (6.45), we have

$$J_z(x, z) = P_0 f_0(x) + \sum_{n=1}^{\infty} P_n f_n(x) e^{-\Gamma_n z}, \tag{6.48}$$

where the P_n are arbitrary constants, and the characteristic functions or eigenfunctions are

$$f_0(x) = \sigma_2, \qquad 0 \le x < b$$
$$= \sigma_1, \qquad b < x \le a + b,$$

$$f_n(x) = \sigma_2 \cos \Gamma_n a \cos \Gamma_n x, \qquad 0 \le x < b$$
$$= \sigma_1 \cos \Gamma_n b \cos \Gamma_n (a + b - x), \qquad b < x \le a + b. \tag{6.49}$$

Similar expressions can be obtained for the remaining field quantities.

From what we learned in the preceding section, we know that equation (6.48) can represent only the current injected into a plate which extends indefinitely in the positive z direction. If there is another junction at $z = l$, for example, we should include a series in which Γ_n is replaced by $-\Gamma_n$.

End conditions may be satisfied in much the same manner as in the preceding section. Thus if $J_z(x, 0)$ is given, the coefficients in the series given by equation (6.48) can be determined if both sides are multiplied by appropriate functions of x and integrated over the interval $(0, a + b)$. In the preceding problem the ease with which such coefficients were obtained was due to the *orthognality property*, equation (6.21), of the cosines. In the present case the functions defined by equation (6.49) are also orthogonal. Thus

$$\int_0^{a+b} [\sigma(x)]^{-1} f_n(x) f_m(x) \, dx = 0, \qquad n \ne m, \tag{6.50}$$

where $\sigma(x) = \sigma_2$ if $0 \le x < b$ and $\sigma(x) = \sigma_1$, if $b < x \le a + b$. To prove, substitute from equation (6.49), integrate, and use the characteristic equation (6.44). Then if both sides of equation (6.48) for $z = 0$ are multiplied by $[\sigma(x)]^{-1}f_m(x)$ and integrated, only one unknown coefficient P_m will be left on the right side.

If there are more layers with different conductivities, the characteristic equation becomes more complex; but the method remains essentially the same. If the conductivity is a continuous function of x, there are still solutions varying exponentially with z; but the eigenfunctions $f_n(x)$ are no longer sinusoidal. Instead they are solutions of a certain ordinary differential equation. This equation can be obtained from equations (6.1) and (6.2). It should be noted that equations (6.3) and (6.4) are no longer valid since they are based on the assumption that σ is at least piecewise independent of x.

When σ is a function of both variables x and z, a further modification of the method becomes necessary. Various field quantities can still be expressed either as sine or cosine series in x for any *particular* value of z. This is known from the theory of Fourier sieries. The coefficients, however, are more general functions of z and the separate terms of the series do not satisfy the field equations and thus do not represent possible fields. Some of these questions will be considered in Chapter 9.

6.3   Direct current in expanding plates

Figure 6.3 shows the top view of a thin expanding plate. We assume that electric current enters the plate along a circular arc AB of radius a and leaves it along another arc CD of radius b. On the average the flow is in the radial direction. The coordinate system that fits this

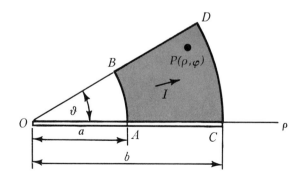

FIGURE 6.3   *The top view of a thin plate whose width increases at a uniform rate.*

geometry best is the cylindrical system. If the field is uniform in the z direction, Laplace's equation (see Appendix III) becomes

$$\rho \frac{\partial}{\partial \rho} \left(\rho \frac{\partial V}{\partial \rho} \right) + \frac{\partial^2 V}{\partial \varphi^2} = 0. \tag{6.51}$$

The components of $\vec{E}$ are

$$E_\rho = -\frac{\partial V}{\partial \rho}, \qquad E_\varphi = -\frac{\partial V}{\rho \partial \varphi}. \tag{6.52}$$

The boundary conditions are

$$E_\varphi(\rho, 0) = E_\varphi(\rho, \vartheta) = 0, \tag{6.53}$$

where ϑ is the angle of the expanding plate. To make the problem definite we should also have some boundary conditions on the circular arcs AB and CD such as a description of the manner in which the current enters and leaves the plate.

The method of solution is essentially the same as in the preceding two problems. We assume a product solution

$$V(\rho, \varphi) = R(\rho)\Phi(\varphi). \tag{6.54}$$

To satisfy the boundary conditions given by equation (6.53), we should have

$$\Phi'(0) = \Phi'(\vartheta) = 0. \tag{6.55}$$

Equations for R and Φ will be obtained if we substitute the product solution in equation (6.51), divide by $R\Phi$, and decide that each term must be a constant. From our experience with a similar problem in Section 6.1 we can avoid a repetition of details by anticipating that Φ should be some sinusoidal function and by choosing the form of the separation constant more directly suitable for obtaining this result. Thus

$$\rho \frac{d}{d\rho} \left(\rho \frac{dR}{d\rho} \right) = \nu^2 R, \qquad \frac{d^2\Phi}{d\varphi^2} = -\nu^2\Phi. \tag{6.56}$$

Equation (6.55) will be satisfied if

$$\Phi = A \cos \nu\varphi, \qquad \sin \nu\vartheta = 0,$$
$$\nu = n\pi/\vartheta, \qquad n = 0, 1, 2, \cdots. \tag{6.57}$$

The equation for R has solutions of the form

$$R = B\rho^\alpha. \tag{6.58}$$

Substituting in the equation, we find

$$\alpha^2 = \nu^2, \qquad \alpha = \pm\nu \tag{6.59}$$

so that the general solution is

$$R = B_n\rho^{n\pi/\vartheta} + C_n\rho^{-n\pi/\vartheta}. \tag{6.60}$$

If n is equal to zero, equation (6.60) reduces to only one independent solution. The general solution is obtained from equation (6.56) as follows:

$$\frac{d}{d\rho}\left(\rho\,\frac{dR}{d\rho}\right) = 0, \qquad \rho\,\frac{dR}{d\rho} = C_0$$

$$R = C_0 \ln \rho + B_0. \tag{6.61}$$

Combining these results, we have

$$V(\rho, \varphi) = B_0 + C_0 \ln \rho + \sum_{n=1}^{\infty}\left[B_n'\left(\frac{\rho}{b}\right)^{n\pi/\vartheta} + C_n'\left(\frac{a}{\rho}\right)^{n\pi/\vartheta}\right]\cos\frac{n\pi\varphi}{\vartheta}. \tag{6.62}$$

Here new arbitrary constants have been introduced: B_n' corresponds largely to the potential distribution on the arc CD, where $\rho = b$, and C_n' corresponds largely to the potential distribution on the arc AB, where $\rho = a$. As b/a increases, the potential distribution on one arc affects less and less the potential distribution on the other. This expansion should be compared with the series given by equation (6.18) for the potential in a plate of constant width and the series given by equation (6.26) for the current density in the general direction of flow. Power functions and exponential functions are related. The former approach the latter when ϑ approaches zero in such a way that $\rho\vartheta$ remains constant.

The logarithmic term in equation (6.61) is particularly important. The radial electric intensity and current density derived from it are inversely proportional to ρ and are independent of φ. This term controls the total radial current in the expanding plate while the remaining terms represent "end-effects."

The problem of expressing the unknown constants in equation (6.62) in terms of radial current distributions on AB and CD is exactly the same as in the case of plates of uniform width.

6.4 Direct current in bent plates

Figure 6.4 shows the upper view of a thin plate bent into a circular strip. The principal difference between this problem and that of an expanding plate is in the direction of flow. In the present case the

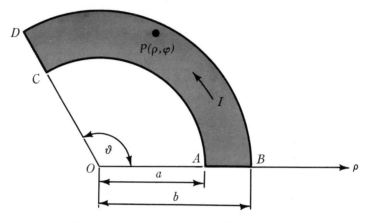

FIGURE 6.4 *A top view of a thin bent plate.*

flow is, on the average, in the φ direction. The boundary conditions are

$$E_\rho(a, \varphi) = E_\rho(b, \varphi) = 0,$$

that is,

$$R'(a) = R'(b) = 0. \tag{6.63}$$

Since ν is no longer given by equation (6.57), we write the general solution, equation (6.60), in the form

$$R = B\rho^\nu + C\rho^{-\nu}. \tag{6.64}$$

Differentiating and using the boundary conditions given by equations (6.63), we have

$$\nu(Ba^{\nu-1} - Ca^{-\nu-1}) = 0,$$

$$\nu(Bb^{\nu-1} - Cb^{-\nu-1}) = 0. \tag{6.65}$$

Both equations are satisfied if

$$\nu = 0. \tag{6.66}$$

In this case the proper solution for Φ in equations (6.56) is

$$\Phi = A_1\varphi + A_0 \tag{6.67}$$

while $R = $ const.

If ν is not equal to zero, equation (6.65) yields

$$C/B = a^{2\nu} = b^{2\nu} \tag{6.68}$$

$$(b/a)^{2\nu} = 1 \tag{6.69}$$

$$\exp\left[2\nu \ln\left(b/a\right)\right] = 1 = e^{j2n\pi}, \qquad n = 1, 2, 3, \cdots,$$

that is,

$$\nu = jk_n, \qquad k_n = \frac{n\pi}{\ln\left(b/a\right)}, \qquad n = 1, 2, 3, \cdots. \tag{6.70}$$

For each characteristic value of ν, equation (6.68) determines the ratio of arbitrary constants

$$C_n = B_n a^{2jk_n}.$$

Hence equation (6.64) becomes

$$R = B_n a^{jk_n}\left[(\rho/a)^{jk_n} + (\rho/a)^{-jk_n}\right]$$

$$= B_n a^{jk_n}\left\{\exp\left[jk_n \ln\left(\rho/a\right)\right] + \exp\left[-jk_n \ln\left(\rho/a\right)\right]\right\} \tag{6.71}$$

$$= P_n \cos\left[k_n \ln\left(\rho/a\right)\right],$$

where P_n is a new arbitrary constant.

Substituting the characteristic values from equation (6.70) into equation (6.56) for Φ, we have

$$\Phi = M_n e^{k_n\varphi} + N_n e^{-k_n\varphi}. \tag{6.72}$$

Collecting the results, we have

$$V(\rho, \varphi) = A_1\varphi + A_0 + \sum_{n=1}^{\infty} (M_n e^{k_n\varphi} + N_n e^{-k_n\varphi}) \cos\left[k_n \ln\left(\rho/a\right)\right] \tag{6.73}$$

where the constants k_n are given by equation (6.70). Various field components can be obtained by differentiation.

As in previous problems the remaining unknown constants can be expressed in terms of $V(\rho, \varphi)$ or $J_\varphi(\rho, \varphi)$ at the ends of the plate where $\varphi = 0$ and $\varphi = \vartheta$. Conveniently enough the characteristic functions given by equation (6.71) and their derivatives turn out to be orthogonal. It is simpler to prove this directly from the differential equations (6.56), and the boundary conditions given by equation (6.63) than by direct calculation of the integrals. Thus for any two characteristic values, we have

$$\frac{d}{d\rho}\left(\rho\,\frac{dR_n}{d\rho}\right) = -k_n^2\rho^{-1}R_n,$$

$$\frac{d}{d\rho}\left(\rho\,\frac{dR_m}{d\rho}\right) = -k_m^2\rho^{-1}R_m.$$

By multiplying the first equation by R_m, the second by R_n, and subtracting, we obtain

$$\frac{d}{d\rho}\left(\rho R_m\,\frac{dR_n}{d\rho} - \rho R_n\,\frac{dR_m}{d\rho}\right) = (k_m^2 - k_n^2)\rho^{-1}R_nR_m,$$

where the left side is a complete derivative. Multiplying by $d\rho$ and integrating from $\rho = a$, to $\rho = b$, we obtain

$$\left(\rho R_m\,\frac{dR_n}{d\rho} - \rho R_n\,\frac{dR_m}{d\rho}\right)\bigg|_a^b = (k_m^2 - k_n^2)\int_a^b \rho^{-1}R_nR_m\,d\rho. \qquad (6.74)$$

In view of the boundary conditions given by equations (6.63) the left side vanishes. Hence,

$$\int_a^b \rho^{-1}R_nR_m\,d\rho = 0, \qquad k_n^2 \neq k_m^2. \qquad (6.75)$$

6.5 Electric current filament between perfectly conducting parallel planes

To illustrate the solution of problems involving static magnetic fields, consider an infinitely long strip of direct current I between a pair of perfectly conducting parallel planes at $x = 0$ and $x = a$. See Figure 6.5. We assume that the strip is parallel to the y axis and that the planes are extending to infinity in the positive and negative z directions. After solution has been obtained, we let the width s of the strip approach zero and thus determine the field of an infinitely thin current filament. In Chapter 2 it was concluded that in current-free regions the magnetic intensity of a static field may be expressed as the negative of the gradient of magnetic potential. Thus the problem reduces to solving Laplace's equation (6.6), and satisfying suitable boundary conditions.

The component of $\bar{H}$ normal to a perfectly conducting surface must vanish. Hence

$$H_x(0, z) = H_x(a, z) = 0.$$

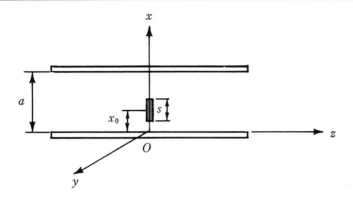

FIGURE 6.5 *A cross section of two parallel conducting planes and an infinite current strip of width s.*

In Section 6.1 we already obtained solutions for E [equation (6.19)] which satisfy these conditions and we can adapt them to the present problem.

At $z = \pm \infty$ the field must vanish. Hence

$$H_x = \sum_{m=1}^{\infty} A_m e^{-m\pi z/a} \sin\left(m\pi x/a\right), \qquad z > 0$$

$$= \sum_{m=1}^{\infty} B_m e^{m\pi z/a} \sin\left(m\pi x/a\right), \qquad z < 0$$

$$\text{(6.76)}$$

$$H_z = \sum_{m=1}^{\infty} A_m e^{-m\pi z/a} \cos\left(m\pi x/a\right), \qquad z > 0$$

$$= -\sum_{m=1}^{\infty} B_m e^{m\pi z/a} \cos\left(m\pi x/a\right), \qquad z < 0.$$

Magnetic lines of force go around the strip so that by symmetry we know that

$$H_z(x, -z) = H_z(x, z),$$

$$\text{(6.77)}$$

$$H_x(x, -z) = -H_x(x, z).$$

Therefore

$$B_m = -A_m. \tag{6.78}$$

By the Ampere-Maxwell law the discontinuity in H_x across the current strip equals the current per unit length normal to the lines of flow. Assuming that the current is distributed uniformly, we have

$$H_z(x, +0) - H_z(x, -0) = I/s, \qquad x_0 - \tfrac{1}{2}s < x < x_0 + \tfrac{1}{2}s.$$

Elsewhere across the plane $z = 0$, H_x is continuous. In view of equation (6.77)

$$H_z(x, +0) = I/2s, \qquad x_0 - \tfrac{1}{2}s < x < x_0 + \tfrac{1}{2}s \qquad (6.79)$$
$$= 0, \qquad \text{outside the interval.}$$

The coefficients A_n of the sine series for $H_z(x, +0)$ are

$$A_n = \frac{2}{a} \int_0^a H_z(x, +0) \sin (n\pi x/a) \, dx.$$

Substituting from equation (6.79) and integrating, we find

$$A_n = \frac{2I}{n\pi s} \sin \frac{n\pi s}{2a} \sin \frac{n\pi x_0}{a}. \qquad (6.80)$$

As s approaches zero

$$A_m \to \frac{I}{a} \sin \frac{m\pi x_0}{a}. \qquad (6.81)$$

These equations together with equation (6.78) determine the magnetic field.

If the current I is alternating slowly, there will exist an electric field parallel to the current,

$$E_y(x, z) = -j\omega\mu \int_0^x H_z \, dx$$

$$\qquad (6.82)$$

$$= j\omega\mu \sum_{n=1}^{\infty} \frac{a}{m\pi} A_m e^{-m\pi z/a} \sin (m\pi x/a), \qquad z > 0.$$

6.6 Point charge inside a hollow metal tube of rectangular cross section

Solution of three-dimensional static problems involves more field components, more terms in series expansions, but no new features. Consider, for instance, a point charge q inside a hollow metal tube of rectangular cross section. In the preceding example a line filament was replaced by a strip of finite width in order to express the condi-

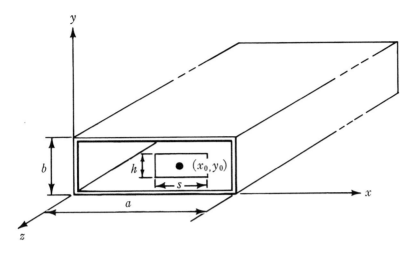

FIGURE 6.6 *A conducting cylinder of rectangular cross section and a rectangle of electric charge.*

tions at the source of the field in a form [see equation (6.79)] convenient for calculating the coefficients A_n. In the present case the point charge at (x_0, y_0) is replaced by a charge distributed uniformly over a rectangular area around (x_0, y_0). See Figure 6.6. Thus if s and h are the sides of the rectangle and Q is the surface density of the charge, then $q = Qhs$. After the solution has been obtained, we allow h and s to approach zero and Q to increase correspondingly.

We start with Laplace's equation

$$\frac{\partial^2 V}{\partial x^2} + \frac{\partial^2 V}{\partial y^2} + \frac{\partial^2 V}{\partial z^2} = 0. \qquad (6.83)$$

Since the potential on the conducting boundary must be constant, let it be equal to zero. From our experience with previous problems we know that linear differential equations with constant coefficients possess exponential and sinusoidal solutions. To satisfy the boundary condition on the surface of the tube we select the following set of functions:

$$V_{mn} = \sin(m\pi x/a)\sin(n\pi y/b)Z_{mn}(z); \qquad m, n = 1, 2, 3, \cdots. \quad (6.84)$$

The general solution is the sum of these solutions taken over all integral values of m and n. From the theory of Fouries series it is known that an almost arbitrary function of x and y can be expressed as a double sine series in x and y. In our case we expect the coefficients to depend on z. The coefficients are obtained by substituting from equation (6.84) into (6.83)

$$\frac{d^2 Z_{mn}}{dz^2} = \Gamma_{mn}^2 Z_{mn}, \qquad \Gamma_{mn}^2 = \left(\frac{m\pi}{a}\right)^2 + \left(\frac{n\pi}{b}\right)^2. \qquad (6.85)$$

Hence

$$Z_{mn} = A_{mn} e^{-\Gamma_{mn} z} + B_{mn} e^{\Gamma_{mn} z}, \qquad (6.86)$$

where A_{mn} and B_{mn} are arbitrary constants of integration. The potential must vanish at infinity. Thus the terms containing negative exponents must be proper for $z > 0$ and those with positive exponents for $z < 0$. The potential must be continuous across the plane $z = 0$ containing the charge. Therefore $B_{mn} = A_{mn}$ and

$$V(x, y, z) = \sum_{m,n} A_{mn} \sin \frac{m\pi x}{a} \sin \frac{n\pi y}{b} \exp\left(-\Gamma_{mn} z\right), \qquad z \geq 0$$

$$= \sum_{m,n} A_{mn} \sin \frac{m\pi x}{a} \sin \frac{n\pi y}{b} \exp\left(\Gamma_{mn} z\right), \qquad z \leq 0.$$

$$(6.87)$$

The component of displacement density normal to the surface charge

$$D_z = \epsilon E_z = -\epsilon \frac{\partial V}{\partial z}$$

is discontinuous. The discontinuity equals the density Q of the surface charge. Hence

$$2\epsilon \Gamma_{mn} A_{mn} = \frac{4}{ab} \iint Q \sin \frac{m\pi x}{a} \sin \frac{n\pi y}{b} \, dx \, dy,$$

where the integration is extended over the area of the rectangle with sides h and s

$$-\tfrac{1}{2}s \leq x - x_0 \leq \tfrac{1}{2}s, \qquad -\tfrac{1}{2}h \leq y - y_0 \leq \tfrac{1}{2}h.$$

If one is interested in obtaining the field of a point charge, there is no need to carry out the integration explicitly. One should merely observe that as h and s approach zero, the coordinates x and y in the integrand approach constant values x_0 and y_0. The sine terms can then be taken outside the integration sign. The remaining integral will represent the total charge q. Thus

$$A_{mn} = \frac{2q}{\epsilon \Gamma_{mn} ab} \sin \frac{m\pi x_0}{a} \sin \frac{n\pi y_0}{b}.$$

6.7   Normal modes of field distribution and wave propagation

All the solutions we have obtained in this chapter have one feature in common: they are represented by infinite series of functions satisfying field equations and certain boundary conditions. Each term of an infinite series, such as the series given by equations (6.87), represents a possible field distribution and is called a *mode of field distribution*. More specifically these fields are called *normal* or *orthogonal modes* because each can exist *without* the others. To generate the field corresponding to one particular pair of values of m and n in equation (6.87), one needs only establish in the plane $z = 0$ a distribution of potential, or of surface charge, proportional to the product of the corresponding sines.

Throughout the rest of this chapter we consider time-harmonic fields which involve wave propagation, and the field generated by a particular source expressed as the result of superposition of *normal modes of propagation*.

6.8   Transverse magnetic (TM) waves between perfectly conducting parallel planes

In this and the following sections we consider waves between perfectly conducting planes. Suppose that the boundaries shown in Figure 6.1 are such planes and not the boundaries of a conducting plate. The medium between the planes is now assumed to be a perfect dielectric. Furthermore let the planes extend indefinitely in the y direction, and assume that the field is uniform in this direction. Maxwell's equations in Cartesian coordinates (see Appendix II) become two independent sets, one connecting H_y, E_x, and E_z and the other connecting E_y, H_x, and H_z. The first one is

$$\frac{\partial E_x}{\partial z} = -j\omega\mu H_y + \frac{\partial E_z}{\partial x}, \qquad j\omega\epsilon E_z = \frac{\partial H_y}{\partial x}$$

$$\tag{6.88}$$

$$\frac{\partial H_y}{\partial z} = -j\omega\epsilon E_x.$$

Parallel planes can be considered as coaxial cylinders of infinitely large radii. Thus our problem is related to the one studied in Chapter 4. There it was assumed that the longitudinal displacement currents were negligible. Let us see if such an assumption is consistent with equations (6.88), the "fine-grained" field equations. One immediate consequence is that H_y is independent of x (see the second equation). From the other two equations we find that E_x and $\partial E_z/\partial x$ are also independent of x. Hence E_z is proportional to $A + Bx$. Since E_z vanishes at both perfectly conducting boundaries, $A = B = 0$ and E_z vanishes identically. Equation (6.88) then reduces to

$$\frac{dE_x}{dz} = -j\omega\mu H_y, \qquad \frac{dH_y}{dz} = j\omega\epsilon E_x. \qquad (6.89)$$

Their solutions are

$$H_y^+ = H_0^+ e^{-j\beta z}, \qquad E_x^+ = \eta H_0^+ e^{-j\beta z}$$

$$H_y^- = H_0^- e^{j\beta z}, \qquad E_x^- = -\eta H_0^- e^{j\beta z} \qquad (6.90)$$

$$\beta = \omega\sqrt{\mu\epsilon}, \qquad \eta = \sqrt{\mu/\epsilon}.$$

The first pair represents waves traveling in the positive z direction, and the second represents waves in the negative z direction. Both field intensities E and H are at right angles to the direction of propagation. Such waves are called *transverse electromagnetic waves* (TEM waves).

Other waves consistent with the field equations (6.88) are called *transverse magnetic waves* (TM waves) because $\vec{H}$ is perpendicular to the direction of propagation. These waves are not only possible, they are necessary because TEM waves alone do not fit the physical conditions at junctions where the distance between parallel planes changes. See Figure 6.1. At $z = 0$, for instance, E_x is not independent of x; it differs from zero in the interval $(0, h)$ and vanishes in (h, a). From our experience with static problems we conclude that E_z can be proportional to $\sin(m\pi x/a)$. If this is the case, E_x and H_y are proportional to $\cos(m\pi x/a)$. Thus

$$E_x = \hat{E}(z) \cos(m\pi x/a),$$

$$(6.91)$$

$$H_y = \hat{H}(z) \cos(m\pi x/a).$$

If we eliminate E_z from the first equation of the set (6.88) by substituting from the second and then using equation (6.91), we obtain

$$\frac{d\hat{E}}{dz} = -\left(j\omega\mu + \frac{m^2\pi^2}{j\omega\epsilon a^2}\right)\hat{H},$$

$$(6.92)$$

$$\frac{d\hat{H}}{dz} = -j\omega\epsilon\hat{E}.$$

The general solution of these equations is

$$\hat{H} = Ae^{-\Gamma_m z} + Be^{\Gamma_m z}$$

$$\hat{E} = K_m Ae^{-\Gamma_m z} - K_m Be^{\Gamma_m z},$$

(6.93)

where Γ_m is the propagation constant and K_m the *wave impedance*

$$\Gamma_m = \sqrt{-\beta^2 + \frac{m^2 \pi^2}{a^2}} = \sqrt{\frac{m^2 \pi^2}{a^2} - \frac{4\pi^2}{\lambda^2}},$$

$$K_m = \Gamma_m / j\omega\epsilon.$$

(6.94)

In these equations λ is the wavelength of plane waves in the dielectric medium of permeability μ and dielectric constant ϵ, so that $f\lambda = 1/\sqrt{\mu\epsilon}$. Observe that at low frequencies all propagation constants are real and the waves are attenuated. They appear only as end effects at junctions (Figure 6.1). As the frequency increases, more and more waves become traveling waves. The *cut-off* wavelengths λ_c and frequencies f_c are given by $\Gamma_m = 0$. Thus

$$\lambda_{c,m} = 2a/m, \qquad f_{c,m} = m/2a\sqrt{\mu\epsilon}.$$

(6.95)

The existence of these *higher order modes of propagation* was anticipated from physical considerations in Section 4.19.

6.9 Transverse electric (TE) waves between perfectly conducting parallel planes

The set of field equations, complementary to the set given by equations (6.88), is

$$\frac{\partial E_y}{\partial z} = j\omega\mu H_x, \qquad j\omega\mu H_z = -\frac{\partial E_y}{\partial x}$$

(6.96)

$$\frac{\partial H_x}{\partial z} = j\omega\epsilon E_y + \frac{\partial H_z}{\partial z}.$$

Waves described by these equations are called *transverse electric waves* (TE waves) because $\vec{E}$ is perpendicular to the direction of propagation.

Again anticipating that E_y and H_z are proportional to $\sin (m\pi x/a)$, let

$$E_y = -\hat{E}(z) \sin (m\pi x/a),$$

$$H_x = \hat{H}(z) \sin (m\pi x/a). \tag{6.97}$$

The negative sign is introduced to make the final form of equations similar to the transmission line equations in Chapter 4. Eliminating H_z from equations (6.96) and substituting from equations (6.97), we have

$$\frac{d\hat{E}}{dz} = -j\omega\mu\hat{H}, \qquad \frac{d\hat{H}}{dz} = -\left(j\omega\epsilon + \frac{m^2\pi^2}{j\omega\mu a^2} \right)\hat{E}. \tag{6.98}$$

Here the propagation constant and the wave impedance are

$$\Gamma_m = \sqrt{-\beta^2 + \frac{m^2\pi^2}{a^2}}, \qquad K_m = j\omega\mu/\Gamma_m. \tag{6.99}$$

The cut-off frequencies are the same as for TM waves. There are no waves corresponding to $m = 0$.

Two perfectly conducting planes $y = 0$ and $y = b$ may be introduced without perturbing the field since they will be perpendicular to $\bar{E}$. Hence, TE waves of the type considered here may exist in hollow metal tubes of rectangular cross section, that is, in *rectangular waveguides*.

6.10 Waves in perfectly conducting rectangular waveguides

In this section we shall consider waves in perfectly conducting waveguides of rectangular cross section. Let the boundaries be

$$x = 0, \qquad x = a, \qquad y = 0, \qquad y = b. \tag{6.100}$$

We start by inquiring whether such a waveguide can support TM waves for which $H_z = 0$ and TE waves for which $E_z = 0$. No risk is involved. If there are no waves in which either one or the other component vanishes, we shall discover it after the appropriate substitutions in the field equations.

For TM waves E_z must vanish on the boundaries defined in equations (6.100). Let us assume waves traveling in the positive z direction. Thus

$$E_z = A \sin \frac{m\pi x}{a} \sin \frac{n\pi y}{b} \exp (-\Gamma_{mn}z), \qquad m, n = 1, 2, 3, \cdots.$$

$$\tag{6.101}$$

For the remaining components we write similar expressions in which either one or the other sine function is replaced by the corresponding cosine function as required by field equations. For example, the first equation given in Appendix II is

$$\frac{\partial E_z}{\partial y} - \frac{\partial E_y}{\partial z} = -j\omega\mu H_z.$$

The derivative of E_z with respect to y is proportional to $\cos(n\pi y/b)$. This equation cannot possibly be satisfied unless E_y and H_x are also proportional to $\cos(n\pi y/b)$. Having written the expressions for the various field components, we substitute them into field equations and obtain linear algebraic equations for the complex amplitudes of the components. These equations are then solved in terms of A. In this manner, the following results are obtained:

$$H_x = \frac{Aj\omega\epsilon n\pi}{\chi_{mn}^2 b} \sin\frac{m\pi x}{a} \cos\frac{n\pi y}{b} \exp(-\Gamma_{mn}z),$$

$$H_y = \frac{Aj\omega\epsilon m\pi}{\chi_{mn}^2 a} \cos\frac{m\pi x}{a} \sin\frac{n\pi y}{b} \exp(-\Gamma_{mn}z),$$

$$\qquad (6.102)$$

$$E_x = K_{mn}H_y, \qquad E_y = -K_{mn}H_x,$$

$$\Gamma_{mn} = \sqrt{\left(\frac{m\pi}{a}\right)^2 + \left(\frac{n\pi}{b}\right)^2 - \beta^2}, \qquad \chi_{mn}^2 = \left(\frac{m\pi}{a}\right)^2 + \left(\frac{n\pi}{b}\right)^2,$$

$$K_{mn} = \Gamma_{mn}/j\omega\epsilon.$$

Similarly for TE waves, start with

$$H_z = B\cos\frac{m\pi x}{a} \cos\frac{n\pi y}{b} \exp(-\Gamma_{mn}z), \qquad m, n = 0, 1, 2, \cdots.$$

$$\qquad (6.103)$$

In the present case either m or n may equal zero, but not both, without yielding a field identically equal to zero. As in the preceding case one obtains

$$E_x = \frac{Bj\omega\mu m\pi}{\chi_{mn}^2 b} \cos\frac{m\pi x}{a} \sin\frac{n\pi y}{b} \exp(-\Gamma_{mn}z),$$

$$E_y = -\frac{Bj\omega\mu m\pi}{\chi_{mn}^2 a} \sin\frac{m\pi x}{a} \cos\frac{n\pi y}{b} \exp(-\Gamma_{mn}z),$$

$$\qquad (6.104)$$

$$H_x = -K_{mn}^{-1}E_y, \quad H_y = K_{mn}^{-1}E_x, \quad K_{mn} = j\omega\mu/\Gamma_{mn}.$$

The expressions for χ_{mn} and Γ_{mn} are the same as those for TM waves.

The double index m, n is used to designate a particular wave or mode of propagation. Thus one may refer to a TE_{mn} wave and TE_{mn} mode or a TM_{mn} wave and TM_{mn} mode. If a is greater than b, then the TE_{10} mode has the lowest cut-off frequency which is given by

$$\omega_c \sqrt{\mu\epsilon} = \pi/a, \quad f_c = 1/2a\sqrt{\mu\epsilon}, \quad \lambda_c = 2a.$$

This wave is called the *dominant wave*. At lower frequencies no waves can travel inside the metal tube.

6.11   Natural oscillations in metal cavities

If the rectangular waveguide considered in the preceding section is closed with two perfectly conducting planes $z = 0$ and $z = l$, a metal cavity is formed. General expressions for possible fields in such a cavity should include positive exponential functions of z as well as the negative. The components E_x and E_y must vanish when $z = 0, l$. This condition cannot be satisfied when Γ_{mn} is real. There must be waves traveling back and forth and adding in phase. Let

$$\Gamma_{mn} = j\beta_{mn}, \quad \beta_{mn} = \sqrt{\beta^2 - \left(\frac{m\pi}{a}\right)^2 - \left(\frac{n\pi}{b}\right)^2}. \quad (6.105)$$

In order that E_x and E_y could vanish at $z = 0, l$ they must be proportional to $\sin \beta_{mn}z$ and it is necessary that

$$\sin \beta_{mn}l = 0, \quad \beta_{mn}l = p\pi, \quad p = 1, 2, \cdots. \quad (6.106)$$

Substituting in the preceding equation, we find

$$\beta^2 = \omega^2\mu\epsilon = \left(\frac{m\pi}{a}\right)^2 + \left(\frac{n\pi}{b}\right)^2 + \left(\frac{p\pi}{l}\right)^2. \quad (6.107)$$

This equation determines the natural frequencies of cavity oscillations.

6.12   Attenuation

The walls of any actual waveguide are not perfectly conducting. Power will be dissipated and waves will be attenuated. Since the power dissipated per unit length of the guide is a small fraction of the power carried by the wave, the attenuation constant can be calculated by using equation (4.38). In order to apply this equation one has to assume that the field distribution over a typical cross section of the guide is not affected much by the conductivity of the walls. We expect this to be the case when the conductivity is large. It is the tangential component of $\bar{H}$ that determines the current in the walls. If the conductivity is infinite, the tangential component of $\bar{E}$ is zero. When the conductivity is large, this component is small. In Section 4.16 we obtained the ratio of E_{tan} to the total current in a conductor; that is, to the tangential magnetomotive force. From it we find the ratio of E_{tan} to H_{tan}. Thus at high frequencies [see equations (4.53) and (4.55) and note that for a cylinder $I(0) = 2\pi a H_{\text{tan}}$] we have

$$E_{\text{tan}} = \eta_c H_{\text{tan}}, \qquad \eta_c = \sqrt{j\omega\mu/\sigma_c} = R_c(1 + j). \qquad (6.108)$$

Using equation (3.3), we obtain the formula for the average power absorbed by the walls of the guide per unit length,

$$P = \tfrac{1}{2}\text{Re} \int E_{\text{tan}} H_{\text{tan}}^* \, ds = \tfrac{1}{2}R_c \int H_{\text{tan}} H_{\text{tan}}^* \, ds, \qquad (6.109)$$

where the integration is round the periphery.

The average power carried by the wave is also obtained by applying equation (3.3) to the transverse components of the field. Thus

$$W = \tfrac{1}{2} \iint \bar{E}_t \times \bar{H}_t^* \, dS, \qquad (6.110)$$

where the integration extends over the cross section of the guide.

We now apply these equations to a special case of a TM wave between parallel planes. The attenuation which we are studying is that of traveling waves, when in absence of power dissipation, the propagation constant given by equation (6.94) is a pure imaginary,

$$\Gamma_m = j\beta_m, \qquad \beta_m = \sqrt{\frac{m^2\pi^2}{a^2} - \beta^2}.$$

From equations (6.91) and (6.93) we have

$$H_y = A \cos(m\pi x/a) \, e^{-j\beta_m z}$$

$$E_x = K_m H_y, \qquad K_m = \beta_m/\omega\epsilon.$$

At the conducting planes $x = 0$ and $x = a$ the tangential $\bar{H}$ is

$$H_y = \pm A e^{-j\beta_m z}.$$

Hence the average power absorbed per unit length *and* unit width by both planes is

$$P = R_c A A^*.$$

The average power carried by the wave, per unit width, is

$$W = \tfrac{1}{2} \int_0^a E_x H_y^* \, dx = \tfrac{1}{2} K_m A A^* \int_0^a \cos^2 \frac{m\pi x}{a} \, dx = \tfrac{1}{4} K_m a A A^*$$

if $m \neq 0$. Otherwise $W = \tfrac{1}{2} K_0 a A A^*$. Therefore

$$\alpha = P/2W = 2R_c/K_m a, \qquad m \neq 0.$$

6.13 Damping constant

The same principle may be applied to the calculation of damping constants of natural oscillations in metal cavities. There the average absorbed power is given by

$$P = \tfrac{1}{2} R_c \iint H_{\tan} H_{\tan}^* \, dS, \tag{6.111}$$

where the integration is extended over the surface of the cavity. The total stored energy is

$$\mathcal{E} = \tfrac{1}{4}\mu \iiint \vec{H} \cdot \vec{H}^* \, dv + \tfrac{1}{4}\epsilon \iiint \vec{E} \cdot \vec{E}^* \, dv,$$

where the first term represents the average magnetic energy and the second the average electric energy. Since the two are equal,

$$\mathcal{E} = \tfrac{1}{2}\mu \iiint \vec{H} \cdot \vec{H}^* \, dv. \tag{6.112}$$

Consider, for example, a mode of oscillation for which $m = n = 1$, $p = 0$, and E_z is given by equation (6.101); that is,

$$E_z = A \sin \frac{\pi x}{a} \sin \frac{\pi y}{b}.$$

Note that according to equation (6.106), $p = 0$ implies that $\Gamma_{11} = 0$. From equation (6.102) we find

$$H_x = \frac{Aj\omega\epsilon\pi}{\chi_{11}^2 b} \sin \frac{\pi x}{a} \cos \frac{\pi y}{b}, \qquad \chi_{11}^2 = \frac{\pi^2}{a^2} + \frac{\pi^2}{b^2}$$

$$H_y = -\frac{Aj\omega\epsilon\pi}{\chi_{11}^2 a} \cos \frac{\pi x}{a} \sin \frac{\pi y}{b}.$$

At two walls of the cavity, $x = 0$ and $x = a$, we have

$$H_y = \mp \frac{A j \omega \epsilon \pi}{\chi_{11}^2 a} \sin \frac{\pi y}{b}.$$

Hence the absorbed power is

$$P_1 = R_c \int_0^l \int_0^b H_y H_y^* \, dy \, dz = \frac{\pi^2 R_c \omega^2 \epsilon^2 bl}{2\chi_{11}^4 a^2} A A^*.$$

For the walls $y = 0$ and $y = b$ we find

$$P_2 = R_c \int_0^l \int_0^a H_z(x, 0) H_z^*(x, 0) \, dx \, dz = \frac{\pi^2 R_c \omega^2 \epsilon^2 al}{2\chi_{11}^4 b^2} A A^*.$$

For the walls $z = 0$ and $z = l$

$$P_3 = R_c \int_0^b \int_0^a (H_x H_x^* + H_y H_y^*) \, dx \, dy = \frac{\pi^2 R_c \omega^2 \epsilon^2 ab}{4\chi_{11}^4} \left(\frac{1}{b^2} + \frac{1}{a^2} \right) A A^*$$

$$= \frac{R_c \omega^2 \epsilon^2 ab}{4\chi_{11}^2} A A^*.$$

The stored energy is

$$\mathcal{E} = \tfrac{1}{2}\mu \int_0^l \int_0^b \int_0^a (H_x H_x^* + H_y H_y^*) \, dx \, dy \, dz = \frac{\mu \omega^2 \epsilon^2 abl}{8\chi_{11}^2} A A^*.$$

From these expressions the damping constant [see equation (3.29) where W_{av} is the present P]

$$\xi = P/2\mathcal{E} = (P_1 + P_2 + P_3)/2\mathcal{E}.$$

is obtained.

6.14   Waveguides and cavities of general shapes

In this chapter we have considered fields, waves, and oscillations bounded mostly by parallel planes. A similar analysis can be carried out when some of the boundaries are cylindrical. The only difference is that we use cylindrical coordinates and some of the functions are Bessel functions instead of circular functions. Except for small values of the argument, Bessel functions resemble sines and cosines or exponential functions. Spherical coordinates are suitable for fields bounded by spheres, cones, and planes. Spherical coordinates can also be separated in the field equations and general solutions can be obtained as infinite series of suitable product solutions.

Only a few coordinate systems permit separation of variables. Even in those that do, this method is not necessarily the best. In Chapters 8 and 9 we shall study a method which is far more general than the method of separation of variables.

While mathematics depend on shapes of boundaries, the physical aspects of fields can be understood by studying what happens when the boundaries are relatively simple. Other boundaries can be thought of as deformations of simple boundaries to which the fields have to adjust.

6.15 Excitation of guided waves

Just as in free space, the basic source of waves in hollow tubes is the current element. Once its field is determined, the field of any given current distribution can be calculated by integration. The current element usually excites all modes. Depending on its position, how-

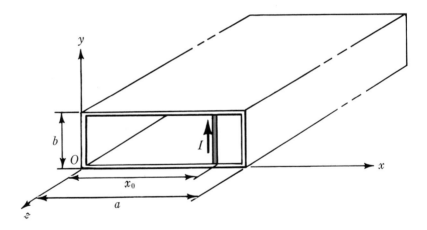

FIGURE 6.7 *A conducting cylinder of rectangular cross section and a transverse current filament.*

ever, some may be missing. In some instances it is simpler to compute the amplitudes of the excited modes directly from the given distribution. For example, in Figure 6.7 when a uniform oscillating current is maintained in a thin wire parallel to the short side of a hollow rectangular tube, the field is independent of the y coordinate and the field intensities are E_y, H_x, H_z. The excited modes are the TE_{m0} modes considered in Section 6.10. The amplitudes of these modes can be calculated as in the static case considered in Section 6.5. In fact one can use some of the results obtained in that section.

From equation (6.98) we have for a typical mode

$$\hat{E}_m(z) = E_m e^{-\Gamma_m z}, \qquad z \geq 0$$

$$= E_m e^{\Gamma_m z}, \qquad z \leq 0$$

since E_y is continuous at $z = 0$. Hence

$$\hat{H}_m(z) = K_m^{-1} E_m e^{-\Gamma_m z}, \qquad z > 0$$

$$= K_m^{-1} E_m e^{\Gamma_m z}, \qquad z < 0.$$

Referring to equation (6.97), we have the general form for the field

$$E_y = -\sum_{m=1}^{\infty} E_m e^{-\Gamma_m z} \sin(m\pi x/a), \qquad z \geq 0$$

$$= -\sum_{m=1}^{\infty} E_m e^{\Gamma_m z} \sin(m\pi x/a), \qquad z \leq 0$$

$$\tag{6.113}$$

$$H_x = \sum_{m=1}^{\infty} K_m^{-1} E_m e^{-\Gamma_m z} \sin(m\pi x/a), \qquad z > 0$$

$$= -\sum_{m=1}^{\infty} K_m^{-1} E_m e^{\Gamma_m z} \sin(m\pi x/a), \qquad z < 0.$$

As β approaches zero, H_x approaches the static expression in equation (6.76) with $A_m = K_m^{-1} E_m$. The discontinuity in H_x is related to the current in the same manner, regardless of the frequency. Hence, for an infinitely thin current filament we use equation (6.81) so that

$$E_m = \frac{K_m I}{a} \sin \frac{m\pi x_0}{a}. \tag{6.114}$$

Thus we have the amplitudes of the transverse field components. The longitudinal component, which can be obtained from the second equation in the set given by equation (6.96), approaches zero as ω increases. At high frequencies the waves tend to become *transverse electromagnetic waves* (TEM waves).

There is another method of calculating the amplitudes of the various modes which is equivalent to the above but has a physical meaning. The current I is driven against its field, work is done, and energy will flow into the field. The average work per second against the field of the mth mode is

$$\tfrac{1}{2}E_m b I^* \sin{(m\pi x_0/a)}.$$

The average power carried in the mth mode in both directions from the plane $z = 0$ is

$$\int_0^b \int_0^a (-E_y H_x^*) \, dx \, dy = \tfrac{1}{2} ab (1/K_m^*) E_m E_m^*.$$

Equating the two and canceling $\tfrac{1}{2}E_m b$, we have

$$(a/K_m^*) E_m^* = I^* \sin{(m\pi x_0/a)},$$

$$E_m^* = (K_m^* I^*/a) \sin{(m\pi x_0/a)}.$$

Taking the conjugates of both sides, we obtain equation (6.114).

This method is particularly easy to apply to a current element. We start with a typical mode which may exist in a hollow tube as determined in Section 6.10, on both sides of the element. The component of $\vec{E}$ *parallel* to the element must be continuous. This condition connects the amplitudes of the fields on both sides of the element. Then we calculate the power expended by the emf impressed on the current element and the power carried by the field, and thus determine the amplitude of the mode.

7

Reflection and Scattering

7.0 Introduction

In this chapter we are concerned with the effect of irregularities or "discontinuities" in media on waves. Depending on the point of view, the effect can be described as either "reflection" from discontinuities or "scattering" by discontinuities.

7.1 Reflection at a junction of transmission lines

In Chapter 4 we considered wave propagation in a uniform transmission line. The basic integral equations (4.11) and differential equations (4.22) are expressed in terms of two variables, the transverse voltage V and the longitudinal current I, which represent, in a gross sense, the intensities of the electric and magnetic fields associated with the transmission line. These equations also contain the *primary parameters*, the series impedance per unit length Z and the shunt admittance per unit length Y, which, in addition, are properties of fields in the large and from which the *secondary parameters* are obtained: the characteristic impedance K, equation (4.25), and the propagation constant Γ, equation (4.29). If we take a section of a transmission line and connect one pair of its terminals to a generator which impresses a voltage of some frequency on the line and the other pair of terminals to a device having impedance K, we shall find that the ratio V/I equals K at all points along the line and thus is independent of the length. Furthermore, the waves are traveling from the generator to the other end. Usually there is some dissipation of energy in the line so that the waves are attenuated with the increasing distance from the generator. In studying wave phenomena it is convenient to assume nondissipative lines and media so that $\Gamma = j\beta$, where the phase constant β equals the rate of change in the phase of V and I per unit length.

If the line is terminated into some impedance other than K, a

wave traveling from the impedance to the generator is originated,
equation (4.41). This is the reflected wave. Its amplitude and phase
in relation to the incident wave are expressed by the reflection coefficient, equation (4.42), depending on the difference between the
terminal impedance and the characteristic impedance.

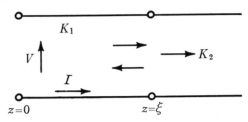

FIGURE 7.1   *Reflection of waves at a junction $z = \xi$ between transmission lines
with different characteristic impedances.*

In Figure 7.1 two uniform nondissipative transmission lines are
joined together. Let

$$K_1 = \sqrt{L_1/C_1}, \qquad K_2 = \sqrt{L_2/C_2},$$
$$\beta_1 = \omega\sqrt{L_1 C_1}, \qquad \beta_2 = \omega\sqrt{L_2 C_2}. \tag{7.1}$$

Assume that the second line is infinite or terminated in the characteristic impedance K_2 and that the generator is to the left of the
junction $z = \xi$. As far as the line to the left of $z = \xi$ is concerned,
the other line is just a device with impedance K_2. Hence from equations in Section 4.12 we obtain

$$I(z) = A \{\exp(-j\beta_1 z) + k \exp(-j\beta_1 \xi) \exp[-j\beta_1(\xi - z)]\}, \tag{7.2}$$

$$V(z) = K_1 A \{\exp(-j\beta_1 z) - k \exp(-j\beta_1 \xi) \exp[-j\beta_1(\xi - z)]\},$$

$$z \leq \xi,$$

where the reflection coefficient for the current wave (ratio of the
amplitudes of the reflected and incident waves) is

$$k = \frac{K_1 - K_2}{K_1 + K_2}. \tag{7.3}$$

Note that there is no reflection if $K_2 = K_1$ even though $\beta_2 \neq \beta_1$
so that the phase velocities in the two lines are different.

Both the voltage and the current must be continuous across the junction. Hence

$$I(z) = I(\xi) \exp\left[-j\beta_2(z - \xi)\right]$$

$$= A \exp\left(-j\beta_1\xi\right) p \exp\left[-j\beta_2(z - \xi)\right], \qquad z \geq \xi,$$

(7.4)

where the *transmission coefficient* for the current wave is

$$p = 1 + k = \frac{2K_1}{K_1 + K_2}.$$

(7.5)

Thus at the junction the amplitude of the incident current wave is multiplied by the transmission coefficient and then the wave continues to travel with a different velocity.

For the voltage wave we have

$$V(z) = K_2 I(z), \qquad z \geq \xi.$$

(7.6)

Hence

$$V(z) = K_1 A \exp\left(-j\beta_1\xi\right) q \exp\left[-j\beta_2(z - \xi)\right], \qquad z \geq \xi$$

(7.7)

where the transmission coefficient for the voltage wave is

$$q = 1 - k = \frac{2K_2}{K_1 + K_2}.$$

(7.8)

7.2   Reflection from a discontinuity in a transmission line

Any discontinuity in impedance gives rise to reflection. Consider a uniform transmission line and introduce a lumped impedance Z_l in series with the line at the point $z = \xi$, as illustrated in Figure 7.2. To solve this problem one could take advantage of short cuts which are developed in comprehensive treatments of networks and transmission lines. Here we use the basic principles from which the short

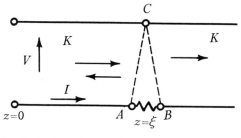

FIGURE 7.2   *Reflection of waves from an impedance discontinuity at point $z = \xi$.*

cuts are developed. The differential equations (4.22) assume continuous parameters and are valid on either side of the lumped impedance but not in the infinitesimal region including it. Thus we write separate solutions, with different arbitrary constants of integration, for $z < \xi$ and $z > \xi$ and join them together with appropriate boundary conditions. For $z < \xi$ we take equations (7.2) with the subscripts dropped and leave the reflection coefficient k arbitrary. To the right of the discontinuity we have

$$I(z) = Be^{-j\beta(z-\xi)},$$

$$V(z) = KBe^{-j\beta(z-\xi)}.$$

(7.9)

The current passing through the lumped impedance is a definite quantity so that it is continuous across the impedance discontinuity

$$I(\xi + 0) = I(\xi - 0).$$

(7.10)

Applying the Faraday–Maxwell law to the circuit $ABCA$ we have

$$V_{AB} + V_{BC} + V_{CA} = 0,$$

(7.11)

assuming that the physical dimensions of the lumped impedance are so small that the magnetic displacement currrent linked with the closed circuit is negligible. In this equation

$$V_{AB} = Z_l I(\xi), \qquad V_{BC} = V(\xi + 0), \qquad V_{CA} = -V(\xi - 0). \quad (7.12)$$

By substituting in equation (7.11) and rearranging the terms, we find

$$V(\xi + 0) - V(\xi - 0) = -Z_l I(\xi).$$

(7.13)

Equations (7.10) and (7.13) are the boundary conditions from which k and B can be determined. Thus

$$B = A(1 + k)e^{-j\beta\xi},$$

$$KB - KA(1 - k)e^{-j\beta\xi} = -Z_l B.$$

The second equation may be written as

$$(K + Z_l)B = KA(1 - k)e^{-j\beta\xi}.$$

Dividing by the first equation, we obtain

$$K + Z_l = K \frac{1 - k}{1 + k}.$$

so that,

$$k = -\frac{Z_l}{2K + Z_l}. \tag{7.14}$$

Therefore

$$B = A \frac{2K}{2K + Z_l} e^{-j\beta\xi}. \tag{7.15}$$

Naturally the reflection coefficient is independent of the amplitude A of the incident wave. The amplitude of the transmitted wave equals the amplitude of the incident wave multiplied by a certain transmission coefficient.

7.3 Reflection of plane waves at normal incidence

Waves generated by a current element are spherical (see Section 5.8). Waves generated by any current distribution in a finite region are obtained by superposition of such spherical waves. Thus they are also waves expanding in all directions; at large distances their amplitudes are inversely proportional to the distance from some point in the region occupied by the sources. If we consider only a *limited* region of space at large distances from the origin of waves, the waves appear essentially plane and uniform. Their amplitudes appear constant over a *wavefront*, that is, a surface of constant phase. Their amplitudes also appear constant in the direction of propagation. In such a region equations (5.25) can be written as follows:

$$H_y = H_0 e^{-j\beta z}, \qquad E_x = \eta H_y,$$

$$\eta = \sqrt{\mu/\epsilon}, \qquad \beta = \omega\sqrt{\mu\epsilon}. \tag{7.16}$$

Here the Cartesian coordinates have been substituted for the spherical: x for θ, y for φ, and z for r.

It is much easier to solve certain important problems for plane waves than to solve them for spherical waves. For this reason the concept of uniform plane waves is very important even though such waves cannot be realized physically except in a restricted

region—and even there only approximately. One such problem is
that of reflection of waves from a plane interface between two semi-
infinite media. First, let us consider the case of normal incidence.
See Figure 7.3. Equations (7.16) are so similar to the equations
for the current and voltage in a transmission line [equations (4.30)

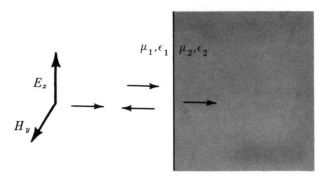

FIGURE 7.3   *Reflection of uniform plane waves incident normally on
the interface between two homogeneous semi-infinite media.*

and (4.33)] that we can write the answer to the problem from the
results obtained in Section 7.1. The magnetic intensity corresponds to
the current (per unit length), the electric intensity to the voltage
(per unit length), and the intrinsic impedance η to the characteristic
impedance K. Thus from equation (7.3) we obtain the reflection
coefficient for H,

$$k = \frac{\eta_1 - \eta_2}{\eta_1 + \eta_2} \tag{7.17}$$

and from equation (7.5) the corresponding transmission coefficient,

$$p = \frac{2\eta_1}{\eta_1 + \eta_2}. \tag{7.18}$$

If the interface is in the plane $z = 0$, the equations for H and E are

$$H_y = H_0 \exp(-j\beta_1 z) + kH_0 \exp(j\beta_1 z), \quad z \leq 0$$
$$= pH_0 \exp(-j\beta_2 z), \quad z \geq 0,$$
$$\tag{7.19}$$

$$E_x = \eta_1 H_0 \exp(-j\beta_1 z) - k\eta_1 H_0 \exp(j\beta_1 z), \quad z \leq 0$$
$$= \eta_2 pH_0 \exp(-j\beta_2 z), \quad z \geq 0.$$

These equations satisfy the boundary conditions at $z = 0$ which require the continuity of E_x and H_y.

7.4 Reflection of plane waves at oblique incidence

In the case of oblique incidence, as shown in Figure 7.4, let the magnetic vector be parallel to the interface. Equations (7.16) for

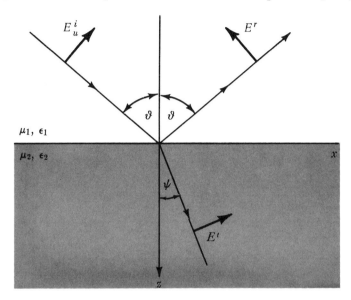

FIGURE 7.4 *Reflection and refraction at oblique incidence.*

the incident wave may be written as follows:

$$H_y^i = H_0 \exp(-j\beta_1 s), \qquad E_u^i = \eta_1 H_y^i, \qquad (7.20)$$

where s is taken in the direction of propagation and u is at right angles to it and to the y axis (which comes out of the paper). If ϑ is the *angle of incidence*, as shown in Figure 7.4, then

$$s = x \sin \vartheta + z \cos \vartheta. \qquad (7.21)$$

Thus

$$H_y^i = H_0 \exp[-j\beta_1(x \sin \vartheta + z \cos \vartheta)]. \qquad (7.22)$$

The components of the incident electric vector in the x and z directions are

$$E_x^i = E_u^i \cos \vartheta = \eta_1 H_0 \cos \vartheta \exp[-j\beta_1(x \sin \vartheta + z \cos \vartheta)],$$

$$(7.23)$$

$$E_z^i = -E_u^i \sin \vartheta = -\eta_1 H_0 \sin \vartheta \exp[-j\beta_1(x \sin \vartheta + z \cos \vartheta)].$$

This wave impinges on the interface and excites waves below it which are traveling away from the interface $z = 0$. The tangential components of $\bar{E}$ and $\bar{H}$ must be continuous at the interface *at all points.* This condition cannot be satisfied unless the field in the lower medium is proportional to

$$\exp\,(-j\beta_1 x \sin \vartheta). \tag{7.24}$$

From the situations considered in the previous sections we conclude that, in general, we cannot satisfy *both* continuity conditions without a wave originating at the interface and traveling away from it in the upper medium. Physically this means that the waves excited in the lower medium will generate, in their turn, reflected waves in the upper medium. The field intensities of the latter should also be proportional to the quantity (7.24).

For the reflected waves we can write immediately

$$H_y^r = kH_0 \exp\,[-j\beta_1(x \sin \vartheta - z \cos \vartheta)], \tag{7.25}$$

where the reflection coefficient k is yet to be determined. This expression has the required dependence on x and it represents a wave moving away from the interface. The reflected wave is just another uniform plane wave and the *angle of reflection equals the angle of incidence.*

The $\bar{E}$ vector must be normal to $\bar{H}$ and to the direction of propagation and, if $\bar{H}$ is coming out of the paper, the $\bar{E}$ vector's direction should be as indicated in Figure 7.4. Thus

$$E_x^r = -\eta_1 kH_0 \cos \vartheta \exp\,[-j\beta_1(x \sin \vartheta - z \cos \vartheta)],$$

$$E_z^r = -\eta_1 kH_0 \sin \vartheta \exp\,[-j\beta_1(x \sin \vartheta - z \cos \vartheta)]. \tag{7.26}$$

We know that the field in the lower medium is proportional to the quantity (7.24) and that the wave is traveling away from the interface. Thus for the transmitted wave we assume

$$H_y^t = pH_0 \exp\,(-j\beta_1 x \sin \vartheta) \exp\,(-j\beta_z z), \tag{7.27}$$

where p is the transmission coefficient and β_z is the phase constant in the z direction. To determine this constant we turn to Maxwell's equations (Appendix II) and set $\partial/\partial y = 0$. Thus

$$\frac{\partial E_x}{\partial z} - \frac{\partial E_z}{\partial x} = -j\omega\mu_2 H_y$$

$$\frac{\partial H_y}{\partial z} = -j\omega\epsilon_2 E_x, \qquad \frac{\partial H_y}{\partial x} = j\omega\epsilon_2 E_z. \tag{7.28}$$

Substituting from the last two equations into the first, we have

$$\frac{\partial^2 H_y}{\partial x^2} + \frac{\partial^2 H_y}{\partial z^2} = -\beta_2^2 H_y, \qquad \beta_2 = \omega\sqrt{\mu_2 \epsilon_2}. \qquad (7.29)$$

Substituting from equation (7.27), we find

$$-\beta_1^2 \sin^2 \vartheta - \beta_z^2 = -\beta_2^2$$

and

$$\beta_z = \sqrt{\beta_2^2 - \beta_1^2 \sin^2 \vartheta}. \qquad (7.30)$$

For β_z we take the positive sign to assure that the wave described in equation (7.27) is traveling away from the interface. The component of $\bar{E}$ parallel to the interface may be obtained from equations (7.27) and (7.28)

$$E_x = (\beta_z/\omega\epsilon_2) pH_0 \exp\left[-j\beta_1 x \sin \vartheta - j\beta_z z\right]. \qquad (7.31)$$

The coefficients k and p can now be determined from the continuity of the tangential field components

$$H_y^i(x, -0) + H_y^r(x, -0) = H_y^t(x, +0)$$

$$E_x^i(x, -0) + E_x^r(x, -0) = E_x^t(x, +0)$$

or

$$H_0 + kH_0 = pH_0$$

$$\eta_1 H_0 \cos \vartheta - \eta_1 kH_0 \cos \vartheta = (\beta_z/\omega\epsilon_2) pH_0.$$

Hence

$$k = \frac{\eta_1 \cos \vartheta - (\beta_z/\omega\epsilon_2)}{\eta_1 \cos \vartheta + (\beta_z/\omega\epsilon_2)} \qquad (7.32)$$

$$p = 1 + k,$$

where β_z is given by equation (7.30).

Depending on the parameters of the media and the angle of incidence, the phase constant β_z can be either real or imaginary. When it is real, the transmitted wave described in equation (7.27) is a uniform plane wave since its amplitude $|pH_0|$ is constant. Thus we assume that it is a wave traveling at some angle ψ to the normal, as shown in Figure 7.4. This is the *angle of refraction*. In optics the transmitted wave is called the *refracted wave*. Thus we rewrite equation (7.27) as

$$H_y^t = pH_0 \exp\left[-j\beta_2(x \sin \psi + z \cos \psi)\right]. \qquad (7.33)$$

Of course, this means that

$$\beta_2 \sin \psi = \beta_1 \sin \vartheta$$

and

$$\beta_2 \cos \psi = \beta_z = \sqrt{\beta_2^2 - \beta_1^2 \sin^2 \vartheta}. \tag{7.34}$$

Both β_1 and β_2 are proportional to ω. Canceling ω, we have

$$\sin \psi = n \sin \vartheta, \qquad n = \sqrt{\mu_1 \epsilon_1 / \mu_2 \epsilon_2}$$

and

$$\cos \psi = \sqrt{1 - n^2 \sin^2 \vartheta}. \tag{7.35}$$

When vacuum is the lower medium, the quantity n is called the *refractive index* of the upper medium. Otherwise it may be called the *relative* refractive index.

The coefficient of reflection can now be expressed as

$$k = \frac{\eta_1 \cos \vartheta - \eta_2 \cos \psi}{\eta_1 \cos \vartheta + \eta_2 \cos \psi}. \tag{7.36}$$

We have seen that the coefficient of reflection given by equation (7.17) at normal incidence is analogous to that in transmission lines, equation (7.3), where it equals the ratio of the difference between two characteristic impedances to their sum. The present equation is also of this form. In fact, *it could have been derived immediately if one had recognized that a uniform plane wave traveling at an angle to the interface can be considered as a phase pattern,* $\exp(-j\beta_1 x \sin \vartheta)$, *traveling normally to the interface.* The *wave impedance normal to the interface* would then be

$$\frac{E_x^i}{H_y^i} = \eta_1 \cos \vartheta. \tag{7.37}$$

Similarly for the transmitted wave

$$\frac{E_x^t}{H_y^t} = \eta_2 \cos \psi.$$

The relation between ϑ and ψ would still have to be determined from the field equations; but the entire derivation would have been much shorter. Furthermore the concept of wave impedance enables one to write the expression for the reflection coefficient when the lower medium is stratified. Thus a great degree of generality can be attained. However, the value of this concept would not have been appreciated without the straightforward analysis based on first principles.

There is an important special case in which $k = 0$ and there is no reflection. This happens when

$$\eta_1 \cos \vartheta = \eta_2 \cos \psi.$$

From this and equation (7.35) we find the angle of incidence

$$\sin \vartheta = \sqrt{\frac{1 - (\mu_2 \epsilon_1 / \mu_1 \epsilon_2)}{1 - (\epsilon_1 / \epsilon_2)^2}}.$$

When $\mu_2 = \mu_1$, this simplifies to

$$\sin \vartheta = \frac{1}{\sqrt{1 + (\epsilon_1 / \epsilon_2)}} = \frac{1}{\sqrt{1 + n^2}} \qquad (7.38)$$

and

$$\sin \psi = \frac{n}{\sqrt{1 + n^2}}.$$

The angle of incidence for which there is no reflection is called the *Brewster angle*.

Equation (7.35) indicates that there may exist a certain critical angle ϑ_c for which the angle of refraction ψ is 90° so the transmitted wave is traveling parallel to the interface. This angle is given by

$$\sin \vartheta_c = 1/n. \qquad (7.39)$$

This can happen only when $n > 1$. In such a case, $\cos \psi$ and β_z are imaginary for any angle of incidence greater than ϑ_c. Equation (7.33) indicates that the transmitted wave will then be attenuated exponentially as the distance from the interface increases. In the expression (7.36) for the reflection coefficient the numerator and denominator become conjugate complex. Thus the absolute value of k is unity, and the amplitude of the reflected wave equals the amplitude of the incident wave. This is *total reflection*.

So far our discussion has applied to incident uniform plane waves with the magnetic vector *parallel* to the interface, as had been assumed in the beginning of this section. A similar analysis can be made for the case in which the electric vector is parallel to the interface. In the formula for the reflection coefficient the cosines will be replaced by the secants as the concept of normal wave impedance immediately indicates. When neither $\bar{E}$ nor $\bar{H}$ is parallel to the interface, the wave can be resolved in two components, one with $\bar{E}$ parallel to the interface and the other with $\bar{H}$ so disposed.

7.5 Waves at grazing incidence over imperfect ground

A perfectly conducting plane introduced at a right angle to the electric vector in a uniform plane wave does not perturb the field. Thus a uniform plane wave may skim the surface of such a plane, as shown in Figure 7.5(a), and in vacuum

$$H_y = H_0 \exp\ (-j\beta_0 z), \qquad E_x = \eta_0 H_0 \exp\ (-j\beta_0 z),$$

$$\beta_0 = \omega\sqrt{\mu_0\epsilon_0}, \qquad \eta_0 = \sqrt{\mu_0/\epsilon_0}. \tag{7.40}$$

An imperfectly conducting plane, on the other hand, *does* perturb the field since H_y implies that an electric current is in the direction of propagation and therefore has a driving electric intensity E_z. Thus if the medium below the plane $x = 0$ is a homogeneous dissipative medium, there must exist a component of $\bar{E}$ in the direction of propagation. Propagation in such a medium was discussed in Section 4.16 and the relation between $\bar{E}$ and $\bar{H}$ at the interface was obtained in Section 6.12, equation (6.108). In the present case this equation becomes

$$E_z = \eta_c H_y, \qquad \eta_c = \sqrt{j\omega\mu/(\sigma_c + j\omega\epsilon)}. \tag{7.41}$$

The dielectric constant, whose effect is negligible in metals at frequencies below 10^{12} cycles per second, should not be neglected in the case of soils. Hence

$$E_z/E_x = \eta_c/\eta_0. \tag{7.42}$$

In obtaining this ratio it was assumed that the field given by equations (7.40) is not affected except for the appearance of E_z at and near the surface. The assumption is reasonable as long as the absolute value of the ratio given in equation (7.42) is small compared with unity which is the case of sea water and various soils.

Equation (7.42) indicates that the electric vector is inclined toward the interface. Since E_z and E_x are not in phase, their resultant will rotate during the cycle. It may be shown that this resultant will describe a narrow ellipse, Figure 7.5(a).

7.6 Wave antenna

An interesting application of the wave tilt over ground is a *wave antenna* consisting of a long wire parallel to the ground, Figure 7.5(b). This wire and the ground form a transmission line. Let us suppose that this line is terminated by its characteristic impedance K

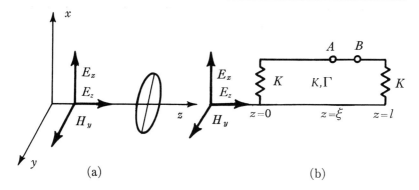

FIGURE 7.5   (a) *Wave tilt at grazing incidence; (b) a wave antenna.*

at both ends. The longitudinal field of a wave skimming the ground will be impressed on the wire. The voltage impressed on a typical element AB of the wire at $z = \xi$ may be obtained from equations (7.40) and (7.41). Thus

$$V_{AB} = E_z(\xi)\, d\xi = \eta_c H_0 \exp\,(-j\beta_0\xi)\, d\xi.$$

This voltage sees impedance K in both directions, that is, the total impedance $2K$. Hence the current through AB due to this voltage will be

$$dI(\xi) = (\eta_c/2K) H_0 \exp\,(-j\beta_0\xi)\, d\xi.$$

This current is propagated in both directions. Thus at point z

$$dI(\xi, z) = (\eta_c/2K) H_0 \exp\,(-j\beta_0\xi) \exp\,[-\Gamma(z-\xi)]\, d\xi, \qquad z \geq \xi$$

$$= (\eta_c/2K) H_0 \exp\,(-j\beta_0\xi) \exp\,[-\Gamma(\xi-z)]\, d\xi, \qquad z \leq \xi;$$

that is,

$$dI(\xi, z) = (\eta_c/2K) H_0 \exp\,[(\Gamma - j\beta_0)\xi]\, e^{-\Gamma z}\, d\xi, \qquad z \geq \xi$$

$$= (\eta_c/2K) H_0 \exp\,[-(\Gamma + j\beta_0)\xi]\, e^{\Gamma z}\, d\xi, \qquad z \leq \xi.$$

The propagation constant Γ is complex since the wire and ground have resistance. Its imaginary part, however, is nearly equal to $j\beta_0$, particularly at high frequencies. Thus in the forward direction the induced currents add in phase. In the backward direction they tend to cancel. At $z = l$ the total current is

$$I(l) = (\eta_c/2K)H_0 e^{-\Gamma l} \int_0^l \exp\left[(\Gamma - j\beta_0)\xi\right] d\xi$$

$$= (\eta_c/2K)H_0 e^{-\Gamma l} \frac{\exp\left[(\Gamma - j\beta_0)l\right] - 1}{\Gamma - j\beta_0}.$$

If Γ is equal to $\alpha + j\beta_0$,

$$I(l) = (\eta_c/2K)H_0 e^{-j\beta_0 l} \frac{1 - e^{-\alpha l}}{\alpha}.$$

When α is small, αl may be small even if l is large. Then

$$I(l) = (\eta_c/2K)H_0 \exp\left(-j\beta_0 l\right) l.$$

The current through the impedance K at $z = l$ will be proportional to the length of the wire.

Thus power may be abstracted from a passing wave. Note that more power will be received when η_c is relatively large and none when $\eta_c = 0$. The wave antenna works better over poor ground than over good ground. The antenna would be inoperative over perfect ground.

7.7 Scattering by a discontinuity in a transmission line

There is another method for obtaining the effect of a discontinuity on wave propagation in a transmission line. See Figure 7.2. If instead of the lumped impedance AB there were a generator, the generator would start waves in both directions. Similarly the voltage across the lumped impedance also generates waves in both directions. These waves are called *scattered waves*. They are superimposed on the

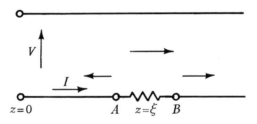

FIGURE 7.6 *Scattering of waves by an impedance discontinuity.*

original incident or *primary* wave, Figure 7.6. From this point of view the equations for the primary wave are

$$I^p(z) = Ae^{-j\beta z},$$
$$V^p(z) = KAe^{-j\beta z} \tag{7.43}$$

on either side of the discontinuity. For the scattered wave we have

$$I^s(z) = Be^{-j\beta(z-\xi)}, \qquad z \geq \xi$$
$$= Be^{-j\beta(\xi-z)}, \qquad z \leq \xi, \tag{7.44}$$

where B is the scattered current through the discontinuity. The corresponding voltages are

$$V^s(z) = KB \exp\left[-j\beta(z - \xi)\right], \qquad z > \xi$$
$$= -KB \exp\left[-j\beta(\xi - z)\right], \qquad z < \xi. \tag{7.45}$$

In this approach the continuity of current, equation (7.10), is satisfied automatically since the primary current is continuous. The total current through the lumped impedance Z_l is

$$I^p(\xi) + I^s(\xi) = Ae^{-j\beta\xi} + B.$$

The voltage discontinuity in the boundary condition (7.13) equals $2KB$ since the primary voltage is continuous. Thus

$$2KB = -Z_l(Ae^{-j\beta\xi} + B)$$

and

$$B = -\frac{Z_l}{2K + Z_l} Ae^{-j\beta\xi}. \tag{7.46}$$

To the left of the discontinuity the scattered wave and reflected wave are identical. Hence the coefficient of A in equation (7.46) is the reflection coefficient. This agrees with equation (7.14). To the right of the discontinuity the transmitted wave equals the sum of the primary and scattered waves. This agrees with equation (7.15) (note that the B in this equation equals $A \exp(-j\beta\xi) + B$ in this section).

This approach is particularly good when the discontinuity is small and one is interested only in the first-order effect. The argument would run as follows: In the first rough approximation the primary wave is not affected by the discontinuity and the current through it is

$$Ae^{-j\beta\xi}.$$

Therefore the voltage drop across it is

$$V_{AB} = Z_l A e^{-j\beta\xi}.$$

This is equivalent to a generator with a voltage

$$-Z_l A e^{-j\beta\xi}$$

driving current in the positive z direction. The impedance seen by this generator is $2K$. Hence the current through the discontinuity due to this voltage is

$$- (Z_l/2K) A e^{-j\beta\xi}.$$

This is the scattered current B, which agrees with equation (7.46) to the extent that Z_l is negligible in comparison with $2K$.

7.8 Scattering by a small perfectly conducting sphere in free space

Consider a small perfectly conducting sphere of radius a in the path of a uniform plane wave, as shown in Figure 7.7. By "small" we mean that the difference in the phase of the wave at any given instant is

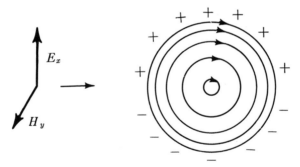

FIGURE 7.7 *Scattering of waves by a small conducting sphere is due to a fluctuating charge as in an electric dipole and to circulating currents as in a ring.*

negligible over the volume occupied by the sphere. Thus it may be assumed that the sphere is in a uniform electric field of intensity E_0 and a uniform magnetic field of intensity H_0, where E_0 and H_0 are the field intensities of the incident wave at the center of the sphere. Under the influence of E_0 electric charge will be displaced up and down with the frequency of the wave and the sphere will become an oscillating dipole. Its electric field is given by equation (5.24). If $\beta a \ll 1$, the field in the vicinity of the sphere varies with the distance r from the center as if it were an electrostatic field. In Section 2.4 we determined the electrostatic moment of this dipole, equation (2.21). The moment of the corresponding current element equals the time derivative of the electrostatic moment

$$j\omega 4\pi\epsilon_0 a^3 E_0.$$

Substituting this for Il in equations (5.23) and (5.24), we obtain the field of the electrically polarized sphere which is a part of the total scattered field.

The other part of the scattered field is due to H_0. At the surface of the sphere the radial component H_r of H_0 must vanish. Hence there must be circulating currents on the sphere which produce an equal and opposite radial magnetic field. The sphere becomes an oscillating magnetic dipole. Its moment may be obtained by a method similar to that in Section 2.4. The moment is

$$-j\omega 2\pi\mu_0 a^3 H_0$$

in the y direction.

In the case of a sphere more exact expressions for the dipole moments can be obtained. Indeed, the exact scattered field for a sphere of any radius can be calculated. The present approximate method, however, applies to small obstacles of shapes for which the exact field is impossible to find while the corresponding electrostatic and magnetostatic problems can be solved.

7.9 Scattering by a small perfectly conducting sphere above a perfectly conducting plane

The method in the preceding section applies to more complex situations such as the one shown in Figure 7.8 where a uniform plane wave strikes a perfectly conducting plane with a small sphere above it. Here the primary wave, impinging on the sphere, is the resultant of the wave incident on the plane and that reflected from it. At the center of the sphere there are two components of $\vec{E}$, one vertical and the other horizontal. Thus the sphere will act as two electric oscillating dipoles and a magnetic dipole. The waves generated by these dipoles are reflected from the plane. The reflected waves will appear to be coming from dipoles on an image sphere. The image of the vertical dipole is in the same direction as the dipole. The same is true of the image of the horizontal magnetic dipole. The image of the horizontal electric dipole is in the opposite direction. These conclusions are drawn from the fact that at the reflecting plane the tan-

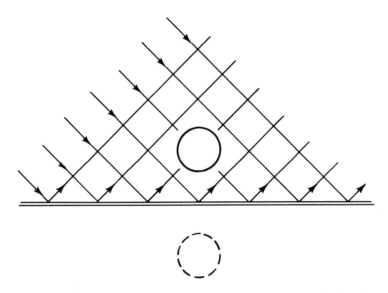

FIGURE 7.8 *Scattering of waves by a small sphere above a conducting plane.*

gential electric intensity must vanish. Since the dipoles have end charges we can use the results of Section 2.12. The currents have to follow suit.

The reflected dipole fields will act on the sphere just as the primary wave did. However, their fields are relatively weak.

7.10 Scattering by a long rectangular loop

In the problem of scattering by a sphere we calculated the electric dipole moment from the electric intensity of the incident wave and suggested that the magnetic dipole moment due to the circulating currents could be obtained from the magnetic intensity. This is the quickest method for small obstacles. Both moments can be obtained from the electric intensity: the electric dipole moment from the incident $\bar{E}$ at the center of the sphere and the magnetic dipole moment from the change in $\bar{E}$ from the near end of the sphere to the far end. Thus in the vicinity of the sphere with the center at $z = 0$, we have

$$E_0 e^{-j\beta z} = E_0 - j\beta E_0 z + \cdots. \tag{7.47}$$

The first term drives the charge up and down. The second term has opposite signs at $z = -a$ and $z = a$ so that it drives the charge round

the sphere. This term is small in comparison with the first but it is
easier to drive the current in a closed conducting path, as in a coil,
than in an open path, as in a capacitor.

To illustrate these points we shall consider a narrow rectangular
loop of length l large in comparison with the separation s between
the axes of the long wires, Figure 7.9(a). Let the field at the center

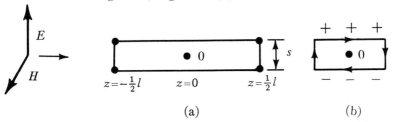

(a)   (b)

FIGURE 7.9   *Scattering by (a) a two-wire line shorted at both ends and (b) by a
small loop.*

of the loop be E_0 and H_0. The voltages *impressed* by the incident wave
on the short sides of the loop at $z = -\tfrac{1}{2}l$ and $z = +\tfrac{1}{2}l$ are, respectively,

$$V_1 = E_0 s \exp\left(j\beta l/2\right), \qquad V_2 = E_0 s \exp(-j\beta l/2). \qquad (7.48)$$

No voltage is impressed on either of the long sides since there is no
component of $\vec{E}$ tangential to them. As long as $l \gg s$, the loop is a
parallel wire transmission line. Let us assume that the dissipation in
the line is negligible and that its characteristic impedance is $K = (L/C)^{\frac{1}{2}}$. The phase constant $\beta = \omega(LC)^{\frac{1}{2}} = \omega(\mu\epsilon)^{\frac{1}{2}}$ equals that of a
plane wave. Hence

$$I(z) = Ae^{-j\beta z} + Be^{j\beta z},$$

$$V(z) = KAe^{-j\beta z} - KBe^{j\beta z}.$$

The total voltage across the short sides must vanish. Therefore

$$KAe^{j\beta l/2} - KBe^{-j\beta l/2} = -V_1,$$

$$KAe^{-j\beta l/2} - KB^{j\beta l/2} = -V_2.$$

Solving for A and B and substituting from equations (7.48), we have

$$A = -E_0 s/K, \qquad B = 0,$$

and

$$I(z) = -(E_0 s/K)e^{-j\beta z}, \qquad V(z) = -E_0 s e^{-j\beta z}. \qquad (7.49)$$

Suppose now that $\beta l/2 \ll 1$ or $l/\lambda \ll 1/\pi$; then

$$I(z) \simeq -E_0 s/K, \qquad V(z) \simeq -E_0 s. \qquad (7.50)$$

That is, the incident wave will induce a uniform current round the "small" loop, Figure 7.9(b), and equal and opposite uniform charge distributions on the longer sides of the loop. If C is the capacitance per unit length, the total charge on the upper wire is $ClsE_0$ and the electrostatic moment of the electric dipole is Cls^2E_0. The area moment of the circulating current is $-lsI = -ls^2E_0/K$, and the equivalent magnetic dipole moment is $-\mu ls^2E_0/K$.

Let us now calculate the current in the loop directly from the magnetic intensity H_0 at the center of the loop. By the Ampere-Maxwell law the induced electromotive force equals $-j\omega\mu lsH_0$. To obtain the current we divide this by the inductive reactance of the loop $j\omega Ll$. Hence

$$I = -\mu H_0 s/L = -\mu\eta^{-1}E_0s/L = -(\mu\epsilon)^{+\frac{1}{2}}E_0s/L = -E_0s/K$$

since

$$LC = \mu\epsilon \quad \text{and} \quad K^2 = L/C,$$

and, therefore,

$$L = K(\mu\epsilon)^{\frac{1}{2}}, \qquad C = (\mu\epsilon)^{\frac{1}{2}}/K. \tag{7.51}$$

The result agrees with equation (7.50).

If we calculate the second term in the power series for the exponential function in the expression (7.49) for $I(z)$, we shall obtain the charging current associated with the electric dipole. This current is small in comparison with the circulating current.

Once we have found the current and charge distributions we can obtain the local and distant fields either with the aid of retarded potentials (5 48) or from equations (5.9) and (5.23). The distant field can be calculated from equations (5 25).

7.11   Scattering by a short wire

In Section 2.3 we obtained the distribution of charge displaced on a thin wire by an electric field parallel to the wire. If $q(z)$ is the charge per unit length at distance z from the center, the moment of two elementary charges $q(z)\,dz$ and $q(-z)\,dz = -q(z)\,dz$ is $2zq(z)\,dz$. The total moment is the integral of the elementary moment from $z = 0$ to $z = l$. The time rate of change of this moment is the moment of the equivalent current element which can be substituted in equations (5.23) and (5.24) to obtain the distant field scattered by a short thin wire in the path of a uniform plane wave. See Figure 7.10.

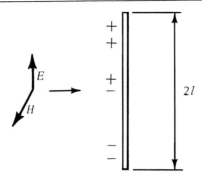

FIGURE 7.10   *A wave impinging on a short thin wire makes it an electric dipole.*

7.12   Scattering by a half-wave wire

In Section 5.12 we concluded that the current and transverse voltage on thin diverging wires (see Figure 5.11) are given essentially by the principal waves. The equations of propagation of principal waves are the same for diverging and parallel wires. For parallel wires the inductance and capacitance per unit length are constant while for diverging wires they vary with the distance from the origin A, B [see equation (5.32)]. The functions involved are logarithmic and hence slowly varying. Thus, they may be approximated by their average values [see equation (5.33)]. Therefore the approximate voltage and current in diverging wires satisfy uniform transmission line equations (Chapter 4).

In the problem of scattering of waves by a wire of arbitrary length $2l$, as shown in Figure 7.11(a), in the path of a plane wave, the current distribution has to be determined first. If the electric intensity at the wire is E_0, the voltage impressed on a typical element of the wire is $E_0\,dz$, that is, $2E_0\,dz$ on two elements equidistant from the center of the wire A, B. This represents an increase in the transverse voltage when z is increased to $z + dz$. At A, B the wire may be continuous, or broken, or have some resistance or impedance as in a receiving antenna. Let us assume that it is continuous. Figure 7.11(b) illustrates the analogous problem for parallel wires. If z is the distance from A, B the equations for the voltage and current are

$$\frac{dV}{dz} = -j\omega LI + 2E_0, \qquad \frac{dI}{dz} = -j\omega CV. \qquad (7.52)$$

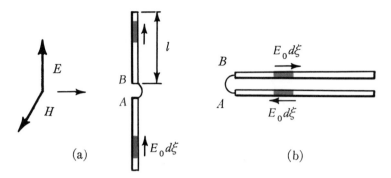

FIGURE 7.11 *Illustrating an approximate calculation of the induced charge and current distribution in* (a) *a thin wire of any length by comparing the wire with* (b) *a two-wire transmission line with voltages impressed in series.*

Eliminating V, we have

$$\frac{d^2 I}{dz^2} = -\beta^2 I - 2j\omega C E_0, \qquad \beta = \omega\sqrt{LC} = \omega\sqrt{\mu\epsilon}. \qquad (7.53)$$

This is a nonhomogeneous differential equation and its general solution is the sum of its particular solution and the general solution of the homogeneous equation ($E_0 = 0$). Equation (7.53) is satisfied by a constant $I = I_0$ which may be found from

$$-\beta^2 I_0 - 2j\omega C E_0 = 0.$$

Thus

$$I_0 = 2E_0/j\omega L.$$

Hence the general solution is

$$I(z) = A \cos \beta z + B \sin \beta z + \frac{2E_0}{j\omega L},$$

$$V(z) = \frac{\beta A}{j\omega C} \sin \beta z - \frac{\beta B}{j\omega C} \cos \beta z.$$

Since $V(0) = 0$ and $I(l) = 0$, we find

$$B = 0, \qquad A = -\frac{2E_0}{j\omega L \cos \beta l},$$

and

$$I(z) = -\frac{2E_0}{j\omega L \cos \beta l} \cos \beta z + \frac{2E_0}{j\omega L}. \qquad (7.54)$$

From this current distribution we can obtain the scattered field.

This field will be approximate since the equations for V and I are based on the assumptions that the wire is so thin that only the principal waves need be considered and that the residual field and hence the radiation may be neglected *as far as their effect on the current distribution is concerned*. The effect of radiation becomes particularly important when the length of the wire equals $\lambda/2$. In this case the first term in equation (7.54) becomes infinite. If the resistance of the wire had been included, the amplitude would have been large but finite. However, for good conductors the resistance of the wire is not an important factor in limiting the amplitude of current. It is the radiation resistance that is important. We may take it into consideration as follows.

As βl approaches $\pi/2$, the first term in equation (7.54) becomes more and more dominant. Thus we expect that when $\beta l = \pi/2$ and the length of the wire is equal to one half of a wavelength, the current is given essentially by the sinusoidal term

$$I(z) = C \cos \beta z \tag{7.55}$$

of some amplitude C. The dotted line in Figure 7.12 shows the shape

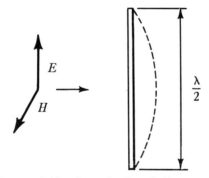

FIGURE 7.12   *Scattering by a half-wave wire.*

of this distribution. If E_0 is the incident electric intensity at the wire, the average work done per second by it, when driving the current, is

$$P = \tfrac{1}{2} \int_{-\lambda/4}^{\lambda/4} E_0 C^* \cos \beta z \, dz = \frac{\lambda}{2\pi} E_0 C^*. \tag{7.56}$$

This must equal the radiated power which for this current distribution is given by equation (5.43),

$$P = 36.55 \, CC^*. \tag{7.57}$$

By equating the two expressions, we find

$$C = \frac{\lambda E_0}{73.1\pi}$$

and

$$I(z) = \frac{\lambda E_0}{73.1\pi} \cos \beta z. \qquad (7.58)$$

The distant scattered field may be obtained from equation (5.42) by setting $I_0 = \lambda E_0/73.1\pi$.

Thus *at resonance* the induced current and the incident electric intensity are in phase and, sufficiently far off resonance, they are in quadrature [see equation (7.54)].

7.13   Scattering by a half-wave receiving antenna

Power may be absorbed from a plane wave if a wire is broken in the middle and the ends are connected to a resistance or, in general, to some impedance. See Figure 7.13. The maximum power is absorbed

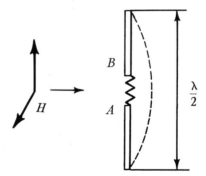

FIGURE 7.13   *Scattering by a half-wave receiving antenna.*

when this impedance is the conjugate of the impedance which would be seen by a generator across these ends when the antenna is used for radiating power. In such a case the reactance is "tuned out" and the resistances are "matched." The half-wave antenna already has zero reactance so that the load resistance should equal 73.1 ohms [see equation (5.44)]. The current in the half-wave antenna is still given by equation (7.55); the average work done by the incident field per second is given by equation (7.56). Part of this work is absorbed by the load and part is reradiated since the current in the antenna generates a spherical wave. Thus instead of equation (7.57) we have

$$P = 73.1 \, CC^*$$

and

$$I(z) = \frac{\lambda E_0}{146.2} \cos \beta z. \qquad (7.59)$$

The intensity of the scattered field, equation (5.42), is only half of that for a wire without a load.

7.14   Scattering in waveguides

Any obstacle in a waveguide, such as the wire in Figure 7.14, will perturb the field of a passing wave. The perturbation can be expressed as a series of modes and their amplitudes can be obtained from the boundary conditions at the surface of the obstacle.

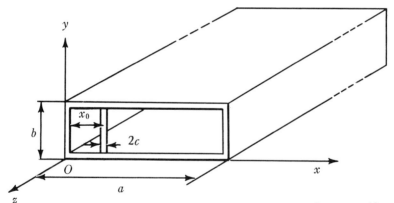

FIGURE 7.14   *Scattering by a transverse wire in a rectangular waveguide.*

Suppose that a dominant wave (TE$_{10}$) impinges on a perfectly conducting transverse wire of radius c. Let the maximum amplitude of this wave be A so that

$$E_y^i = A \exp(-j\beta_1 z) \sin(\pi x/a), \qquad \beta_1 = \sqrt{\beta^2 - (\pi/a)^2}. \qquad (7.60)$$

Assuming that the axis of the wire is at $z = 0$, we conclude that the scattered field will be of the form (6.113). Thus

$$E_y^s = - \sum_{m=1}^{\infty} E_m \exp\left(-\Gamma_m z\right) \sin\left(m\pi x/a\right), \qquad z \geq c,$$

(7.61)

$$= - \sum_{m=1}^{\infty} E_m \exp\left(\Gamma_m z\right) \sin\left(m\pi x/a\right), \qquad z \leq -c,$$

where

$$\Gamma_m = \sqrt{(m\pi/a)^2 - \beta^2}.$$

In the region $-c < z < c$ the field will consist of modes propagating in both directions because the current in the wire is distributed on its surface and it may be subdivided into infinitely thin current filaments, each of which excites modes propagating in opposite directions.

On the surface of the wire the total E_y must vanish. This is the condition from which the coefficients E_m will be determined. If the wire is thin, E_y^i and therefore E_y^s will be substantially uniform on its surface. One would expect that the scattered field due to current I in the wire is nearly equal to the field which would be generated if I were on the axis of the wire. Therefore, the coefficients in equation (7.61) are given approximately by equation (6.114), and outside the wire for $z \geq c$,

$$E_y^s = - \sum_{m=1}^{\infty} a^{-1} K_m I \exp\left(-\Gamma_m z\right) \sin\frac{m\pi x_0}{a} \sin\frac{m\pi x}{a}. \quad (7.62)$$

For $z \leq -c$, z should be replaced by $-z$. To the extent to which E_y^s is the same round the wire, it can be calculated at some point of our choosing, at point (x_0, c), for example. The intensity of the incident field will be taken equal to that on the axis of the wire

$$E_0 = A \sin\left(\pi x_0/a\right). \quad (7.63)$$

Thus from the boundary condition we have

$$E_0 = I \sum_{m=1}^{\infty} a^{-1} K_m \exp\left(-\Gamma_m c\right) \sin^2\left(m\pi x_0/a\right). \quad (7.64)$$

Thus I may be expressed in terms of either E_0 or A.

The ratio

$$Z = E_0 b/I = \sum_{m=1}^{\infty} (b/a) K_m \exp\left(-\Gamma_m c\right) \sin^2\left(m\pi x_0/a\right)$$

is the impedance seen from the wire. If $a < \lambda < 2a$, only the TE_{10} mode will be traveling. The remaining modes will be attenuated and will represent a local field associated with the current in the wire. Only K_1 will be real

$$K_1 = \omega\mu/\beta_1, \qquad K_m = j\omega\mu/\Gamma_m \quad \text{for} \quad m = 2, 3, \cdots.$$

Therefore

$$Z = R + jX,$$

where

$$R = \frac{\omega\mu b}{\beta_1 a} \sin^2 (\pi x_0/a) = \frac{\eta b}{a}\left[1 - \left(\frac{\lambda}{2a}\right)^2\right]^{-\frac{1}{2}} \sin^2 (\pi x_0/a),$$

$$(7.65)$$

$$jX = (j\omega\mu b/a) \sum_{m=2}^{\infty} \Gamma_m^{-1} \exp (-\Gamma_m c) \sin^2 (m\pi x_0/a).$$

To the wire each half of the guide will appear as a transmission line of characteristic impedance

$$K = 2R = \frac{2\eta b}{a}\left[1 - \left(\frac{\lambda}{2a}\right)^2\right]^{-\frac{1}{2}} \sin^2 (\pi x_0/a). \qquad (7.66)$$

The wire itself will have an inductive reactance X. See Figure 7.15.

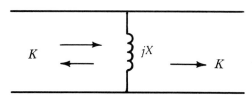

FIGURE 7.15 *Equivalent transmission line and shunt reactance representing the physical situation in Figure 7.14 under certain conditions.*

The series for X converges slowly. However, an approximate value may be obtained from the nearly static case and the correction term may be expressed as a more rapidly converging series. From equations (6.81) and (6.82), we have

$$E_y(x, z) = -\frac{j\omega\mu I}{\pi} \sum_{m=1}^{\infty} \frac{1}{m} e^{-m\pi z/a} \sin \frac{m\pi x_0}{a} \sin \frac{m\pi x}{a}. \qquad (7.67)$$

In this case, the reactance of the wire is

$$E_0 b/I = -E_y b/I = j\omega L_0,$$

$$L_0 = \frac{\mu b}{\pi} \sum_{m=1}^{\infty} \frac{1}{m} e^{-m\pi c/a} \sin^2 \frac{m\pi x_0}{a}. \qquad (7.68)$$

It is possible to sum the series (7.67). The product of the sines may be expressed in terms of exponential functions

$$\sin \frac{m\pi x_0}{a} \sin \frac{m\pi x}{a} = \tfrac{1}{2} \cos \frac{m\pi(x - x_0)}{a} - \tfrac{1}{2} \cos \frac{m\pi(x + x_0)}{a}$$

$$= \tfrac{1}{4} \exp \left[jm\pi(x - x_0)/a \right] + \cdots.$$

These exponentials we substitute in equation (7.67). Setting

$$w = \frac{\pi}{a}(z + jx), \qquad w_0 = \frac{j\pi x_0}{a}, \tag{7.69}$$

we obtain

$$E_y = -\frac{j\omega\mu I}{4\pi} \sum_{m=1}^{\infty} \frac{1}{m} \left\{ \exp \left[-m(w - w_0) \right] + \exp \left[-m(w^* - w_0^*) \right] \right.$$

$$\left. - \exp \left[-m(w + w_0) \right] - \exp \left[-m(w^* + w_0^*) \right] \right\}.$$

Since

$$\sum_{m=1}^{\infty} \frac{1}{m} p^m = -\ln(1 - p),$$

we have

$$E_y = -\frac{j\omega\mu I}{4\pi} \ln \frac{[1 - \exp(-w - w_0)][1 - \exp(-w^* - w_0^*)]}{[1 - \exp(-w + w_0)][1 - \exp(-w^* + w_0^*)]}$$

$$= -\frac{j\omega\mu I}{4\pi} \ln \frac{\sinh \tfrac{1}{2}(w + w_0) \sinh \tfrac{1}{2}(w^* + w_0^*)}{\sinh \tfrac{1}{2}(w - w_0) \sinh \tfrac{1}{2}(w^* - w_0^*)}$$

$$= -\frac{j\omega\mu I}{2\pi} \ln \frac{\sinh \tfrac{1}{2}|w + w_0|}{\sinh \tfrac{1}{2}|w - w_0|}. \tag{7.70}$$

From equations (7.69) we find

$$|w - w_0| = \frac{\pi}{a} \sqrt{z^2 + (x - x_0)^2} = \frac{\pi r_1}{a},$$

$$|w + w_0| = \frac{\pi}{a} \sqrt{z^2 + (x + x_0)^2} = \frac{\pi r_2}{a},$$

where r_1 and r_2 are, respectively, the distances from a typical point (x, z) to the point $(x_0, 0)$ through which the current filament is passing and from its mirror image in the plane $x = 0$ to the same point. Hence

$$E_y = -\frac{j\omega\mu I}{2\pi} \ln \frac{\sinh(\pi r_2/2a)}{\sinh(\pi r_1/2a)}. \qquad (7.71)$$

Setting $r_1 = c$ and $r_2 = 2x_0$, a closed form for the inductance of the wire is obtained at frequencies for which $\lambda \gg 2a$,

$$L_0 = \frac{\mu b}{2\pi} \ln \frac{\sinh(\pi x_0/a)}{\sinh(\pi c/2a)}. \qquad (7.72)$$

In this formula x_0 should be greater than $2c$. Otherwise the current distribution round the wire will depart too much from uniformity on account of the proximity to the wall of the guide. If $\pi x_0/a \ll 1$, the hyperbolic functions may be approximated by their arguments and

$$L_0 = \frac{\mu b}{2\pi} \ln \frac{2x_0}{c}. \qquad (7.73)$$

This is the inductance of the wire near a single conducting plane.

In our scattering problem $a < \lambda < 2a$. The major difference between the impedance (7.65) seen by the wire in this case and the low-frequency impedance (7.68) is in the first term of the series. In the low-frequency case the first term is reactive while for the frequencies we are considering it is resistive. The series for the reactance in equations (7.65) begins with $m = 2$. The first approximation to this reactance may be obtained by setting $\Gamma_m = m\pi/a$ for $m \geq 2$. Thus we obtain the series (7.68) except for the first term so that

$$jX = j\omega\left(L_0 - \frac{\mu b}{\pi} e^{-\pi c/a} \sin^2 \frac{\pi x_0}{a}\right). \qquad (7.74)$$

8

Coupled Oscillations

8.0 Introduction

Starting with oscillations in coupled circuits, we develop the idea of concentrated coupling between modes of oscillation in distributed circuits and then the idea of distributed coupling between such modes. This idea of coupling between modes of oscillation leads to the representation of structures with distributed circuit parameters by equivalent networks with lumped circuit parameters.

8.1 Oscillations in two coupled circuits

In Chapter 3, we considered several examples of a periodic transformation of electric energy into magnetic, and vice versa when the electric energy is concentrated mostly in one region and the magnetic energy in another. Next in complexity is the case of two separate concentrations of electric energy, Figure 8.1 (a, b). Case (a) suggests three separate coils with three corresponding concentrations of magnetic energy, one of which is common to both circuits. Case (b) suggests two coils with overlapping magnetic fields. The circuit equations are the same for both cases

$$\left(j\omega L_{11} + \frac{1}{j\omega C_{11}}\right) I_1 + j\omega L_{12} I_2 = 0,$$

$$j\omega L_{12} I_1 + \left(j\omega L_{22} + \frac{1}{j\omega C_{22}}\right) I_2 = 0, \qquad (8.1)$$

where in the first case $L_{11} = L_1 + L_M$, $L_{22} = L_2 + L_M$, and in the second, $L_{11} = L_1$, $L_{22} = L_2$. In both cases, $L_{12} = L_M$, $C_{11} = C_1$, and $C_{22} = C_2$.

From these equations we obtain the ratio of the currents

$$\frac{I_1}{I_2} = \frac{\omega^2 L_{12} C_{11}}{1 - \omega^2 L_{11} C_{11}} = \frac{1 - \omega^2 L_{22} C_{22}}{\omega^2 L_{12} C_{22}}. \qquad (8.2)$$

268

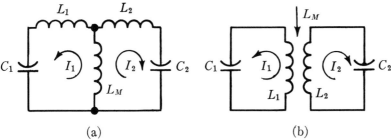

(a)   (b)

FIGURE 8.1   *Coupled circuits.*

Hence,

$$(\omega^2 L_{11} C_{11} - 1)(\omega^2 L_{22} C_{22} - 1) = \omega^4 L_{12}^2 C_{11} C_{22},$$

and

$$\omega_{1,2}^2 = \frac{L_{11} C_{11} + L_{22} C_{22} \pm \sqrt{(L_{11} C_{11} - L_{22} C_{22})^2 + 4 L_{12}^2 C_{11} C_{22}}}{2(L_{11} L_{22} - L_{12}^2) C_{11} C_{22}}. \quad (8.3)$$

There are two natural frequencies. For each frequency we may obtain the ratio of the currents in the two meshes from equation (8.2).

8.2   Beats

An important special case arises when the natural frequencies of two coupled circuits are equal in the absence of coupling

$$L_{11} C_{11} = L_{22} C_{22} = \omega_0^{-2}. \quad (8.4)$$

In this case, equation (8.3) becomes

$$\omega_{1,2}^2 = \frac{\omega_0^2 (1 \pm k)}{1 - k^2},$$

where

$$k = \frac{L_{12}}{\sqrt{L_{11} L_{22}}} \quad (8.5)$$

is the *coupling coefficient*. Hence,

$$\omega_1 = \frac{\omega_0}{\sqrt{1 - k}}, \qquad \omega_2 = \frac{\omega_0}{\sqrt{1 + k}}. \quad (8.6)$$

One of these natural frequencies is higher than the frequency of the uncoupled circuits, and the other is lower.

For the higher frequency ω_1 the current ratio is

$$I_1/I_2 = -\sqrt{L_{22}/L_{11}} = -p, \qquad (8.7)$$

and for the lower frequency

$$I_1/I_2 = \sqrt{L_{22}/L_{11}} = p. \qquad (8.8)$$

For the lower frequency the relative directions of currents in the two meshes are as shown in Figure 8.1. For the higher frequency the direction of current in one mesh is opposite. Thus, if A is the complex amplitude of the current in the second mesh for the higher *mode of oscillation*, then,

$$I_1(t) = -pA \exp (j\omega_1 t), \qquad I_2(t) = A \exp (j\omega_1 t). \qquad (8.9)$$

Similarly, if B is the complex amplitude of the current in the second mesh for the lower mode of oscillation, then

$$I_1(t) = pB \exp (j\omega_2 t), \qquad I_2(t) = B \exp (j\omega_2 t). \qquad (8.10)$$

The two modes of oscillation may exist simultaneously, and in general

$$I_1(t) = -pA \exp (j\omega_1 t) + pB \exp (j\omega_2 t),$$

and $\qquad\qquad\qquad\qquad\qquad\qquad\qquad\qquad\qquad$ (8.11)

$$I_2(t) = A \exp (j\omega_1 t) + B \exp (j\omega_2 t).$$

If $B = -A$, then there is no current in the second mesh at the instant $t = 0$. At any other time

$$I_1(t) = -pA [\exp (j\omega_1 t) + \exp (j\omega_2 t)]$$

$$= -2pA \exp [j(\omega_1 + \omega_2)t/2] \cos \tfrac{1}{2}(\omega_1 - \omega_2)t, \qquad (8.12)$$

$$I_2(t) = 2j A \exp [j(\omega_1 + \omega_2)t/2] \sin \tfrac{1}{2}(\omega_1 - \omega_2)t.$$

Thus, the oscillations appear to be taking place with the angular frequency $\tfrac{1}{2}(\omega_1 + \omega_2)$, while the amplitudes of the currents are varying periodically with the frequency $\tfrac{1}{2}(\omega_1 - \omega_2)$. When the amplitude of the current in one mesh is zero, the amplitude of the current in the other mesh is maximum. In addition to a periodic transfer of electric energy into magnetic, we have also a periodic complete transfer of energy from one mesh to the other.

In each *mode of oscillation*, however, the energy is evenly divided between the two meshes. To show this, multiply equation (8.7) or equation (8.8) by its conjugate

$$I_1 I_1^* / I_2 I_2^* = L_{22}/L_{11}.$$

Hence,

$$\tfrac{1}{2} L_{11} I_1 I_1^* = \tfrac{1}{2} L_{22} I_2 I_2^*. \tag{8.13}$$

Thus, the maximum energies stored in the coils are equal. The amplitudes of I_1 and I_2 are constant, and hence, in each mode of oscillation there is no transfer of energy between the meshes. Thus, equation (8.13) represents the total energy in each circuit.

If $L_1 = L_2 = L$, $p = 1$, and we have a symmetric circuit, Figure 8.2, which can be easily analyzed from symmetry considerations. In

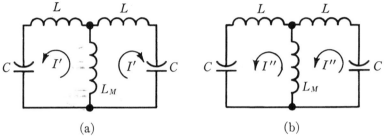

(a)   (b)

FIGURE 8.2   *Two modes of oscillation in symmetric coupled circuits.*

case (a) the inductance L_M may be considered as two inductances in parallel, each equal to $2L_M$. The two halves of the complete circuit may then be separated without disturbing the oscillations. The total inductance in each half is $L + 2L_M$, and the natural frequency is

$$\omega = \frac{1}{\sqrt{(L + 2L_M)C}}. \tag{8.14}$$

In case (b) there is no current in the mutual inductance L_M, and the same current flows through both inductances. The inductance of the big mesh is $2L$ and the capacitance $\tfrac{1}{2}C$. Hence, the natural frequency is

$$\omega = \frac{1}{\sqrt{LC}}. \tag{8.15}$$

8.3 Concentrated coupling between sections of transmission lines

The exchange of energy between two identical coupled circuits takes place no matter how small the coupling coefficient is [see equation (8.5)]. The smaller k is, the lower is the frequency of exchange.

Consider now a long section of a two-wire transmission line, "shorted" in the middle. The shorting bar has a small inductance, quite negligible in comparison with the total inductance of each section; but it is common to both sections and provides coupling between them. Thus, the originally equal natural frequencies will be slightly altered

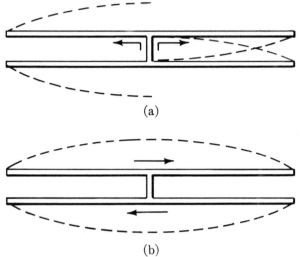

(a)

(b)

FIGURE 8.3 *Two modes of oscillation in a two-wire transmission line "shorted" in the middle.*

and there will be two modes of oscillation as indicated in Figure 8.3 (a, b). If oscillations are excited only in one section, there will be a gradual transfer of energy to the other section. After all energy has been transferred, the reverse flow of energy will begin.

8.4 An equivalent network for a shorted section of a uniform non-dissipative transmission line and its admittance in terms of resonant frequencies

Let us consider a uniform nondissipative transmission line of length l which is connected to a generator of zero internal impedance at $z = 0$, and shorted at $z = l$, Figure 8.4(a). Let the impressed voltage be $V^i \exp{(j\omega t)}$. Thus, if $V^i = 0$, we have a section shorted at both ends, Figure 8.4(b). The complex amplitudes of the transverse voltage and longitudinal current $V(z)$ and $I(z)$, satisfy equations (4.22)

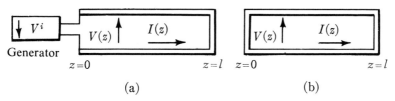

FIGURE 8.4   (a) A transmission line driven by a generator with zero internal
impedance (so that the impressed voltage is independent of the line impedance)
and shorted at the far end $z = l$; (b) a line shorted at both ends.

in the interval $0 < z \leq l$. These equations are

$$\frac{dV}{dz} = -j\omega LI, \qquad \frac{dI}{dz} = -j\omega CV. \tag{8.16}$$

In Chapter 4 the solutions were obtained in a form particularly
suitable to the analysis of wave propagation in transmission lines.
In this section we shall express the solutions in a different form and
obtain a network with lumped circuit parameters which is equivalent
to the line section with distributed circuit parameters.

Whatever the current $I(z)$ may be, it can be expressed as a cosine
series

$$I(z) = \sum_{n=0}^{\infty} I_n \cos (n\pi z/l), \qquad 0 \leq z \leq l, \tag{8.17}$$

where

$$I_0 = l^{-1} \int_0^l I(z) \, dz,$$

$$\tag{8.18}$$

$$I_n = (2/l) \int_0^l I(z) \cos (n\pi z/l) \, dz.$$

Let the voltage be expressed as a sine series so that the boundary
condition $V(l) = 0$ is satisfied automatically. Thus,

$$V(z) = \sum_{n=1}^{\infty} V_n \sin (n\pi z/l), \qquad 0 < z \leq l, \tag{8.19}$$

where

$$V_n = (2/l) \int_0^l V(z) \sin (n\pi z/l) \, dz. \tag{8.20}$$

Since $V(0) \neq 0$, the sine series (8.19) does not converge uniformly in the *closed* interval $(0, l)$. At $z = 0$, there is the condition

$$V(0) = V^i \tag{8.21}$$

to supplement the series for other values of z.

Taking $I(z)$ from the first equation in the set (8.16), and substituting in equations (8.18), we have

$$I_0 = -\frac{1}{j\omega Ll} \int_0^l \frac{dV}{dz} dz = -\frac{1}{j\omega Ll} [V(l) - V(0)]$$

$$= \frac{V^i}{j\omega Ll}, \tag{8.22}$$

$$I_n = -\frac{2}{j\omega Ll} \int_0^l \frac{dV}{dz} \cos \frac{n\pi z}{l} dz.$$

Integrating by parts, we find

$$I_n = -\frac{2}{j\omega Ll} \left[V(l) \cos n\pi - V(0) + \frac{n\pi}{l} \int_0^l V(z) \sin \frac{n\pi z}{l} dz \right].$$

Using equations (8.20) and (8.21), we obtain

$$I_n = \frac{2}{j\omega Ll} (V^i - \tfrac{1}{2} n\pi V_n). \tag{8.23}$$

Similarly, the second equation in the set (8.16), and equation (8.18) may be used to express the V_n in terms of the I_n

$$V_n = -\frac{2}{j\omega Cl} \int_0^l \frac{dI}{dz} \sin \frac{n\pi z}{l} dz$$

$$= -\frac{2}{j\omega Cl} \left[I(l) \sin n\pi - I(0) \sin 0 - \frac{n\pi}{l} \int_0^l I(z) \cos \frac{n\pi z}{l} dz \right].$$

The latter integral is given by equations (8.18). Thus,

$$V_n = \frac{n\pi I_n}{j\omega Cl}. \tag{8.24}$$

Substituting this in equation (8.23), we find

$$I_n = \frac{V^i}{(j\omega Ll/2) + (n^2\pi^2/2j\omega Cl)}. \tag{8.25}$$

Thus, all the coefficients in the series for $I(z)$ and $V(z)$ have been determined.

In particular the input current is

$$I(0) = \sum_{n=0}^{\infty} I_n$$

$$= \frac{Vi}{j\omega Ll} + Vi \sum_{n=1}^{\infty} \frac{1}{(j\omega Ll/2) + (n^2\pi^2/2j\omega Cl)},$$

and the input admittance

$$Y_{in} = \frac{I(0)}{Vi} = \frac{1}{j\omega Ll} + \sum_{n=1}^{\infty} \frac{1}{(j\omega Ll/2) + (n^2\pi^2/2j\omega Cl)}. \quad (8.26)$$

The first term is the admittance of an inductance Ll. The typical term in the summation is the admittance of an inductance $\frac{1}{2}Ll$ in

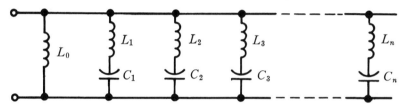

FIGURE 8.5 *An equivalent network for the physical transmission line shorted at the far end.*

series with a capacitance $2Cl/n^2\pi^2$. Hence, Y_{in} is the admittance of the network shown in Figure 8.5, where

$$L_0 = Ll, \qquad L_n = \tfrac{1}{2}Ll, \qquad C_n = \frac{2Cl}{n^2\pi^2}. \quad (8.27)$$

The input admittance becomes infinite, and the impedance zero, at the following frequencies

$$\omega_0 = 0, \qquad \omega_n = \frac{1}{\sqrt{L_n C_n}} = \frac{n\pi}{l\sqrt{LC}}. \quad (8.28)$$

These are the *resonant frequencies* of the transmission line section in Figure 8.4(a), and also the natural frequencies of the section shorted at both ends, Figure 8.4(b). In terms of these frequencies we have

$$Y_{in} = \frac{1}{j\omega Ll} + \sum_{n=1}^{\infty} \frac{2j\omega}{Ll(\omega_n^2 - \omega^2)}. \quad (8.29)$$

As $\omega \to 0$, we have,

$$Y_{in} \to \frac{1}{j\omega Ll} + \frac{2j\omega}{Ll} \sum_{n=1}^{\infty} \frac{1}{\omega_n^2} \to \frac{1}{j\omega Ll} + \frac{j\omega 2Cl}{\pi^2} \sum_{n=1}^{\infty} \frac{1}{n^2}.$$

Since

$$\sum_{n=1}^{\infty} \frac{1}{n^2} = \frac{\pi^2}{6},$$

we have

$$Y_{in} \to \frac{1}{j\omega Ll} + \tfrac{1}{3}j\omega Cl. \tag{8.30}$$

This low-frequency equivalent circuit for a shorted section of the line was obtained directly from energy considerations in Section 3.6. With the aid of this result, equation (8.29) may be expressed as

$$Y_{in} = \frac{1}{j\omega Ll} + \tfrac{1}{3}j\omega Cl + \sum_{n=1}^{\infty} \frac{2j\omega}{Ll} \left[\frac{1}{\omega_n^2 - \omega^2} - \frac{1}{\omega_n^2} \right] \tag{8.31}$$

$$= \frac{1}{j\omega Ll} + \tfrac{1}{3}j\omega Cl + \sum_{n=1}^{\infty} \frac{2j\omega^3}{Ll\omega_n^2(\omega_n^2 - \omega^2)}.$$

In this expression, the series is more rapidly convergent than the series in equation (8.29).

8.5 Another equivalent network for a shorted section of a uniform nondissipative transmission line and its impedance in terms of antiresonant frequencies

A different equivalent network may be obtained if a different set of functions is used to represent $I(z)$ and $V(z)$. Suppose the voltage and the current are represented by the following series:

$$V(z) = \sum_{n=0}^{\infty} V_n \cos \frac{(2n+1)\pi z}{2l}, \qquad 0 \le z \le l,$$

$$\tag{8.32}$$

$$I(z) = \sum_{n=0}^{\infty} I_n \sin \frac{(2n+1)\pi z}{2l}, \qquad 0 < z \le l,$$

$$= I^i \qquad\qquad\qquad\qquad z = 0,$$

where I^i is the input current. The cosine functions have been selected to satisfy the boundary condition $V(l) = 0$. This time it is the current that is represented by a nonuniformly convergent series. The coefficients in these series are

$$V_n = \frac{2}{l} \int_0^l V(z) \cos \frac{(2n+1)\pi z}{2l} \, dz,$$

(8.33)

$$I_n = \frac{2}{l} \int_0^l I(z) \sin \frac{(2n+1)\pi z}{2l} \, dz.$$

In this representation there is a fixed input current which ideally can be obtained when the internal impedance of the generator is infinite so that the impedance of the line has no effect on the input current, Figure 8.6(a). When $I^i = 0$, the line is open at $z = 0$,

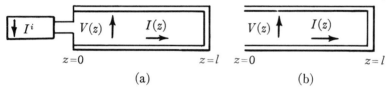

(a)   (b)

FIGURE 8.6   (a) A transmission line driven by a generator of infinite internal impedance (so that the input current is independent of the line admittance) and shorted at the far end z = l; (b) a line open at one end and shorted at the other.

Figure 8.6(b). This is dual of the case in the preceding section where the internal impedance of the generator was assumed to be equal to zero so that the impedance of the line had no effect on the input voltage All real generators have a finite internal impedance. If this impedance is explicitly inserted in series with the external circuit, we have in effect a generator of zero impedance. Similarly, if the admittance of the generator is explicitly inserted in parallel with the external circuit, we have in effect a generator of infinite impedance.

From equation (8.32), we obtain the input voltage

$$V(0) = \sum_{n=0}^{\infty} V_n,$$

and the input impedance

$$Z_{in} = V(0)/I^i = \sum_{n=0}^{\infty} V_n/I^i. \qquad (8.34)$$

The method of expressing the V_n and the I_n in terms of I^i is the same as in the preceding section. We substitute into equations (8.33) the expressions for $V(z)$ and $I(z)$ in terms of the derivatives $dI(z)/dz$ and $dV(z)/dz$ from equations (8.16). The integrals are differentiated by parts and equations (8.33) are used once more. Thus, we obtain

$$V_n = \frac{I^i}{j\omega(Cl/2) + [(2n+1)^2\pi^2/8j\omega Ll]},$$

(8.35)

$$I_n = \frac{(2n+1)\pi V_n}{2j\omega Ll}.$$

The input impedance can now be expressed as

$$Z_{in} = \sum_{n=0}^{\infty} \frac{1}{j\omega C_n + (1/j\omega L_n)},$$

(8.36)

$$C_n = \tfrac{1}{2}Cl, \qquad L_n = 8Ll/(2n+1)^2\pi^2.$$

This is the impedance of parallel resonant circuits connected in series, Figure 8.7.

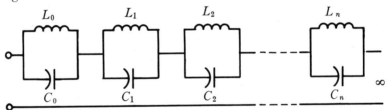

FIGURE 8.7 *An alternate equivalent network for a transmission line shorted at the far end.*

The input impedance becomes infinite at the resonant frequency of each parallel circuit [which is also the natural frequency of a section open at one end and shorted at the other, Figure 8.6(b)]. These frequencies are

$$\omega_n = \frac{1}{\sqrt{L_n C_n}} = \frac{(2n+1)\pi}{2l\sqrt{LC}}.$$

(8.37)

Therefore,

$$Z_{in} = \sum_{n=0}^{\infty} \frac{2j\omega}{Cl(\omega_n^2 - \omega^2)}.$$

(8.38)

As $\omega \to 0$, this impedance approaches

$$Z_{\text{in}} = \frac{2j\omega}{Cl} \sum_{n=0}^{\infty} \frac{1}{\omega_n^2} = \frac{8j\omega Ll}{\pi^2} \sum_{n=0}^{\infty} \frac{1}{(2n+1)^2} = j\omega Ll \qquad (8.39)$$

since the sum equals $\pi^2/8$. Here Ll is, of course, the direct current inductance of the loop. The input impedance can now be expressed as follows:

$$Z_{\text{in}} = j\omega Ll + \sum_{n=0}^{\infty} \frac{2j\omega}{Cl} \left(\frac{1}{\omega_n^2 - \omega^2} - \frac{1}{\omega_n^2} \right)$$

$$(8.40)$$

$$= j\omega Ll + \sum_{n=0}^{\infty} \frac{j8Ll\omega^3}{(2n+1)^2\pi^2(\omega_n^2 - \omega^2)}.$$

This is the impedance of the network shown in Figure 8.8. The primary circuit is the transmission line section, regarded as a simple

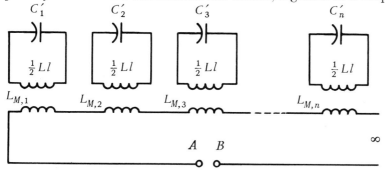

FIGURE 8.8   *A third type of equivalent network for a transmission line shorted at the far end.*

loop of inductance Ll which is coupled to parallel resonant circuits for which

$$C_n' = \frac{8Cl}{(2n+1)^2\pi^2}, \qquad L_{M,n} = \frac{2Ll}{(2n+1)\pi}. \qquad (8.41)$$

The impedance between A and B is

$$Z_{\text{in}} = j\omega Ll + \sum_{n=0}^{\infty} \frac{j\omega^3 L_{M,n}^2}{(Ll/2)(\omega_n^2 - \omega^2)}. \qquad (8.42)$$

8.6 Equivalent networks for nonuniform transmission lines

In this section network equations will be derived for a section of length l of a nonuniform transmission line, Figure 8.9. Let us assume

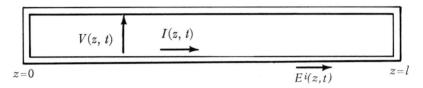

$z=0$ $E^i(z,t)$ $z=l$

FIGURE 8.9 *A nonuniform transmission line, shorted at both ends, with a distributed impressed series voltage varying arbitrarily with time.*

a general time-variable case, and a distributed impressed series voltage. Thus, let

$$E^i(z, t) = \text{impressed voltage per unit length,}$$

$$I(z, t) = \text{longitudinal current,}$$

$$V(z, t) = \text{transverse voltage,}$$

$$q(z, t) = \text{electric charge per unit length.}$$

In this case the transmission equations are

$$\frac{\partial V(z, t)}{\partial z} = -L(z)\,\frac{\partial I(z, t)}{\partial t} + E^i(z, t) \qquad (8.43)$$

$$\frac{\partial I(z, t)}{\partial z} = -C(z)\,\frac{\partial V(z, t)}{\partial t}. \qquad (8.44)$$

Since

$$q(z, t) = C(z)\,V(z, t), \qquad (8.45)$$

equation (8.44) may be written as

$$\frac{\partial I(z, t)}{\partial z} = -\frac{\partial q(z, t)}{\partial t}. \qquad (8.46)$$

If the line is shorted at both ends

$$V(0, t) = V(l, t) = 0;$$

therefore,

$$q(0, t) = q(l, t) = 0. \qquad (8.47)$$

At any instant, $I(z, t)$ may be expressed as a cosine series, and at all instants by such a series with coefficients depending on time

$$I(z, t) = \sum_{n=0}^{\infty} I_n(t) \cos (n\pi z/l). \tag{8.48}$$

In this representation, $I_0(t)$ is the current circulating round the loop, and $I_n(t)$ the current passing at the antinodes of the nth space harmonic, taken by itself. The current $I_n(t)$ equals $\dot{q}_n(t)$, the time rate of charge $q_n(t)$ passing through these antinodes.

Substituting from equation (8.48) into (8.46), we have

$$\frac{\partial q(z, t)}{\partial t} = \sum_{n=1}^{\infty} (n\pi/l)\dot{q}_n(t) \sin (n\pi z/l).$$

Integrating from $t = 0$ to $t = t$ we find,

$$q(z, t) - q(z, 0) = \sum_{n=1}^{\infty} (n\pi/l)q_n(t) \sin (n\pi z/l)$$

$$- \sum_{n=1}^{\infty} (n\pi/l)q_n(0) \sin (n\pi z/l).$$

Hence,

$$q(z, t) = \sum_{n=1}^{\infty} (n\pi/l)q_n(t) \sin (n\pi z/l) + Q(z), \tag{8.49}$$

where $Q(z)$ is a static charge distribution maintained by a static impressed field. This distribution may be found from equations (8.43) and (8.45). Thus,

$$\frac{d}{dz} \frac{Q(z)}{C(z)} = E_{st}^i(z).$$

Suppose that such distribution, if any, has been found and deleted from the time-variable distribution (8.49). Then,

$$q(z, t) = \sum_{n=1}^{\infty} (n\pi/l)q_n(t) \sin (n\pi z/l). \tag{8.50}$$

Equations (8.44), (8.46), and the boundary conditions are satisfied on account of our choice of time variables $q_n(t)$ and the forms of Fourier series. It remains to satisfy equation (8.43). First we substitute from equation (8.45)

$$\frac{\partial}{\partial z} \left[\frac{q(z, t)}{C(z)} \right] + L(z) \frac{\partial I(z, t)}{\partial t} = E^i(z, t).$$

This equation must be satisfied for all z. To ensure this we expand both sides in a cosine series in z, and equate the coefficients. Thus,

$$\int_0^l \left(\frac{\partial}{\partial z} \left[\frac{q(z, t)}{C(z)} \right] + L(z) \frac{\partial I(z, t)}{\partial t} \right) \cos \frac{m\pi z}{l} \, dz$$

$$= \int_0^l E^i(z, t) \cos \frac{m\pi z}{l} \, dz, \qquad m = 0, 1, 2, \cdots. \qquad (8.51)$$

The first part of the integrand on the left may be integrated by parts

$$\int_0^l \cos \frac{m\pi z}{l} \frac{\partial}{\partial z} \left[\frac{q(z, t)}{C(z)} \right] dz = \cos \frac{m\pi z}{l} \frac{q(z, t)}{C(z)} \Big|_0^l$$

$$+ \int_0^l \frac{(m\pi/l) \sin (m\pi z/l) q(z, t)}{C(z)} \, dz.$$

The first term on the right vanishes, and equation (8.51) becomes

$$\int_0^l \frac{(m\pi/l) \sin (m\pi z/l) q(z, t)}{C(z)} \, dz + \int_0^l L(z) \cos \frac{m\pi z}{l} \frac{\partial I(z, t)}{\partial t} \, dz$$

$$= \int_0^l E^i(z, t) \cos \frac{m\pi z}{l} \, dz.$$

Substituting from equations (8.48) and (8.50), we obtain

$$L_{00}\dot{I}_0(t) + L_{01}\dot{I}_1(t) + L_{02}\dot{I}_2(t) + \cdots = V_0^i(t)$$

$$L_{m0}\dot{I}_0(t) + \left[L_{m1}\dot{I}_1(t) + \frac{q_1(t)}{C_{m1}} \right]$$

$$\qquad\qquad (8.52)$$

$$+ \left[L_{m2}\dot{I}_2(t) + \frac{q_2(t)}{C_{m2}} \right] + \cdots = V_m^i(t)$$

for $m = 1, 2, 3, \cdots$, where

$$L_{0m} = \int_0^l L(z) \cos (m\pi z/l) \, dz,$$

$$L_{mn} = \int_0^l L(z) \cos (m\pi z/l) \cos (n\pi z/l) \, dz, \qquad m, n = 0, 1, 2, \cdots,$$

$$\qquad\qquad (8.53)$$

$$1/C_{mn} = \int_0^l \frac{\sin (m\pi z/l) \sin (n\pi z/l)}{(l^2/mn\pi^2) C(z)} \, dz, \qquad m, n = 1, 2, 3, \cdots,$$

$$V_m^i(t) = \int_0^l E^i(z, t) \cos (m\pi z/l) \, dz, \qquad m = 0, 1, 2, \cdots.$$

Equations (8.52) are the mesh equations for a network. The inductance and capacitance in the mth mesh are given by L_{mm}, and C_{mm}. The mutual inductances and capacitances are L_{mn}, and C_{mn} when $m \neq n$.

8.7 Lagrange's equations in circuit theory

Equations (8.52) can be derived from Lagrange's equations if the kinetic energy is equated to magnetic energy $\mathcal{E}_m$, and the potential energy to electric energy $\mathcal{E}_e$. Both $\mathcal{E}_m$ and $\mathcal{E}_e$ should be expressed in terms of the "generalized coordinates" of the system, $q_n(t)$, and the "generalized velocities," $I_n(t)$. Thus,

$$\mathcal{E}_m = \frac{1}{2} \int_0^l L(z)[I(z)]^2 \, dz. \tag{8.54}$$

By substituting from equation (8.48), we have

$$\mathcal{E}_m = \frac{1}{2} \int_0^l \sum_{m,n} L(z) I_m(t) I_n(t) \, \cos \frac{mz}{l} \cos \frac{nz}{l} \, dz$$

$$= \tfrac{1}{2} \sum_{m,n} L_{mn} I_m(t) I_n(t),$$

$$\tag{8.55}$$

where the inductance coefficients are given by equations (8.53). Similarly,

$$\mathcal{E}_e = \frac{1}{2} \int_0^l \frac{[q(z)]^2}{C(z)} \, dz$$

$$= \frac{1}{2} \sum_{m,n} \frac{q_m(t) q_n(t)}{C_{mn}},$$

$$\tag{8.56}$$

where the capacitance coefficients are also given by equations (8.53). The "generalized forces" are obtained from their definition

$$\delta W = \sum_m V_m^i(t) \, \delta q_m \tag{8.57}$$

where δW is the work done by the impressed electric intensity during a virtual displacement of the system $(\delta q_1, \delta q_2, \cdots)$. Since

$$\delta W = \int_0^l E^i(z, t) [I(z, t) \, \delta t] \, dz$$

and

$$I(z, t) \, \delta t = \sum_m \dot{q}_m(t) \, \delta t \cos (m\pi z/l)$$

$$= \sum_m \cos (m\pi z/l) \, \delta q_m,$$

we have

$$V_m^i(t) = \int_0^l E_z^i(z, t) \cos (m\pi z/l) \, dz. \tag{8.58}$$

Lagrange's equations are

$$\frac{d}{dt} \left[\frac{\partial(\mathcal{E}_m - \mathcal{E}_e)}{\partial I_m} \right] - \frac{\partial(\mathcal{E}_m - \mathcal{E}_e)}{\partial q_m} = V_m^i(t). \tag{8.59}$$

By substituting from equations (8.55) and (8.56), we obtain the network equations (8.52).

9

Generalized Telegraphist's Equations

9.0 Introduction

Developments in this chapter run parallel to those in the preceding chapter. Instead of coupling between circuits we consider coupling between transmission lines. Instead of coupling between modes of oscillation we have coupling between modes of wave propagation. Mathematically this idea of coupling between modes of propagation leads to the conversion of Maxwell's partial differential equations with given boundary conditions into a set of ordinary differential equations analogous to the equations for coupled transmission lines developed by Lord Kelvin, the so-called "telegraphist's equations." Kelvin's equations are approximate while the generalized telegraphist's equations obtained in this chapter are exact.

9.1 Coupled transmission lines

The transverse voltage and longitudinal current in two-conductor transmission lines satisfy a simple pair of linear differential equations (4.22). From the results obtained in Sections 2.15, 2.16, and 2.17 it may be concluded that for three conductors, Figure 9.1, we should have the following equations:

$$\frac{dV_1}{dz} = -Z_{11}I_1 - Z_{12}I_2, \qquad \frac{dI_1}{dz} = -Y_{11}V_1 - Y_{12}V_2,$$

$$\tag{9.1}$$

$$\frac{dV_2}{dz} = -Z_{12}I_1 - Z_{22}I_2, \qquad \frac{dI_2}{dz} = -Y_{12}V_1 - Y_{22}V_2.$$

The coefficients in these equations depend on the geometry and physical properties of the system. The equations are obtained from Maxwell's equations in precisely the same manner as for two conductors. Thus the Faraday-Maxwell equation is applied to rectangular

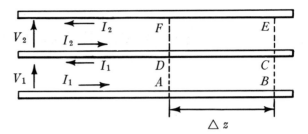

FIGURE 9.1   *Three parallel wires, constituting a system of two coupled transmission lines.*

circuits $ABCD$ and $DCEF$ to obtain the rates of change of V_1 and V_2 with z. The Ampere-Maxwell equation is needed to obtain the magnetic intensity of the field and the magnetic current linked with these circuits. The rates of change of I_1 and I_2 with z are obtained by calculating the transverse leakage currents.

For $n + 1$ conductors there are n pairs of equations in which the derivatives dV_m/dz are linear functions of I_1, I_2, $\cdots$ and dI_m/dz linear functions of V_1, V_2, $\cdots$. The coefficients Z_{mm} are called the series self-impedances per unit length and Z_{mk}, $m \neq k$, the mutual impedances, also per unit length. Similarly, Y_{mk} is the self or mutual shunt admittance per unit length, depending on whether $m = k$ or $m \neq k$.

If the coefficients are independent of z, equations (9.1) possess exponential solutions

$$V_1 = Ae^{-\Gamma z}, \qquad I_1 = Be^{-\Gamma z},$$
$$V_2 = Ce^{-\Gamma z}, \qquad I_2 = De^{-\Gamma z}. \tag{9.2}$$

The equations for the unknown constants are obtained by substitution in equations (9.1)

$$\Gamma A = Z_{11}B + Z_{12}D, \qquad \Gamma B = Y_{11}A + Y_{12}C,$$
$$\Gamma C = Z_{12}B + Z_{22}D, \qquad \Gamma D = Y_{12}A + Y_{22}C. \tag{9.3}$$

These are homogeneous equations in A, B, C, and D. They possess nonvanishing solutions only when the determinant of the system of equations vanishes. Thus we shall have a fourth-order equation for the propagation constant Γ. In fact this equation will be quadratic in Γ^2 so that if Γ is a solution, then $-\Gamma$ is also a solution. Physically, this was to be expected since the propagation constants in both directions should be the same. Thus there will be two distinct propagration constants, Γ_1 and Γ_2. For each value, the ratios B/A, C/A, and D/A may be determined from equations (9.3). The waves corresponding to the two values of Γ are two *modes of propagation*. In the case of $n + 1$ conductors there will be n modes of propagation.

9.2 Weak coupling

Even for two coupled transmission lines the solution is rather complicated. The complexity increases rapidly with the number of transmission lines. Approximate solutions can be obtained in the important special case of weak coupling when Z_{12} and Y_{12} are small in comparison with Z_{11}, Z_{22} and Y_{11}, Y_{22}, respectively. First the coupling is neglected and each pair of equations is solved separately. Then the solutions are substituted in the neglected terms and the resulting nonhomogeneous equations are solved. This technique can be simplified still further as shown below.

Consider two coupled transmission lines, Figure 9.2. Suppose that

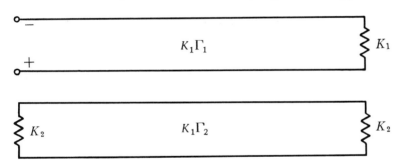

FIGURE 9.2 *Two coupled transmission lines.*

a voltage is impressed on one end of one transmission line while its other end is terminated into its characteristic impedance K_1. Let the other line be terminated by its characteristic impedance K_2 at both ends. In the first approximation

$$I_1(z) = Ae^{-\Gamma_1 z}, \qquad V_1(z) = K_1\,Ae^{-\Gamma_1 z},$$

$$I_2(z) = 0, \qquad V_2(z) = 0.$$

$$(9.4)$$

The quantity $-Z_{12}I_1$ in equations (9.1) is the series voltage per unit length impressed on the second line. At $z = \xi$ the elementary impressed voltage is

$$-Z_{12}I_1(\xi)\, d\xi = -Z_{12}A e^{-\Gamma_1\xi}\, d\xi.$$

This voltage sees an impedance $2K_2$ so that the current at $z = \xi$ is

$$-(Z_{12}/2K_2)\, A e^{-\Gamma_1\xi}\, d\xi,$$

and at other points

$$-(Z_{12}/2K_2)\, A \exp\left[-\Gamma_1\xi - \Gamma_2(z - \xi)\right] d\xi, \qquad z \geq \xi$$

$$-(Z_{12}/2K_2)\, A \exp\left[-\Gamma_1\xi - \Gamma_2(\xi - z)\right] d\xi, \qquad z \leq \xi.$$

(9.5)

Thus the total induced current is

$$-(Z_{12}/2K_2)\, A e^{-\Gamma_2 z} \int_0^z e^{(\Gamma_2-\Gamma_1)\xi}\, d\xi +$$

$$-(Z_{12}/2K_2)\, A e^{\Gamma_2 z} \int_z^l e^{-(\Gamma_1+\Gamma_2)\xi}\, d\xi. \qquad (9.6)$$

Integrating as indicated, we have the total current produced by the coupling voltages impressed in series,

$$-\frac{Z_{12}A}{2K_2}\left[\frac{e^{-\Gamma_1 z} - e^{-\Gamma_2 z}}{\Gamma_2 - \Gamma_1} + \frac{e^{-\Gamma_1 z} - \exp\left[-\Gamma_1 l - \Gamma_2(l - z)\right]}{\Gamma_1 + \Gamma_2}\right]. \qquad (9.7)$$

From equations (9.5) we find that the transverse voltages induced in the second line are

$$-\tfrac{1}{2}Z_{12}A e^{-\Gamma_1\xi}e^{-\Gamma_2(z-\xi)}\, d\xi, \qquad z > \xi$$

$$+\tfrac{1}{2}Z_{12}A e^{-\Gamma_1\xi}e^{-\Gamma_2(\xi-z)}\, d\xi, \qquad z < \xi.$$

(9.8)

Integrating with respect to ξ from $\xi = 0$ to $\xi = l$, we obtain the total transverse voltage due to the series coupling

$$-\tfrac{1}{2}Z_{12}A\left[\frac{e^{-\Gamma_1 z} - e^{-\Gamma_2 z}}{\Gamma_2 - \Gamma_1} - \frac{e^{-\Gamma_1 z} - \exp\left[-\Gamma_1 l - \Gamma_2(l - z)\right]}{\Gamma_1 + \Gamma_2}\right]. \qquad (9.9)$$

At $z = \xi$ in the second transmission line we have an induced shunt current $-Y_{12}V_1\, d\xi$, one half of which goes to the left and the other half to the right. From there on the induced current is propagated along the line. Thus the elementary induced current is

$$-\tfrac{1}{2}Y_{12}V_1 e^{-\Gamma_2(z-\xi)}\, d\xi = -\tfrac{1}{2}Y_{12}K_1 A e^{-\Gamma_1\xi}e^{-\Gamma_2(z-\xi)}\, d\xi, \qquad z > \xi,$$

$$\tfrac{1}{2}Y_{12}V_1 e^{-\Gamma_2(\xi-z)}\, d\xi = \tfrac{1}{2}Y_{12}K_1 A e^{-\Gamma_1\xi}e^{-\Gamma_2(\xi-z)}\, d\xi, \qquad z < \xi.$$

(9.10)

Integrating this with respect to ξ from 0 to l, we obtain the total current in the line produced by the impressed elementary shunt currents

$$-\tfrac{1}{2}Y_{12}K_1A\left[\frac{e^{-\Gamma_1 z}-e^{-\Gamma_2 z}}{\Gamma_2-\Gamma_1}-\frac{e^{-\Gamma_1 z}-\exp\left[-\Gamma_1 l-\Gamma_2(l-z)\right]}{\Gamma_1+\Gamma_2}\right].$$

$$(9.11)$$

The sum of this and expression (9.7) is the entire current induced in the second line by the wave traveling in the first

$$I_2(z) = -\tfrac{1}{2}A\left(Z_{12}K_2^{-1}+Y_{12}K_1\right)\frac{e^{-\Gamma_1 z}-e^{-\Gamma_2 z}}{\Gamma_2-\Gamma_1}$$

$$+\tfrac{1}{2}A\left(Y_{12}K_1-Z_{12}K_2^{-1}\right)\frac{e^{-\Gamma_1 z}-\exp\left[-\Gamma_1 l-\Gamma_2(l-z)\right]}{\Gamma_1+\Gamma_2}. \qquad (9.12)$$

From equations (9.10) we obtain the elementary transverse voltage induced in the second line if we multiply the expression for $z > \xi$ by K_2 and that for $z < \xi$ by $-K_2$. Then we integrate over the interval $(0, l)$ and add to equation (9.9) to obtain $V_2(z)$.

In the same manner one can calculate the transverse voltage and longitudinal current induced back into the first line by $I_2(z)$ and $V_2(z)$. This should be added to $I_1(z)$ and $V_1(z)$ in equations (9.4). The correction would be of the second order in small quantities Z_{12} and Y_{12} and in many practical applications is negligible.

There is one very important exception, however. If $\Gamma_2 = \Gamma_1$, then the first integral in the expression (9.6) equals z. In this case when the length of the line is large, the induced $V_2(z)$ and $I_2(z)$ will also become large (for large z) and higher order approximations are necessary. This "degenerate" case is best treated by the exact method of Section 9.1.

9.3   Directional coupling

In the preceding section it was concluded that the case in which the propagation constants of the coupled lines are equal requires special attention. In this case

$$Z_{11}Y_{11} = Z_{22}Y_{22},$$

or if the lines are nondissipative

$$L_{11}C_{11} = L_{22}C_{22}. \qquad (9.13)$$

Consider first a subcase in which $L_{11} = L_{22} = L$ and therefore $C_{11} =$

$C_{22} = C$. Equations (9.1) become

$$\frac{dV_1}{dz} = -j\omega L I_1 - j\omega L_{12} I_2, \qquad \frac{dI_1}{dz} = -j\omega C V_1 - j\omega C_{12} V_2,$$

(9.14)

$$\frac{dV_2}{dz} = -j\omega L_{12} I_1 - j\omega L I_2, \qquad \frac{dI_2}{dz} = -j\omega C_{12} V_1 - j\omega C V_2.$$

Assume exponential solutions of the form (9.2), substitute them in equation (9.14) and obtain a set of linear algebraic equations of the form (9.3). From there on proceed as outlined in Section 9.1 and obtain the expressions for the propagation constants of two possible modes of propagation and the corresponding amplitudes.

One may also take advantage of the symmetry of equations (9.14). Adding the equations in the left column, and also in the right column, we have

$$\frac{d(V_1 + V_2)}{dz} = -j\omega(L + L_{12})(I_1 + I_2),$$

(9.15)

$$\frac{d(I_1 + I_2)}{dz} = -j\omega(C + C_{12})(V_1 + V_2).$$

Thus the sums of the transverse voltages and longitudinal currents in two transmission lines are propagated with the phase constant

$$\beta_1 = \omega\sqrt{(L + L_{12})(C + C_{12})}$$

(9.16)

and velocity

$$v_1 = \frac{1}{\sqrt{(L + L_{12})(C + C_{12})}}.$$

(9.17)

The characteristic impedance is

$$K_1 = \sqrt{\frac{L + L_{12}}{C + C_{12}}}.$$

(9.18)

Subtracting equations in the left and right columns, we have

$$\frac{d(V_1 - V_2)}{dz} = -j\omega(L - L_{12})(I_1 - I_2),$$

(9.19)

$$\frac{d(I_1 - I_2)}{dz} = j\omega(C - C_{12})(V_1 - V_2).$$

Thus the differences between the transverse voltages and longitudinal currents are propagated with the phase constant and velocity given by

$$\beta_2 = \omega\sqrt{(L - L_{12})(C - C_{12})}, \qquad v_2 = \frac{1}{\sqrt{(L - L_{12})(C - C_{12})}}.$$

(9.20)

The characteristic impedance is

$$K_2 = \sqrt{\frac{L - L_{12}}{C - C_{12}}}.$$

(9.21)

The symmetry in equations (9.14) reflects the physical symmetry. Consider for instance three equidistant parallel wires, Figure 9.3.

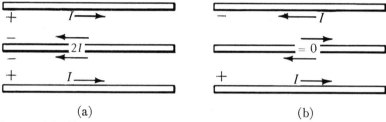

(a)   (b)

FIGURE 9.3   *Two modes of propagation in symmetric coupled transmission lines.*

It is evident that these wires may support two *independent* modes of propagation. In the mode (a) equal currents in the *same* direction in the outer wires return via the middle wire. In the mode (b) there is no current in the middle wire and the outer wires act as a transmission line.

Returning to equations (9.15) and (9.19), we have

$$I_1(z) + I_2(z) = Ae^{-j\beta_1 z},$$

$$I_1(z) - I_2(z) = Be^{-j\beta_2 z},$$

for waves traveling in the positive z direction. Hence

$$I_1(z) = \tfrac{1}{2}Ae^{-j\beta_1 z} + \tfrac{1}{2}Be^{-j\beta_2 z},$$

(9.22)

$$I_2(z) = \tfrac{1}{2}Ae^{-j\beta_1 z} - \tfrac{1}{2}Be^{-j\beta_2 z}.$$

Suppose that at $z = 0$ a voltage is applied across the first line but not across the second line. For instance, in the case of three wires, Figure 9.3, a voltage may be applied between the two lower wires and the terminal of the upper wire left floating. Then $I_2(0) = 0$ and $B = A$. Equations (9.22) become

$$I_1(z) = \tfrac{1}{2}A(e^{-j\beta_1 z} + e^{-j\beta_2 z}) = A \exp[-j(\beta_1 + \beta_2)z/2]\cos\tfrac{1}{2}(\beta_1 - \beta_2)z,$$

$$(9.23)$$

$$I_2(z) = \tfrac{1}{2}A(e^{-j\beta_1 z} - e^{-j\beta_2 z}) = jA \exp[-j(\beta_1 + \beta_2)z/2]\sin\tfrac{1}{2}(\beta_2 - \beta_1)z.$$

At $z = 0$, $I_1(0) = A$ and $I_2(0) = 0$. At distance $z = l$ such that

$$\tfrac{1}{2}|\beta_2 - \beta_1|l = \tfrac{1}{2}\pi, \tag{9.24}$$

the current in the first line equals zero and the amplitude of the current in the second line is A. Thus if the two lines are *uncoupled* beyond $z = l$, the energy delivered to the first line at $z = 0$ will have passed entirely into the second line and there will be no wave in the first beyond $z = l$. If the lines remain coupled, the energy will start flowing back into the first line. The phenomenon is similar to beats in coupled circuits (see Section 8.3). In the present case it is called *directional coupling*. As the coupling between the lines decreases, $\beta_2 - \beta_1$ also decreases and l increases.

9.4 Waves in stratified media between perfectly conducting parallel planes

In Section 6.8 we considered wave propagation in a homogeneous dielectric between two perfectly conducting parallel planes. Suppose now that the medium is nonhomogeneous. Let us keep the assumptions that the field does not depend on the y coordinate, Figure 6.1, that the magnetic intensity is parallel to the planes, and that μ is constant. Eliminating E_x and E_z from equations (6.88), we obtain

$$\frac{\partial}{\partial x}\left(\epsilon^{-1}\frac{\partial H_y}{\partial x}\right) + \frac{\partial}{\partial z}\left(\epsilon^{-1}\frac{\partial H_y}{\partial z}\right) = -\omega^2\mu H_y. \tag{9.25}$$

If ϵ depends on both coordinates, it is easy to establish that this equation has no solution in the product form

$$H_y = X(x)Z(z). \tag{9.26}$$

The method of separation of variables no longer works. However, if ϵ is a function of only one coordinate, then the variables can still be separated.

Suppose, for example, that $\epsilon = \epsilon(z)$ varies only in the direction of propagation. By substituting from equation (9.26) into (9.25) and dividing by XZ, we obtain

$$\frac{\epsilon(z)}{Z} \frac{d}{dz} \left[\frac{1}{\epsilon(z)} \frac{dZ}{dz} \right] = -\omega^2 \mu \epsilon(z) - \frac{1}{X} \frac{d^2 X}{dx^2}.$$

This equation cannot be true unless the last term is constant just as in the homogeneous case. Referring to equations (6.91) we have

$$X(x) = \cos(m\pi x/a), \qquad m = 0, 1, 2, \cdots.$$

The particular form and the values of m are dictated by the fact that E_z and hence $X'(x)$ must vanish at the boundaries $x = 0, a$. The equation for Z becomes

$$\epsilon(z) \frac{d}{dz} \left[\frac{1}{\epsilon(z)} \frac{dZ}{dz} \right] = -\left[\omega^2 \mu \epsilon(z) - \frac{m^2 \pi^2}{a^2} \right] Z. \qquad (9.27)$$

When $\epsilon = \epsilon(x)$, equation (9.25) becomes

$$\frac{\epsilon(x)}{X} \frac{d}{dx} \left[\frac{1}{\epsilon(x)} \frac{dX}{dx} \right] = -\omega^2 \mu \epsilon(x) - \frac{1}{Z} \frac{d^2 Z}{dz^2}.$$

This equation possesses solutions, exponential in z,

$$Z = e^{-\Gamma z}.$$

Hence

$$\epsilon(x) \frac{d}{dx} \left[\frac{1}{\epsilon(x)} \frac{dX}{dx} \right] = -[\omega^2 \mu \epsilon(x) + \Gamma^2] X. \qquad (9.28)$$

This is essentially the same differential equation as equation (9.27). The important difference is that Γ is not known and must be determined from the boundary conditions

$$X'(0) = X'(a) = 0. \qquad (9.29)$$

There will be an infinite set of characteristic values Γ_m and corresponding characteristic functions X_m which will satisfy equations (9.29). These functions are orthogonal in the interval $(0, a)$. To prove this we take two solutions, X_m and X_n, and write equation (9.28) as

$$\frac{d}{dx} \left[\frac{1}{\epsilon(x)} \frac{dX_m}{dx} \right] = -\left[\omega^2 \mu + \frac{\Gamma_m^2}{\epsilon(x)} \right] X_m,$$

$$\frac{d}{dx} \left[\frac{1}{\epsilon(x)} \frac{dX_n}{dx} \right] = -\left[\omega^2 \mu + \frac{\Gamma_n^2}{\epsilon(x)} \right] X_n.$$

Multiplying the first equation by $X_n\,dx$, the second by $X_m\,dx$ and subtracting, we find that the left-hand side is a complete differential

$$d\left[\frac{1}{\epsilon(x)}\left(X_n\frac{dX_m}{dx} - X_m\frac{dX_n}{dx}\right)\right] = \frac{\Gamma_n^2 - \Gamma_m^2}{\epsilon(x)}X_mX_n\,dx.$$

Integrating over the interval $(0, a)$, we have

$$\frac{1}{\epsilon(x)}(X_nX_m' - X_mX_n')\;\Big|_0^a = (\Gamma_n^2 - \Gamma_m^2)\int_0^a\frac{1}{\epsilon(x)}X_mX_n\,dx.$$

In view of the boundary conditions (9.29) the left side vanishes and

$$\int_0^a\frac{1}{\epsilon(x)}X_m(x)X_n(x)\,dx = 0, \quad\text{if}\quad \Gamma_n \neq \Gamma_m.$$

This is as far as we can go without specifying $\epsilon(x)$. The complete solution of the problem of stratified media depends essentially on our ability to handle the second-order differential equation (9.27). In general, one has to resort to approximations or to numerical methods.

9.5 Waves in completely nonhomogeneous media between perfectly conducting planes

If ϵ is a function of both coordinates the method of separation of variables fails. In this case we shall not attempt to solve the partial differential equation (9.25). Instead we shall deal directly with the first-order Maxwell's equations (6.88). Two are propagation equations, in the z direction,

$$\frac{\partial E_x}{\partial z} = -j\omega\mu H_y + \frac{\partial E_z}{\partial x}, \qquad \frac{\partial H_y}{\partial z} = -j\omega\epsilon E_x, \qquad (9.30)$$

and one is a coupling equation between the transverse and longitudinal fields,

$$E_z = \frac{1}{j\omega\epsilon}\frac{\partial H_y}{\partial x}. \qquad (9.31)$$

For a given value of z, E_x and H_y can be expressed as cosine series in x. This follows from the theory of Fourier series. Hence this is true *for all values of z* when the coefficients are permitted to depend on z. Thus we assume

$$E_x = \frac{V_0(z)}{a} + \sum_{m=1}^{\infty} N_m V_m(z) \cos (m\pi x/a),$$

$$\tag{9.32}$$

$$H_y = \frac{I_0(z)}{b} + \sum_{m=1}^{\infty} N_m I_m(z) \cos (m\pi x/a).$$

In these equations $V_0(z)$ is the transverse voltage between the planes and $I_0(z)$ is the current which would flow in a strip of width b (in the y direction) if the wave were purely transverse electromagnetic. The constants N_m are chosen so that the average complex power flow through the area ab is given by the following expression

$$P = \tfrac{1}{2} \sum_{m=0}^{\infty} V_m(z) I_m^*(z), \tag{9.33}$$

which is always valid for any number of uncoupled transmission lines. Since

$$P = \tfrac{1}{2} \int_0^b \int_0^a E_x H_y^* \, dx \, dy$$

$$= \tfrac{1}{2} V_0(z) I_0^*(z) + \tfrac{1}{2} \sum_{m=1}^{\infty} \tfrac{1}{2} ab N_m^2 V_m(z) I_m^*(z),$$

we have

$$N_m = (2/ab)^{\frac{1}{2}} = N. \tag{9.34}$$

Thus in the present case N_m is independent of m.

Integrating equations (9.32) over the rectangle $x = 0, a$ and $y = 0, b$, we obtain

$$V_0(z) = b^{-1} \int_0^b \int_0^a E_x \, dx \, dy = \int_0^a E_x \, dx,$$

$$\tag{9.35}$$

$$I_0(z) = a^{-1} \int_0^b \int_0^a H_y \, dx \, dy = (b/a) \int_0^a H_y \, dx.$$

Multiplying equations (9.32) by $\cos (n\pi x/a)$ and integrating over the same rectangle, we find that the terms for which $m \neq n$ vanish. Thus

$$V_n(z) = N \int_0^b \int_0^a E_x \cos \frac{n\pi x}{a} \, dx \, dy = bN \int_0^a E_x \cos \frac{n\pi x}{a} \, dx,$$

$$(9.36)$$

$$I_n(z) = N \int_0^b \int_0^a H_y \cos \frac{n\pi x}{a} \, dx \, dy = bN \int_0^a H_y \cos \frac{n\pi x}{a} \, dx.$$

In the present case the field is independent of y and we could have dispensed with integration in this direction. In waveguides, however, the field is usually a function of both coordinates and the integration has to be performed over the cross-sectional area. Furthermore, in anticipation of the final form of the results we have chosen the coefficients V_n and I_n deliberately in such a way that their physical dimensions are those of voltage and current. The preceding equations give these coefficients in terms of the transverse field components just as equations (9.32) express the transverse field in terms of the coefficients.

Differentiating equations (9.35) and (9.36) with respect to z, we have

$$\frac{dV_0(z)}{dz} = \int_0^a \frac{\partial E_x}{\partial z} \, dx, \qquad \frac{dI_0(z)}{dz} = (b/a) \int_0^a \frac{\partial H_y}{\partial z} \, dx,$$

$$(9.37)$$

$$\frac{dV_n(z)}{dz} = bN \int_0^a \frac{\partial E_x}{\partial z} \cos \frac{n\pi x}{a} \, dx,$$

$$\frac{dI_n(z)}{dz} = bN \int_0^a \frac{\partial H_y}{\partial z} \cos \frac{n\pi x}{a} \, dx.$$

To obtain the equations connecting the V_n and the I_n, it is necessary only to substitute from Maxwell's equations (9.30) into (9.37) and to perform the integrations. Thus

$$\frac{dV_0(z)}{dz} = -j\omega\mu \int_0^a H_y \, dx + \int_0^a \frac{\partial E_z}{\partial x} \, dx.$$

The last term equals $E_z(a) - E_z(0) = 0$. Substituting H_y from equations (9.32) and integrating, we have

$$\frac{dV_0(z)}{dz} = -j\frac{\omega\mu a}{b} I_0(z).$$ (9.38)

Similarly

$$\frac{dI_0(z)}{dz} = -j\omega(b/a) \int_0^a \epsilon(x, z) E_x \, dx$$

(9.39)

$$= -\sum_{m=0}^{\infty} Y_{0m} V_m(z),$$

where

$$Y_{00} = j\omega(b/a^2) \int_0^a \epsilon(x, z) \, dx,$$

$$Y_{0m} = j\omega(b/a) N \int_0^a \epsilon(x, z) \cos \frac{m\pi x}{a} \, dx, \qquad m \neq 0.$$

In the same manner

$$\frac{dI_n(z)}{dz} = -j\omega bN \int_0^a \epsilon(x, z) E_x \cos \frac{n\pi x}{a} \, dx$$

(9.40)

$$= -\sum_{m=0}^{\infty} Y_{nm} V_m(z),$$

where

$$Y_{n0} = j\omega(b/a) N \int_0^a \epsilon(x, z) \cos \frac{n\pi x}{a} \, dx,$$

$$Y_{nm} = j\omega bN^2 \int_0^a \epsilon(x, z) \cos \frac{m\pi x}{a} \cos \frac{n\pi x}{a} \, dx, \qquad m \neq 0$$

$$= (2j\omega/a) \int_0^a \epsilon(x, z) \cos \frac{m\pi x}{a} \cos \frac{n\pi x}{a} \, dx.$$

For the middle equation in the set (9.37) we have

$$\frac{dV_n}{dz} = -j\omega\mu bN \int_0^a H_y \cos \frac{n\pi x}{a} \, dx + bN \int_0^a \frac{\partial E_z}{\partial x} \cos \frac{n\pi x}{a} \, dx. \quad (9.41)$$

In view of equations (9.32) and the orthogonality of the cosines, the first integral on the right is

$$\int_0^a H_y \cos \frac{n\pi x}{a} \, dx = \tfrac{1}{2} a N I_n(z). \tag{9.42}$$

The second integral we integrate by parts

$$\int_0^a \frac{\partial E_z}{\partial x} \cos \frac{n\pi x}{a} \, dx = E_z \cos \frac{n\pi x}{a} \Big|_0^a + \frac{n\pi}{a} \int_0^a E_z \sin \frac{n\pi x}{a} \, dx.$$

The first term vanishes at both limits since E_z vanishes there. In the second term we substitute from equation (9.31), integrate by parts once more, and substitute from equations (9.32). Thus we have

$$\frac{n\pi}{j\omega a} \int_0^a \frac{1}{\epsilon} \frac{\partial H_y}{\partial x} \sin \frac{n\pi x}{a} \, dx = \frac{n\pi}{j\omega a} H_y \epsilon^{-1} \sin \frac{n\pi x}{a} \Big|_0^a +$$

$$- \frac{n\pi}{j\omega a} \int_0^a H_y \frac{d}{dx} \left[\epsilon^{-1} \sin \frac{n\pi x}{a} \right] dx.$$

The first term on the right vanishes and the second becomes, after the substitution from equations (9.32),

$$- \frac{n\pi I_0(z)}{j\omega a b} \int_0^a \frac{d}{dx} \left[\epsilon^{-1} \sin \frac{n\pi x}{a} \right] dx$$

$$- \sum_{m=1}^{\infty} \frac{n\pi N I_m(z)}{j\omega a} \int_0^a \cos \frac{m\pi x}{a} \frac{d}{dx} \left[\epsilon^{-1} \sin \frac{n\pi x}{a} \right] dx.$$

The first term may be integrated immediately, and it vanishes. The integrals in the second term may be integrated by parts. Thus the entire expression becomes

$$- \sum_{m=1}^{\infty} I_m(z) \frac{nm\pi^2 N}{j\omega a^2} \int_0^a \epsilon^{-1} \sin \frac{n\pi x}{a} \sin \frac{m\pi x}{a} \, dx.$$

This is our final expression for the second integral in equation (9.41) The first integral is given by equation (9.42). Therefore

$$\frac{dV_n(z)}{dz} = - \sum_{m=1}^{\infty} Z_{nm} I_m(z),$$

$$Z_{nm} = \frac{2nm\pi^2}{j\omega a^3} \int_0^a \epsilon^{-1} \sin \frac{n\pi x}{a} \sin \frac{m\pi x}{a} \, dx, \qquad m \neq n \tag{9.43}$$

$$Z_{nn} = j\omega\mu + \frac{2n^2\pi^2}{j\omega a^3} \int_0^a \epsilon^{-1} \sin^2 \frac{n\pi x}{a} \, dx.$$

Thus an infinite set of ordinary differential equations (9.38), (9.39), (9.40), and (9.43) of the type connecting the voltages and currents in an infinite system of coupled transmission lines has been obtained. Here there are no "transmission lines" in a physical sense; instead one could speak of *coupled modes of propagation*. Summarizing the results and isolating the terms involving the self-impedances and self-admittances from the mutual terms, we have

$$\frac{dV_0(z)}{dz} = -j\,\frac{\omega\mu a}{b}\,I_0(z),$$

$$\frac{dI_0(z)}{dz} = -Y_{00}V_0(z) - \sum_{m=1}^{\infty} Y_{0m}V_m(z),$$

(9.44)

$$\frac{dV_n(z)}{dz} = -Z_{nn}I_n(z) - \sum_{m=1}^{\infty}{}' Z_{nn}I_m(z),$$

$$\frac{dI_n(z)}{dz} = -Y_{nn}V_n(z) - \sum_{m=0}^{\infty}{}' Y_{nm}V_m(z),$$

where the primes denote the omission from the summation of the terms for which $m = n$. For the principal mode the admittance Y_{00} depends solely on the average dielectric constant over the interval $0 \le x \le a$. For the higher modes the self-admittance also depends largely on the average dielectric constant,

$$Y_{nn} = (j\omega/a) \int_0^a \epsilon(x, z)\, dx + (j\omega/a) \int_0^a \epsilon(x, z)\, \cos\frac{2n\pi x}{a}\, dx$$

except when $\epsilon(x, z)$ is a periodic function of x, proportional to $\cos(2n\pi x/a)$, so that the last term becomes significant. The mutual admittances tend to be small in general. They all vanish if $\epsilon(x, z)$ is independent of x. If $\epsilon(x, z) = \epsilon_{av} + \Delta\,\epsilon(x, z)$, then they will depend only on the deviation of ϵ from its average value ϵ_{av}. There will be further cancellations after these deviations are multiplied by oscillating functions of x. The same may be said about the impedances. Thus it is possible to obtain approximate solutions by the method explained in Section 9.2. First we neglect the coupling and solve the equations for the individual modes. We then use these solutions to obtain their effects on other modes.

Equations (9.44) are called the *generalized telegraphist's equations*. For certain physical systems additional terms appear on the right side. In the equation for a typical dV_n/dz there appears a linear function of the V_m as well as of the I_m. Similarly, the equation for dI_n/dz would include a linear function of the I_m.

9.6 Waves between uniformly bent planes

In the preceding problem the modes were coupled by the variations in the dielectric constant. In the case of uniformly bent planes, Figure 9.4, they are coupled by the curvature. Let us use bent cylin-

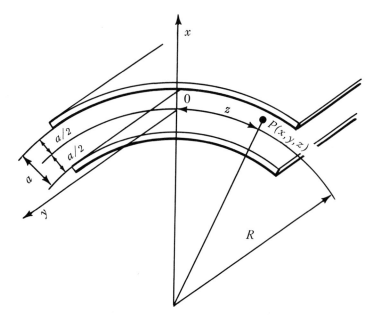

FIGURE 9.4 *Bent parallel planes.*

drical coordinates as indicated. The y coordinate will be measured along the axis of bending, the x coordinate from the cylindrical surface half-way between the uniformly bent planes (cylinders, of course), and the z coordinate in this surface. If R is the radius of the mean cylindrical surface, then the differential element of distance is

$$ds^2 = dx^2 + dy^2 + \left(1 + \frac{x}{R}\right)^2 dz^2$$

since the distances along the z lines for equal increments dz are proportional to their radii of curvature $R + x$. Hence, Maxwell's equations in uniformly bent cylindrical coordinates may be obtained from the general equations in curvilinear coordinates (Appendix II) by letting

$$e_1 = e_2 = 1, \qquad e_3 = 1 + \frac{x}{R}.$$

Considering again fields independent of y and with magnetic intensity parallel to the axis of bending, we have

$$\frac{\partial E_x}{\partial z} = -j\omega\mu \left(1 + \frac{x}{R}\right) H_y + \frac{\partial}{\partial x}\left[\left(1 + \frac{x}{R}\right) E_z\right]$$

$$(9.45)$$

$$\frac{\partial H_y}{\partial z} = -j\omega\epsilon \left(1 + \frac{x}{R}\right) E_x, \qquad E_z = \frac{1}{j\omega\epsilon}\frac{\partial H_y}{\partial x}.$$

Had we defined x as the distance from one of the bent planes, we would have expressed the transverse field components by a cosine series (9.32). As it is, one should replace in these series x by $x + (a/2)$. Thus

$$E_x = \frac{V_0(z)}{a} + N \sum_{m=1}^{\infty} V_m(z) \cos \frac{m\pi}{a}\left(x + \frac{a}{2}\right),$$

$$(9.46)$$

$$H_y = \frac{I_0(z)}{b} + N \sum_{m=1}^{\infty} I_m(z) \cos \frac{m\pi}{a}\left(x + \frac{a}{2}\right),$$

where we have taken into consideration that N_m is independent of m.

The generalized telegraphist's equations are obtained exactly as in the preceding section. They will be of the form (9.44) except for the first equation which will be more general, that is,

$$\frac{dV_0(z)}{dz} = -\frac{j\omega\mu a}{b} I_0(z) - \sum_{m=1}^{\infty} Z_{0m} I_m(z),$$

where

$$Z_{0m} = \frac{j\omega\mu N}{R} \int_{-a/2}^{a/2} x \cos \frac{m\pi}{a}\left(x + \frac{a}{2}\right) dx. \qquad (9.47)$$

The remaining impedances and admittances are

$$Y_{0m} = \frac{j\omega\epsilon bN}{aR} \int_{-a/2}^{a/2} x \cos\frac{m\pi}{a}\left(x + \frac{a}{2}\right) dx, \qquad m = 0, 1, 2, \cdots,$$

$$Z_{nm} = \frac{1}{aR}\left(j\omega\mu + \frac{mn\pi^2}{j\omega\epsilon a^2}\right) \int_{a-/2}^{a/2} x \cos\left[(m - n)\pi\left(\frac{x}{a} + \frac{1}{2}\right)\right] dx$$

$$\hspace{6cm} (9.48)$$

$$+ \frac{1}{aR}\left(j\omega\mu - \frac{mn\pi^2}{j\omega\epsilon a^2}\right) \int_{-a/2}^{a/2} x \cos\left[(m + n)\pi\left(\frac{x}{a} + \frac{1}{2}\right)\right] dx,$$

$$Y_{nm} = \frac{2j\omega\epsilon}{aR} \int_{-a/2}^{a/2} x \cos\frac{m\pi}{a}\left(x + \frac{a}{2}\right) \cos\frac{n\pi}{a}\left(x + \frac{a}{2}\right) dx.$$

The last two equations are valid when neither n nor m is equal to zero.

9.7   Waves between imperfectly conducting parallel planes

Let us return to parallel planes and assume that they are not perfect conductors. The fields which *between* the planes are described by equations (9.30) and (9.31) will be considered. At the boundaries E_z is proportional to H_y. Thus

$$E_z(0, z) = Z_1 H_y(0, z), \qquad E_z(a, z) = -Z_2 H_y(a, z), \quad (9.49)$$

where Z_1 and Z_2 are the surface impedances whose real parts are positive. The difference in algebraic signs is due to the fact that the power flows downward into the lower plane, $x = 0$, Figure 6.1, and upward into the upper plane $x = a$.

The transverse field components shall be expressed as cosine series, equations (9.32). The longitudinal component E_z *between* the planes may be obtained from equation (9.31) by differentiation

$$E_z = -\frac{N}{j\omega\epsilon} \sum_{m=1}^{\infty} \frac{m\pi}{a} I_m(z) \sin\frac{m\pi x}{a}, \qquad 0 < z < a. \quad (9.50)$$

At $x = 0$ and $x = a$ it is given by equations (9.49) while the series vanishes there. From the theory of Fourier series, and particularly of sine series, it is known that a function which *does not vanish at the ends of a closed interval*, such as $(0, a)$, may be expressed by a sine series in an *open* interval $(0+, a - 0)$. The series is nonuniformly convergent. That is, as x approaches zero or a, the series approaches the right values; but these values cannot be obtained simply by setting $x = 0$ or $x = a$ in the series itself. All terms of the series vanish at these points. Furthermore, the derivative series does not converge. Thus it is not permissible to substitute from equation (9.50) into equations (9.30). However, in Section 9.5 we have explained a method of obtaining the equations for the coefficients $V_n(z)$, $I_n(z)$ which does not involve such a substitution. For example, from equations (9.37) and (9.30) we have

$$\frac{dV_0(z)}{dz} = \int_0^a \frac{\partial E_x}{\partial z}\, dx = -j\omega\mu \int_0^a H_y\, dx + \int_0^a \frac{\partial E_z}{\partial x}\, dx$$

$$= -\frac{j\omega\mu a}{b} I_0(z) + E_z(x, z) \Big|_{x=0}^{x=a}$$

$$= -\frac{j\omega\mu a}{b} I_0(z) + E_z(a, z) - E_z(0, z).$$

Using the boundary conditions (9.49) and equations (9.32) for $H_y(a, z)$ and $H_y(0, z)$, we obtain

$$\frac{dV_0(z)}{dz} = -\left(\frac{Z_1 + Z_2}{b} + j\,\frac{\omega\mu a}{b}\right) I_0(z) - \sum_{m=1}^{\infty} Z_{0m} I_m(z),$$

$$\text{(9.51)}$$

$$Z_{0m} = N[Z_1 + (-)^m Z_2], \qquad N = \sqrt{2/ab}.$$

Similarly

$$\frac{dV_n(z)}{dz} = -j\omega\mu bN \int_0^a H_y \cos\frac{n\pi x}{a}\, dx + bN \int_0^a \frac{\partial E_z}{\partial x} \cos\frac{n\pi x}{a}\, dx.$$

The first term on the right is calculated by using the series for H_y. The second integral may be integrated by parts

$$\int_0^a \frac{\partial E_z}{\partial x} \cos\frac{n\pi x}{a}\, dx = E_z \cos\frac{n\pi x}{a}\Big|_0^a$$

$$+ \frac{n\pi}{a} \int_0^a E_z \sin\frac{n\pi x}{a}\, dx \quad \frac{-Z_1 + (-)^n Z_2}{b} I_0(z) - \sum_{m=1}^{\infty} \quad \text{(9.52)}$$

$$\times [Z_1 + (-)^{n+m} Z_2] N I_m(z) + \frac{n\pi}{a} \int_0^a E_z \sin\frac{n\pi x}{a}\, dx.$$

We could substitute from equation (9.50) for E_z and integrate. In this case we would obtain the correct result. However, the integration of nonuniformly converging series should be performed with care. This integration can be avoided by substituting from equation (9.31) and integrating by parts

$$\int_0^a \frac{\partial H_y}{\partial x} \sin \frac{n\pi x}{a}\, dx = H_y \sin \frac{n\pi x}{a} \Big|_0^a - \frac{n\pi}{a} \int_0^a H_y \cos \frac{n\pi x}{a}\, dx$$

$$= \tfrac{1}{2} n\pi N I_n(z).$$

Using this result and equation (9.52), we have

$$\frac{dV_n(z)}{dz} = -Z_{nn} I_n(z) - \sum_m Z_{nm} I_n(z),$$

$$Z_{nn} = j\omega\mu + \frac{n^2\pi^2}{j\omega\epsilon a^2} + \frac{2(Z_1 + Z_2)}{a}, \tag{9.53}$$

$$Z_{nm} = \frac{2[Z_1 + (-)^{n+m} Z_2]}{a}, \qquad n, m = 1, 2, 3, \cdots.$$

When n or m vanishes (but not both), Z_{nm} is given in equations (9.51).

No special difficulties arise in obtaining

$$\frac{dI_n(z)}{dz} = -j\omega\epsilon V_n(z). \tag{9.54}$$

9.8   Generalized coordinates

The coefficients in such series as in equations (9.32) may be properly called the *generalized coordinates* of the electromagnetic field. They are similar to the generalized coordinates used for describing the state of a mechanical system or to mesh currents in the network analysis. There is no unique set of such coordinates for any given problem. It is clear from the preceding sections that it is desirable to choose them in such a way that the coupling coefficients are small. It would seem that the optimum choice would be a set for which all mutual coefficients vanish. However, this is not necessarily the case. In the problem of uniformly bent planes a choice of cylindrical coordinates and separation of variables would yield generalized coordinates (the coefficients of certain Bessel functions) for which all coupling coefficients vanish. Nevertheless when R is large, the analysis by the method given in Section 9.6 is much simpler.

Appendix I

A.1 Coordinate systems and vector components

The most frequently used coordinate systems are the *rectangular* or *Cartesian*, *cylindrical*, and *spherical*; in these systems a typical point P is denoted by (x, y, z), (ρ, φ, z), (r, θ, φ), respectively. The meaning of these coordinates is explained in Figure A.1. Thus x, y, z

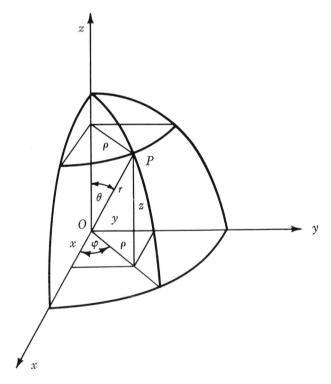

FIGURE A.1 *Coordinate systems.*

are the distances from three mutually perpendicular reference planes; ρ is the distance from the z axis; r is the distance from the origin O; the "polar angle" θ is the angle from the z axis to the radius OP; the "longitude" φ is the angle from the half plane determined by the z axis and the positive x axis to the half plane through P. Any vector

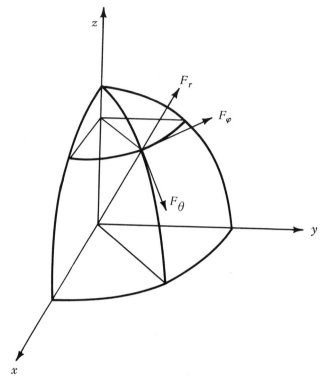

FIGURE A.2 *Vector components.*

$\bar{F}$ can be resolved along three mutually perpendicular directions. Figure A.2 illustrates such a resolution in a spherical frame of reference. The components F_r, F_θ, and F_φ are positive in the directions of increasing r, θ, and φ, respectively.

A.2 Transformation of coordinates

From Figure A.1 we deduce the following relations between Cartesian, cylindrical, and spherical coordinates:

$$x = \rho \cos \varphi = r \sin \theta \cos \varphi; \qquad \rho = \sqrt{x^2 + y^2} = r \sin \theta$$
$$y = \rho \sin \varphi = r \sin \theta \sin \varphi; \qquad \varphi = \tan^{-1}(y/x) = \varphi$$
$$z = z = r \cos \theta; \qquad z = z = r \cos \theta$$
$$r = \sqrt{x^2 + y^2 + z^2} = \sqrt{\rho^2 + z^2};$$
$$\theta = \tan^{-1}\left[(x^2 + y^2)^{\frac{1}{2}}/z\right] = \tan^{-1}(\rho/z);$$
$$\varphi = \tan^{-1}(y/x) = \varphi.$$

A.3 Elements of length, area, and volume

The square of the hypotenuse of a right triangle equals the sum of the squares of its sides. From this theorem it follows that

$$ds^2 = dx^2 + dy^2 + dz^2,$$

where ds is the distance between two neighboring points. Although the theorem of Pythagoras does not hold for large curvilinear triangles on the surface of a sphere and most other curved surfaces, it does hold for infinitesimal right triangles and we have the following expression:

$$ds^2 = ds_u^2 + ds_v^2 + ds_w^2,$$

where ds_u, ds_v, and ds_w are the infinitesimal sides of a right-angled

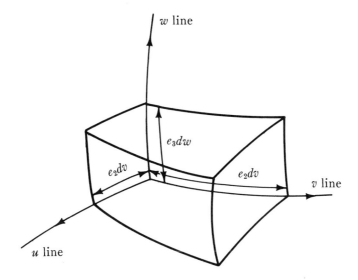

FIGURE A.3 *An elementary coordinate cell in orthogonal curvilinear coordinates.*

curvilinear parallelpiped (see Figure A.3) formed by mutually perpendicular surfaces, such as spheres, cones, and half planes of spherical coordinate system. Curvilinear coordinates may be defined in various ways but invariably the differential lengths along coordinate lines are proportional to the differentials of the coordinates,

$$ds_u = e_1\, du, \qquad ds_v = e_2\, dv, \qquad ds_w = e_3\, dw.$$

Hence

$$ds^2 = e_1^2\, du^2 + e_2^2\, dv^2 + e_3^2\, dw^2.$$

The elements of area and volume are

$$dS_{uv} = ds_u\, ds_v = e_1 e_2\, du\, dv,$$

$$dS_{vw} = ds_v\, ds_w = e_2 e_3\, dv\, dw,$$

$$dS_{wu} = ds_w\, ds_u = e_3 e_1\, dw\, du,$$

$$dV = ds_u\, ds_v\, ds_w = e_1 e_2 e_3\, du\, dv\, dw.$$

In spherical coordinates (r, θ, φ) we have

$$e_1 = 1, \qquad e_2 = r, \qquad e_3 = r \sin \theta.$$

In cylindrical coordinates (ρ, φ, z)

$$e_1 = 1, \qquad e_2 = \rho, \qquad e_3 = 1.$$

A.4   Gradient

Consider a function $V(u, v, w)$ which depends only on the coordinates of a point. Loci of equal values of this function

$$V(u, v, w) = \text{constant}$$

are called *level surfaces* or *contour surfaces*; in the two dimensional cases we have *level lines* or *contour lines*. Electric potential is an example of such a function.

The maximum rate of change of V is along the normals to contour surfaces. This rate of change is called the *gradient* of V and is a vector whose magnitude is

$$|\operatorname{grad} V| = \frac{dV}{ds},$$

where ds is taken along the normal to the contour surface. The component of this vector along the u line is obtained if we multiply this magnitude by the cosine of the angle between the normal and the u line, ds/ds_u. Hence

$$\operatorname{grad}_u V = \frac{dV}{ds_u}, \qquad \operatorname{grad}_v V = \frac{dV}{ds_v}, \qquad \operatorname{grad}_w V = \frac{dV}{ds_w}.$$

In Cartesian, cylindrical, and spherical coordinates we have

$$\text{grad } V = \left(\frac{\partial V}{\partial x}, \frac{\partial V}{\partial y}, \frac{\partial V}{\partial z} \right),$$

$$\text{grad } V = \left(\frac{\partial V}{\partial \rho}, \frac{1}{\rho} \frac{\partial V}{\partial \varphi}, \frac{\partial V}{\partial z} \right),$$

$$\text{grad } V = \left(\frac{\partial V}{\partial r}, \frac{1}{r} \frac{\partial V}{\partial \theta}, \frac{1}{r \sin \theta} \frac{\partial V}{\partial \varphi} \right).$$

A.5 Circulation of a vector and curl of a vector

Circulation of a vector $\vec{F}$ round a closed curve is the line integral of its tangential component round the curve. Thus the electromotive force round a closed curve is the circulation of $\vec{E}$, and the magnetomotive force the circulation of $\vec{H}$.

Consider an infinitesimal element of area centered at a point P. For a certain orientation of the area the circulation of $\vec{F}$ round its edge per unit area is maximum. This vector quantity is called the curl of $\vec{F}$ and is denoted by curl $\vec{F}$. Referring to Maxwell's laws, we observe that electric current density is the curl of $\vec{H}$, and magnetic current density is the negative of the curl of $\vec{E}$. Thus for time-harmonic fields

$$\text{curl } \vec{E} = -j\omega\mu\vec{H}, \qquad \text{curl } \vec{H} = (\sigma + j\omega\epsilon)\vec{E}.$$

The components of curl $\vec{F}$ in orthogonal coordinates may be calculated from its definition. Consider Figure A.4 which shows an infinitesimal curvilinear rectangle $ABCD$ in a surface formed by v and w lines when u is constant. The contribution to the circulation from the sides BC and DA is

$$\frac{\partial}{\partial v} (F_w \, ds_w) \, dv = \frac{\partial}{\partial v} (e_3 F_w) \, dw \, dv.$$

The contribution from AB and CD is

$$-\frac{\partial}{\partial w} (F_v \, ds_v) \, dw = -\frac{\partial}{\partial w} (e_2 F_v) \, dv \, dw.$$

The area of the rectangle is $e_2 e_3 \, dv \, dw$. Hence

$$\text{curl}_u \vec{F} = \frac{1}{e_2 e_3} \left[\frac{\partial}{\partial v} (e_3 F_w) - \frac{\partial}{\partial w} (e_2 F_v) \right].$$

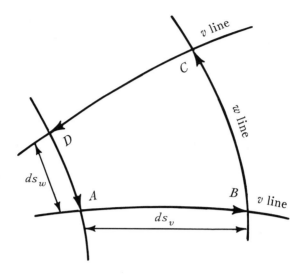

FIGURE A.4 *Assisting in the calculation of the u component of the curl of a vector.*

The remaining components may be obtained by cyclic permutation of u, v, w and 1, 2, 3.

A.6 Flux of a vector and divergence

The flux of a vector $\vec{F}$ through a closed surface is the surface integral of its normal component. If we choose such a surface around some point P and let it shrink to zero, the limit of the flux per unit volume is called the *divergence* of vector $\vec{F}$ and denoted by div $\vec{F}$.

Consider an elementary coordinate cell about P (see Figure A.3). The area of a u surface through P intercepted by the cell, is $e_2 e_3 \, dv \, dw$ and the flux across it is $e_2 e_3 F_u \, dv \, dw$. The rate of change of this flux in the u direction is

$$\frac{\partial}{\partial u} (e_2 e_3 F_u) \, dv \, dw$$

and the residual flux through the u faces of the cell is

$$\frac{\partial}{\partial u} (e_2 e_3 F_u) \, du \, dv \, dw.$$

By a cyclic permutation of u, v, w and 1, 2, 3 we obtain the residual fluxes through the remaining pairs of faces and

$$\text{div } \bar{F} = \frac{1}{e_1 e_2 e_3} \left[\frac{\partial}{\partial u} (e_2 e_3 F_u) + \frac{\partial}{\partial v} (e_3 e_1 F_v) + \frac{\partial}{\partial w} (e_1 e_2 F_w) \right].$$

A.7   Laplacian

The *Laplacian* is defined as the divergence of a gradient

$$\Delta V = \text{div grad } V.$$

Thus

$$\Delta V = \frac{1}{e_1 e_2 e_3} \left[\frac{\partial}{\partial u} \left(\frac{e_2 e_3}{e_1} \frac{\partial V}{\partial u} \right) + \frac{\partial}{\partial v} \left(\frac{e_3 e_1}{e_2} \frac{\partial V}{\partial v} \right) + \frac{\partial}{\partial w} \left(\frac{e_1 e_2}{e_3} \frac{\partial V}{\partial w} \right) \right].$$

Appendix II

Maxwell's differential equations

In Cartesian coordinates

$$\frac{\partial E_z}{\partial y} - \frac{\partial E_y}{\partial z} = -j\omega\mu H_x, \qquad \frac{\partial H_z}{\partial y} - \frac{\partial H_y}{\partial z} = (\sigma + j\omega\epsilon) E_x$$

$$\frac{\partial E_x}{\partial z} - \frac{\partial E_z}{\partial x} = -j\omega\mu H_y, \qquad \frac{\partial H_x}{\partial z} - \frac{\partial H_z}{\partial x} = (\sigma + j\omega\epsilon) E_y$$

$$\frac{\partial E_y}{\partial x} - \frac{\partial E_x}{\partial y} = -j\omega\mu H_z, \qquad \frac{\partial H_y}{\partial x} - \frac{\partial H_x}{\partial y} = (\sigma + j\omega\epsilon) E_z.$$

In cylindrical coordinates

$$\frac{\partial E_z}{\partial \varphi} - \rho \frac{\partial E_\varphi}{\partial z} = -j\omega\mu\rho H_\rho, \qquad \frac{\partial H_z}{\partial \varphi} - \rho \frac{\partial H_\varphi}{\partial z} = (\sigma + j\omega\epsilon)\rho E_\rho,$$

$$\frac{\partial E_\rho}{\partial z} - \frac{\partial E_z}{\partial \rho} = -j\omega\mu H_\varphi, \qquad \frac{\partial H_\rho}{\partial z} - \frac{\partial H_z}{\partial \rho} = (\sigma + j\omega\epsilon) E_\varphi,$$

$$\frac{\partial}{\partial \rho} (\rho E_\varphi) - \frac{\partial E_\rho}{\partial \varphi} = -j\omega\mu\rho H_z, \qquad \frac{\partial}{\partial \rho} (\rho H_\varphi) - \frac{\partial H_\rho}{\partial \varphi} = (\sigma + j\omega\epsilon)\rho E_z.$$

In spherical coordinates

$$\frac{\partial}{\partial \theta} (\sin \theta E_\varphi) - \frac{\partial E_\theta}{\partial \varphi} = -j\omega\mu r \sin \theta H_r,$$

$$\frac{\partial}{\partial \theta} (\sin \theta H_\varphi) - \frac{\partial H_\theta}{\partial \varphi} = (\sigma + j\omega\epsilon) r \sin \theta E_r,$$

$$\frac{\partial E_r}{\partial \varphi} - \sin \theta \frac{\partial}{\partial r} (r E_\varphi) = -j\omega\mu r \sin \theta H_\theta,$$

$$\frac{\partial H_r}{\partial \varphi} - \sin \theta \frac{\partial}{\partial r} (r H_\varphi) = (\sigma + j\omega\epsilon) r \sin \theta E_\theta,$$

$$\frac{\partial}{\partial r} (r E_\theta) - \frac{\partial E_r}{\partial \theta} = -j\omega\mu r H_\varphi,$$

$$\frac{\partial}{\partial r} (r H_\theta) - \frac{\partial H_r}{\partial \theta} = (\sigma + j\omega\epsilon) r E_\varphi.$$

In general curvilinear coordinates

$$\frac{\partial(e_3 E_w)}{\partial v} - \frac{\partial(e_2 E_v)}{\partial w} = -j\omega\mu e_2 e_3 H_u,$$

$$\frac{\partial(e_3 H_w)}{\partial v} - \frac{\partial(e_2 H_v)}{\partial w} = (\sigma + j\omega\epsilon) e_2 e_3 E_u,$$

$$\frac{\partial(e_1 E_u)}{\partial w} - \frac{\partial(e_3 E_w)}{\partial u} = -j\omega\mu e_3 e_1 H_v,$$

$$\frac{\partial(e_1 H_u)}{\partial w} - \frac{\partial(e_3 H_w)}{\partial u} = (\sigma + j\omega\epsilon) e_3 e_1 E_v,$$

$$\frac{\partial(e_2 E_v)}{\partial u} - \frac{\partial(c_1 E_u)}{\partial v} = -j\omega\mu e_1 e_2 H_w,$$

$$\frac{\partial(e_2 H_v)}{\partial u} - \frac{\partial(e_1 H_u)}{\partial v} = (\sigma + j\omega\epsilon) e_1 e_2 E_w.$$

Appendix III

Laplace's equation

In Cartesian coordinates

$$\frac{\partial^2 V}{\partial x^2} + \frac{\partial^2 V}{\partial y^2} + \frac{\partial^2 V}{\partial z^2} = 0.$$

In cylindrical coordinates

$$\rho \frac{\partial}{\partial \rho}\left(\rho \frac{\partial V}{\partial \rho}\right) + \frac{\partial^2 V}{\partial \varphi^2} + \rho^2 \frac{\partial^2 V}{\partial z^2} = 0.$$

In spherical coordinates

$$\sin^2 \theta \frac{\partial}{\partial r}\left(r^2 \frac{\partial V}{\partial r}\right) + \sin \theta \frac{\partial}{\partial \theta}\left(\sin \theta \frac{\partial V}{\partial \theta}\right) + \frac{\partial^2 V}{\partial \varphi^2} = 0.$$

In general curvilinear coordinates

$$\frac{\partial}{\partial u}\left(\frac{e_2 e_3}{e_1}\frac{\partial V}{\partial u}\right) + \frac{\partial}{\partial v}\left(\frac{e_3 e_1}{e_2}\frac{\partial V}{\partial v}\right) + \frac{\partial}{\partial w}\left(\frac{e_1 e_2}{e_3}\frac{\partial V}{\partial w}\right) = 0.$$

Problems

1.2–1   Two homogeneous spheres of mass m are equally and uniformly charged. Express the charge q on each sphere in terms of m when the force of repulsion just annihilates the force of gravitational attraction.

   Answer: $q = 86\,m$ micro-microcoulombs.

1.4–1   Show that the following equations are the differential equations for the electric lines of force:

$$\frac{dx}{E_x} = \frac{dy}{E_y} = \frac{dz}{E_z}, \quad \text{in Cartesian coordinates}$$

$$\frac{d\rho}{E_\rho} = \frac{\rho\,d\varphi}{E_\varphi} = \frac{dz}{E_z}, \quad \text{in cylindrical coordinates}$$

$$\frac{dr}{E_r} = \frac{r\,d\theta}{E_\theta} = \frac{r\sin\theta\,d\varphi}{E_\varphi}, \quad \text{in spherical coordinates.}$$

See Appendix A.1 for the definitions of r, ρ, θ, and φ.

1.10–1   A copper sphere of radius a is submerged in sea water far below its surface. An insulated wire conveys to it current I. Calculate the following:

(a)   the power P dissipated in sea water;
(b)   the voltage V from the sphere to infinity along a radius or a line made up of segments of radii and circular arcs concentric with the sphere.

   Answer: $P = I^2/4\pi\sigma a,\qquad V = I/4\pi\sigma a$

   $\qquad\qquad = I^2/20\pi a,\qquad\ \ = I/20\pi a.$

1.11–1   Consider a current element of moment Il in a conducting medium. Calculate the voltage from point (r_0, θ_0) to infinity along two paths:

(a)   along the radius $\theta = \theta_0$,

(b)   along the meridian from (r_0, θ_0) to (r_0, θ_1) and then along the
radius $\theta = \theta_1$.

Answer: $V = \dfrac{Il \cos \theta_0}{4\pi\sigma r_0^2}$.

1.15–1   A charged ring (thin circular wire) of mean radius a is
in the xy plane and coaxial with the z axis. The total charge is q.
Find the electric intensity on the axis of the ring.

Answer: $E_z = (qz/4\pi\epsilon)\,(a^2 + z^2)^{-3/2}$.

1.15–2   A sphere of radius a is imbedded in free space. Let q be
the charge on the sphere. Find the voltage along a radius from the
sphere to infinity.

Answer: $V = q/4\pi\epsilon_0 a$.

In circuit theory the quantity $C = 4\pi\epsilon_0 a$ is called the *capacitance*
of the sphere.

1.15–3   Assume that in Problem 1.15–2 we bring in infinitesimal
quantities of charge, dq. Work is done against the field of the charged
sphere. Calculate the work done in raising the charge on the sphere
from $q = q_1$ to $q = q_2 > q_1$.

Answer: $W = (q_2^2 - q_1^2)/8\pi\epsilon_0 a$.

1.15–4   Consider a metal sphere of radius a with a negative charge
$-q$. Suppose that an electron, originally at rest, starts moving. Find
its speed at infinity (assuming that this speed turns out to be a
small fraction of the speed of light).

Answer: $v = \sqrt{q(e/m)/2\pi\epsilon_0 r}$ $r \gg a$.

1.16–1   Consider an electric dipole along the z axis at the origin
of the coordinate system. Obtain the equation for an electric line
of force passing through the point $r = r_0,\ \theta = \frac{1}{2}\pi,\ \varphi = \varphi_0$.

Answer: $r = r_0 \sin^2 \theta,\ \varphi = \varphi_0$.

1.17–1   Assume that a uniform magnetic field of flux density
B_0 is parallel to the z axis. Suppose that at time $t = 0$, an electron

(charge $-e$, mass m) is at the origin and is moving in the direction of the y axis with a speed v_0.

(a) Show that the equations of motion are

$$\frac{dv_x}{dt} = -(e/m)B_0v_y, \qquad \frac{dv_y}{dt} = (e/m)B_0v_x.$$

(b) Prove that thereafter the speed of the electron remains constant.

(c) Show that the electron is moving in a circle whose center is on the negative x axis and whose radius equals $v_0B_0^{-1}(e/m)^{-1}$, and that the angular frequency is $\omega = (e/m)B_0$.

1.21–1   Find the magnetic intensity in the interior of a cylinder of radius a if the current in the cylinder is I and is distributed uniformly.

Answer: $H_\varphi = I\rho/2\pi a^2$.

1.22–1   Calculate the magnetic intensity on the axis of a thin circular ring of mean radius a. Let I be the current and z the distance from the plane of the ring.

Answer: $H_z = \frac{1}{2}a^2I(a^2 + z^2)^{-3/2}$.

1.22–2   Using the result of Problem 1.22–1, calculate the magnetic ·field on the axis of a solenoid of radius a, extending from $z = 0$ to $z = l$. Assume that the current in the winding is I and the number of turns per unit length is n. Assume that the winding is so thin that the current can be smoothed over the cylindrical surface of the solenoid. In particular, compare the magnetic intensities at the center of the solenoid and at its ends when $l \gg 2a$.

Answer: $H_z = \frac{1}{2}nI[(l - z)r_1^{-1} + zr^{-1}]$, where

$$r = (a^2 + z^2)^{\frac{1}{2}}, \quad r_1 = [a^2 + (l - z)^2]^{1/2}$$

and

$$H_z(l/2) \simeq nI \simeq 2H_z(0).$$

1.22–3   For the solenoid in Problem 1.22–2 discuss the "end effects" by computing H_z at $z = 0$, a, $2a$, $\cdots$. Assume that l is large compared with a. Show that if $z = ma$ and $m > 1$, then

$$H_z = nI\left(1 - \frac{1}{4m^2} + \frac{3}{16m^4} - \frac{15}{96m^6} + \cdots\right).$$

1.22–4   A thin wire of radius b is bent into a circular ring of mean radius a. Assume that a uniform magnetic field is created at a uniform rate in τ seconds, from $t = 0$ to $t = \tau$. Assume that magnetic flux is perpendicular to the plane of the ring and its final density is B_0. Calculate the current in the ring and the energy dissipated in the wire.

Answer: $I = \pi \sigma a b^2 B_0 / 2\tau, \quad 0 \le t \le \tau$

$\quad\quad\quad \mathcal{E} = \pi^2 \sigma a^3 b^2 B_0^2 / 2\tau.$

1.22–5   Consider a long solenoid of length l and cross sectional area S. Assume that the current is I and the number of turns per unit length is n. Find the voltage between the ends of the winding.

Answer: $V = \mu_0 n^2 S l \dot{I}$. In circuit theory the coefficient of proportionality, $L = \mu_0 n^2 S l$, is called the *inductance* of the solenoid.

1.22–6   Consider a current filament I, extending along the z axis from $z = 0$ to $z = \infty$. Superimpose on it another infinite filament $-I$ from $z = l$ to $z = \infty$. A current element of moment Il is thus obtained. Derive equation (1.57) from equation (1.56).

1.22–7   Referring to Section 1.22 and the equation preceding equation (1.56), show that we can also write

$$2\pi r \sin \theta H_\varphi = -\int_\theta^\pi \int_0^{2\pi} J_r r^2 \sin \theta \, d\theta \, d\varphi.$$

On the right the integration is performed over the spherical cap "complementary" to the one used in the text. This is a variant method of calculating the magnetic intensity of the field generated by a semi-infinite current filament. (See Figure 1.8).

1.26–1   A conducting cylinder of radius a is coaxial with the z axis. It is uniformly charged. The charge per unit length is q. From symmetry considerations and equation (1.79) find the field

Answer: $E_\rho = q/2\pi\epsilon\rho, \quad\quad \rho \ge a$

$\quad\quad\quad = 0, \quad\quad\quad\quad \rho < a$

$\quad E_\varphi = E_z = 0$

1.26–2   Assume that in Problem 1.26–1 there is another conducting cylinder, also coaxial with the z axis. Let $b > a$ be its inner radius and $-q$ the charge per unit length. Find the field and the voltage V between the cylinders.

$$Answer: \quad E_\rho = 0, \qquad \rho > b$$
$$= q/2\pi\epsilon\rho, \qquad a \le \rho \le b$$
$$= 0, \qquad \rho < a,$$
$$E_\varphi = E_z = 0,$$
$$V = (q/2\pi\epsilon) \ln (b/a).$$

1.26–3   From equations (1.31) and (1.47) which define, respectively, the dielectric constant ϵ and the permeability μ show that the quantity $c = (\mu\epsilon)^{-1/2}$ has the physical dimensions of velocity and $\eta = (\mu/\epsilon)^{1/2}$ has the dimensions of resistance [see equation (1.17)]. This means that $\vec{E}$ and $\eta\vec{H}$ have the same physical dimensions and their magnitudes can thus be compared.

Show that in terms of these "secondary parameters" of a medium Maxwell's equations for nondissipative isotropic media can be written as

$$\oint E_{\tan} ds = -\frac{1}{c}\frac{\partial}{\partial t}\int (\eta H_{nor}) dS,$$

$$\oint \eta H_{\tan} ds = \frac{1}{c}\frac{\partial}{\partial t}\int E_{nor} dS.$$

Note that for free space c equals approximately 3×10^8 m/sec.

1.26–4   In order to obtain an idea of the order of magnitude of the interaction between electric and magnetic fields assume that

$$\vec{E}(x, y, z; t) = \vec{E}(x, y, z)e^{pt},$$
$$\vec{H}(x, y, z; t) = \vec{H}(x, y, z)e^{pt}.$$

Note that the ratio of the time derivative of $\vec{E}$ to $\vec{E}$ itself equals p so that p is the *relative rate* of change or fractional rate of change of $\vec{E}$ (and $\vec{H}$). Show that for this time dependence Maxwell's equations become

$$\oint E_{\tan} ds = -(p/c)\int (\eta H_{nor}) dS,$$

$$\oint \eta H_{\tan} ds = (p/c)\int E_{nor} dS.$$

Suppose that $p = 1/T$ so that in T seconds the field increases in the ratio of e to 1 (that is, 2.718 $\cdots$ to 1). Show that the length cT is indicative of the linear dimensions of the field for which the electromagnetic interaction becomes significant. The same is true when $p = -1/T$ and the field is decreasing.

1.26–5 Assume that $\vec{E}$ and $\vec{H}$ are varying with the angular frequency ω

$$\vec{E} = \vec{E}^c \cos \omega t + \vec{E}^s \sin \omega t,$$

$$\vec{H} = \vec{H}^c \cos \omega t + \vec{H}^s \sin \omega t.$$

Show that for nondissipative media Maxwell's equations become

$$\oint E^c_{\text{tan}} \, ds = -(\omega/c) \int \eta H^s_{\text{nor}} \, dS,$$

$$\oint E^s_{\text{tan}} \, ds = (\omega/c) \int \eta H^c_{\text{nor}} \, dS,$$

$$\oint H^c_{\text{tan}} \, ds = (\omega/c) \int E^s_{\text{nor}} \, dS,$$

$$\oint H^s_{\text{tan}} \, ds = -(\omega/c) \int E^c_{\text{nor}} \, dS.$$

Note that ω plays the same role as p in the preceding problem and that $T = 1/\omega$.

1.27–1 Consider an infinitesimal rectangle in free space whose vertices are: $A(x, y, z)$, $B(x + \Delta x, y, z)$, $C(x + \Delta x, y + \Delta y, z)$, and $D(x, y + \Delta y, z)$. Let E_x, E_y, E_z, H_x, H_y, and H_z be the Cartesian components of $\vec{E}$ and H at point A. Apply Maxwell's equations (1.76) and (1.77) to this rectangle and show that

$$\frac{\partial E_y}{\partial x} - \frac{\partial E_x}{\partial y} = -\mu_0 \frac{\partial H_z}{\partial t},$$

$$\frac{\partial H_y}{\partial x} - \frac{\partial H_x}{\partial y} = \epsilon_0 \frac{\partial E_z}{\partial t}.$$

Try some variations in the method of calculating electromotive and magnetomotive forces round the closed circuit $ABCDA$ in the following ways:

(a) Since Δx is infinitesimal, $V_{AB} = E_x \Delta x$ and

$$V_{DC} = E_x \Delta x + \frac{\partial}{\partial y} (E_x \Delta x) \Delta y$$

except for infinitesimals of higher order. Since $V_{CD} = -V_{DC}$, these two equations yield $V_{AB} + V_{CD}$.

(b) More directly, $V_{AB} + V_{CD} = -(V_{DC} - V_{AB})$. The quantity in parentheses is an increment in V_{AB} when y is increased by Δy and therefore is equal to the rate of change of V_{AB} in the y direction multiplied by Δy,

$$\frac{\partial}{\partial y} (E_x \Delta x) \Delta y.$$

Four other partial differential equations are obtained by applying Maxwell's integral equations to infinitesimal rectangles in planes parallel to the remaining coordinate planes. On account of symmetry, however, these equations are readily obtained by cyclic permutation of x, y, and z.

Similar equations may be obtained in cylindrical coordinates. Choose a curvilinear rectangle $A(\rho, \varphi, z)$, $B(\rho + \Delta\rho, \varphi, z)$, $C(\rho + \Delta\rho, \varphi + \Delta\varphi, z)$ $D(\rho, \varphi + \Delta\varphi, z)$ and show that

$$\frac{\partial}{\partial \rho} (\rho E_\varphi) - \frac{\partial E_\rho}{\partial \varphi} = -\mu_0 \rho \frac{\partial H_z}{\partial t}.$$

1.27–2   Apply equation (1.79) to an infinitesimal parallelopided formed by three coordinate planes passing through point (x, y, z) and three planes passing through $(x + \Delta x, y + \Delta y, z + \Delta z)$ and show that

$$\frac{\partial D_x}{\partial x} + \frac{\partial D_y}{\partial y} + \frac{\partial D_z}{\partial z} = q_v,$$

where q_v is the volume density of charge.

1.27–3   Consider a perfectly conducting sphere of radius a imbedded in an imperfect dielectric medium of conductivity σ and dielectric constant ϵ. At time $t = 0$ an electric charge q_0 is placed on the sphere. Show that (see equation 1.78) at subsequent time the radial electric intensity satisfies the following equation

$$\sigma E_r + \epsilon \frac{\partial E_r}{\partial t} = 0$$

and that

$$E_r = \frac{q_0 e^{-\sigma t/\epsilon}}{4\pi\epsilon r^2}.$$

Note that the first equation implies that the displacement current is equal and opposite to the conduction current density. This equality is possible because the electric field decays extremely fast (substitute the constants of sea water or soil).

1.28–1   Consider two circular metal plates of radius a and coaxial with the z axis, one in the plane $z = 0$ and the other in the plane $z = h \ll a$. Let V_0 be the voltage from the lower plate to the upper. Show that approximately $E_z = V_0/h$, $D_z = \epsilon V_0/h$, and that the charge on the lower plate is

$$q = (\pi\epsilon a^2/h) V_0.$$

Note that in circuit theory the coefficient $C = \pi\epsilon a^2/h$ is called the capacitance of the pair of plates.

Show that if V_0 is varying slowly with time, the magnetic intensity due to the vertical displacement current is $H_\varphi = \epsilon\rho\dot{V}_0/2h = I_0\rho/2\pi a^2$. Compare this intensity with that in a circular wire (see Problem 1.21–1).

1.28–2   Consider two uniformly and oppositely charged planes, $z = 0$ and $z = h$. Let q_S be the surface density of charge on $z = 0$ and $-q_S$ on $z = h$. Explain why the field exists only between the planes and show that $E_z = q_S/\epsilon$.

2.1–1   Show that the field of an infinitely long uniformly charged linear filament or cylinder (see Problem 1.26–1) can be expressed as the gradient of the following *logarithmic potential*

$$V = -(q/2\pi\epsilon) \ln \rho + A, \tag{1}$$

where A is an arbitrary constant. This constant may be chosen to make V equal to zero at some reference distance $\rho = \rho_0$. Then

$$V = -(q/2\pi\epsilon) \ln (\rho/\rho_0). \tag{2}$$

The form of equation (2) is quite proper since ρ/ρ_0 is dimensionless.

The form of equation (1), on the other hand, is ambiguous since $\ln \rho$ depends on the unit of length. The ambiguity, however, is absorbed in the arbitrary constant A. Neither the field nor potential differences depend on this constant. For this reason A is often dropped from equation (1).

Show also that a uniform electric field of intensity E_0 parallel to the z axis may be obtained from the potential function

$$V = -E_0 z + A.$$

If the field is parallel to the x axis, then $V = -E_0 x + A$.

2.1–2   Consider two infinite uniformly and oppositely charged filaments parallel to the z axis in the xz plane. Let the positively charged filament pass through point $x = \frac{1}{2}s$ and the negatively charged through $x = -\frac{1}{2}s$. Assume that s is infinitesimal. Express the potential and the field in terms of the positive charge q per unit length.

Answer: $V = (qs \cos \varphi)/2\pi\epsilon\rho$.

$E_\rho = (qs \cos \varphi)/2\pi\epsilon\rho^2$.

$E_\varphi = (qs \sin \varphi)/2\pi\epsilon\rho^2$.

2.1–3   Obtain the potential difference between two spheres of radius a when the charge on one is q and on the other $-q$. Assume that the distance s between their centers is rather large in comparison with $2a$.

Answer: $V_1 - V_2 = \dfrac{q}{2\pi\epsilon a} (1 - a/s).$

2.1–4   Obtain the potential difference between two infinitely long parallel wires of radius a when the distance s between their axes is rather large in comparison with $2a$. Let q be the charge per unit length on one wire and $-q$ on the other.

Answer: $V_1 - V_2 = \dfrac{q}{\pi\epsilon} \ln (s/a).$

2.1–5   Obtain the potential difference V between concentric spheres of radii a and $b > a$ when they are equally and oppositely charged.

Answer: $V = \dfrac{q(b - a)}{4\pi\epsilon ab}.$

2.1–6   Show that the potential difference in Problem 2.1–5 may be expressed as

$$V = \frac{qh}{4\pi\epsilon c^2}\left(1 + \frac{h^2}{4c^2} + \frac{h^4}{16c^4} + \frac{h^6}{64c^6} + \cdots\right),$$

where $h = b - a$ and $c = (a + b)/2$. Note that $S = 4\pi c^2$ is the area of the sphere of mean radius c so that when $(h/2c)^2 \ll 1$ we have a simple approximate formula

$$V = qh/\epsilon S.$$

2.1–7   Obtain an expression for the potential difference in Problem 1.26–2 similar to the one in Problem 2.1–6.

Answer: $$V = \frac{qh}{2\pi\epsilon} \sum_{n=0}^{\infty} \frac{1}{2n + 1}\left(\frac{h}{2c}\right)^{2n}.$$

2.1–8   Consider a thin conducting circular disk of thickness h. Let its inner radius be a and the outer b. Let the potential difference between the edges be V. Find the current I.

Answer: $I = GV, G = 2\pi\sigma h/\ln(b/a)$.

2.1–9   Consider a thin conducting spherical shell concentric with the origin. Let there be two holes in this shell. The edge of one is the intersection of a cone $\theta = \theta_1$ with the sphere. The edge of the other is the intersection of a coaxial cone $\theta = \theta_2$ with the sphere. Find the relation between the current I and the voltage V between the edges. Let h be the thickness of the shell.

Answer: $$I = GV, G = \frac{2\pi\sigma h}{\ln \tan\left(\frac{1}{2}\theta_2\right) - \ln \tan\left(\frac{1}{2}\theta_1\right)}.$$

2.1–10   Consider two uniformly charged spheres of radius a. Let the distance s between their centers be rather large in comparison with $2a$. Show that the force between them (in vacuum) equals approximately

$$F = 4\pi\epsilon_0(a/r)^2 V^2[1 + (a/s)]^{-2},$$

where V is the potential of each sphere.

Calculate the potential which is just sufficient to neutralize the gravitational force between the spheres when a/s is negligible in comparison with unity.

Answer: $V = 0.77\,(m/a)$ volts.

2.1–11   Consider direct current flow in a square mesh plane screen of conducting wires. Choose some junction of two wires as the origin of a Cartesian system of coordinates, and the wires passing through it as the axes. The coordinates of a typical junction will then be (m, n), where m and n are integers. Since the voltage between any two junctions is independent of the path connecting them, we can ascribe a potential $V(m, n)$ to each junction (m, n). The voltage from junction (m, n) to junction (p, q) will then be $V(m, n) - V(p, q)$.

Assume that the conductance between any two adjacent junctions is G_1. Suppose that the current from junction (m, n) to $(m + 1, n)$ is $I(m, n; m + 1, n)$. Then

$$I(m, n; m + 1, u) = G_1[V(m, n) - V(m + 1, n)].$$

Show that

$V(m, n)$

$$= \tfrac{1}{4}[V(m - 1, n) + V(m + 1, n) + V(m, n - 1) + V(m, n + 1)]$$

so that the potential of each junction is the average of the potentials of the four adjacent junctions.

Discuss the analogy between the condition imposed on the currents leaving a junction and equation (1.76) for the case of time-invariable fields. Discuss the analogy between

$$V(m, n; m + 1, n) = V(m, n) - V(m + 1, n),$$

where the left side is the voltage from junction (m, n) to junction $(m + 1, n)$, and equations (2.6), (2.7), and (2.8).

Show that for a three dimensional lattice of wires the *potential of any junction is the average of the potentials of the six adjacent junctions.*

2.1–12   Using the result of Problem 1.27–2, show that the potential satisfies Poisson's equation

$$\frac{\partial^2 V}{\partial x^2} + \frac{\partial^2 V}{\partial y^2} + \frac{\partial^2 V}{\partial z^2} = -q_v/\epsilon$$

where q_v is the volume density of charge.

In the special case of charge free regions this equation is called Laplace's equation.

2.1–13   The potential function of the dipole type of field, equation (2.10) varies as $\cos \theta$ where θ is the angle between the axis of the dipole and a line to a typical point in space. Are there other potential functions which vary as $\cos \theta$ but have a different dependence on r,

$R(r)$ let us say? Using Laplace's equation in spherical coordinates (Appendix III) show that we must have

$$\frac{d}{dr}\left(r^2\,\frac{dR}{dr}\right) = 2R$$

and that the general solution is

$$R = Ar^{-2} + Br.$$

The first term gives the dipole type potential. The second term gives

$$V = Br \cos \theta = Bz.$$

This is the potential in a uniform field.

2.1–14   Show that there is no potential function which varies as $\cos 2\theta$ for *all* values of r.

2.1–15   Show that if $E_\theta = 0$ for $a < r < b$, then the field in this region is either radial or zero.

2.2–1   Three equidistant and equally charged metal spheres of radius a are centered on the z axis at points $z = 0$ and $z = \pm s$. Let q be the charge on each sphere and assume that $s \gg a$. Obtain the approximate potentials of the spheres.

Answer: $V_0 = \dfrac{q}{4\pi\epsilon a}\left(1 + \dfrac{2a}{s}\right)$, for the middle sphere

$$V_1 = \frac{q}{4\pi\epsilon a}\left(1 + \frac{3a}{2s}\right),\ \text{for an outside sphere.}$$

2.2–2   An electric tripole is on the z axis: charge $-2q$ at $z = 0$ and q at $z = \pm s$. Assume that s is infinitesimal and obtain the potential and the electric intensity of the field.

Answer: $V = \dfrac{qs^2}{8\pi\epsilon r^3}\,(1 + 3\cos 2\theta),$

$$E_r = \frac{3qs^2}{8\pi\epsilon r^4}\,(1 + 3\cos 2\theta),\ E_\theta = \frac{3qs^2\sin 2\theta}{4\pi\epsilon r^4}.$$

2.2–3   Assume that a uniformly charged filament extends on the z axis from $z = -\frac{1}{2}l$ to $z = \frac{1}{2}l$. Show that as l increases the potential approaches

$$V = (q/2\pi\epsilon) \ln (l/\rho) = -(q/2\pi\epsilon) \ln \rho + (q/2\pi\epsilon) \ln l$$

in an increasingly large volume surrounding the origin. This yields the logarithmic potential introduced in Problem 2.1–1.

2.2–4   Find the potential of a uniformly charged thin circular ring of radius a on its axis. Let q be the total charge.

Answer: $V = q/4\pi\epsilon\sqrt{a^2 + z^2}$.

2.2–5   Find the potential at the center of a thin, uniformly charged square loop. Let q be the total charge and a the side of the square. Compare this potential with the corresponding potential of a circular ring of diameter $2a$.

Answer: $V = q/2\pi\epsilon a \ln (1 + \sqrt{2})$.

V (square) $= 0.88 \times V$ (ring).

2.2–6   Assume that a thin wire of radius a and length $l \gg a$ is uniformly charged and that the charge per unit length is q. Find the average potential.

Answer: $V = \dfrac{q}{2\pi\epsilon} \left(\ln \dfrac{2l}{a} - 1 \right) = \dfrac{q}{2\pi\epsilon} \left(\ln \dfrac{l}{a} - 0.31 \right).$

2.2–7   A square loop, length l on each side, is made of a thin wire of radius a ($a \ll l$). Assume that it is uniformly charged and that q is the charge per unit length. Find the potentials at the corners and in the middle of a side.

Answer: $V = \dfrac{q}{2\pi\epsilon} \left(\ln \dfrac{l}{a} + \ln (2 + 2\sqrt{2}) \right) = \dfrac{q}{2\pi\epsilon} \left(\ln \dfrac{l}{a} + 1.57 \right),$

$V = \dfrac{q}{2\pi\epsilon} \left(\ln \dfrac{l}{a} + \ln \dfrac{7 + 3\sqrt{5}}{2} \right) = \dfrac{q}{2\pi\epsilon} \left(\ln \dfrac{l}{a} + 1.93 \right).$

Note: Since the average potential of a thin wire whose length equals the *perimeter* of the square is

$$\dfrac{q}{2\pi\epsilon} \left(\ln \dfrac{l}{a} + 1.08 \right),$$

it appears that the average potentials of a uniformly charged wire, a square loop, a regular polygon, and a circle are approximately equal if their perimeters are equal; in terms of the perimeter p the potential is approximately

$$V = \frac{q}{2\pi\epsilon}\left(\ln\frac{p}{a} - 0.3\right).$$

For polygons and circles a better value would be obtained by taking the average potential round the square.

2.2–8   Consider two parallel thin wires of radius a and length l, disposed as in Figure 2.33 (Section 2.18). Let the interaxial distance s be fairly large in comparison with $2a$ (at least twice as large) and l be considerably larger than s. Assume that the wires are uniformly and oppositely charged. Express the transverse potential difference in terms of the distance ns from one end of the pair ($ns < l/2$) and find how quickly the "end effect" disappears.

Answer: $$V = \frac{q}{\pi\epsilon}\ln\frac{s}{a} + \frac{q}{2\pi\epsilon}\ln\frac{ns + \sqrt{(ns)^2 + a^2}}{ns + s\sqrt{n^2 + 1}}.$$

Calculate the values of the second term for $n = 1, 2, 3$.

2.2–9   Suppose that in Problem 2.2–8 the wires are similarly charged. Obtain a simplified expression for the potential, not too near the ends. Assume that the charge per unit length on each wire is $\frac{1}{2}q$. Express the result in a form which can be compared with equation (2.12).

Answer: $$V = \frac{q}{4\pi\epsilon}\ln\frac{4z(l - z)}{as}.$$

2.2–10   Consider two infinitely long thin parallel wires, arranged symmetrically about the axis of a cylinder of large radius b in one of its radial planes. Let a be the radius of each wire and $s \ll b$ the distance between their axes. Let the charge per unit length of each wire be $\frac{1}{2}q$ and that on the cylinder $-q$. Obtain the potential difference V between the wires and the cylinder and compare it with that of a single wire coaxial with the cylinder.

Answer: $$V = \frac{q}{2\pi\epsilon}\ln\frac{b}{\sqrt{as}}.$$

A single wire of radius $\sqrt{as}$ would be at the same potential.

2.2–11   Consider two uniformly and oppositely charged thin wires of radius a and length l, forming a V, as shown in the Figure

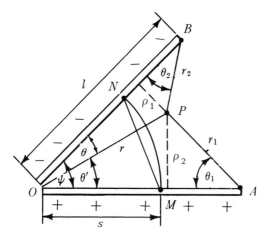

FIGURE 2.2–11

2.2–11. Let the charge per unit length on OA be q. Show that the potential at any point P is

$$V = \frac{q}{4\pi\epsilon} \ln \frac{\rho_2^2 r_1 \, (1 + \cos\theta)\,(1 + \cos\theta_1)}{\rho_1^2 r_2 \, (1 + \cos\theta')\,(1 + \cos\theta_2)}$$

and the potential difference between the elements of the wires, equidistant from the apex and not too near the ends, is

$$V_{MN} = \frac{q}{2\pi\epsilon} \ln \frac{4\rho_2^2(l - s)}{a^2 r_2 \, (1 + \cos\psi)\,(1 + \cos\theta_2)}$$

$$= \frac{q}{\pi\epsilon} \ln \frac{d}{a} + \frac{q}{2\pi\epsilon} \ln \frac{2(l - s)}{r_2 + l - s \cos\psi},$$

where ψ is the angle between the wires and d is the distance between the elements.

2.2–12   Consider $2n + 1$ metal spheres of radius a, centered on the z axis at $z = 0, \pm c, \pm 2c, \cdots \pm nc$. Let q_1 be the charge on each sphere. Show that the potential of the sphere centered at the origin is approximately

$$V_0 = \frac{q_1}{4\pi\epsilon a} + \frac{q_1}{2\pi\epsilon c} \sum_{m=1}^{m=n} \frac{1}{m}.$$

Let l be the distance between the centers of the extreme spheres and q the charge per unit length of the array. Noting that for large n

$$1 + \tfrac{1}{2} + \tfrac{1}{3} + \cdots + \frac{1}{n} \simeq \ln n + C,$$

where $C = 0.577 \cdots$ is Euler's constant, show that

$$V_0 = \frac{qc}{4\pi\epsilon a} + \frac{q}{2\pi\epsilon}\left(\ln\frac{l}{2c} + C\right).$$

Note that if this formula is used for spheres almost touching each other, then the potential

$$V_0 = \frac{q}{2\pi\epsilon}\left(\ln\frac{l}{a} + 0.2\right)$$

differs only a little from the potential at points half way between the ends of a thin cylinder coaxial with a uniformly charged filament [see equation (2.12)].

2.2–13   In Problem 2.2–2 we obtained the potential function of a tripole and its field. Show that there is another potential function which has the same dependence on θ, namely,

$$V = Ar^2(1 + 3\cos 2\theta).$$

2.2–14   Using the results of Problems 2.2–2 and 2.2–13 show that if we have a distribution of charge of density

$$q_s = P(1 + 3\cos 2\theta)$$

on a spherical surface $r = a$, then the potential function of the field is

$$V = P(a/5\epsilon)(a/r)^3(1 + 3\cos 2\theta), \qquad r \geq a,$$

$$= P(a/5\epsilon)(r/a)^2(1 + 3\cos 2\theta), \qquad r \leq a.$$

2.3–1   Consider a thin wire of radius a on the z axis from $z = -l$ to $z = l$. Assume a point charge q on the x axis at $x = s$. Calculate approximately the charge distribution on the wire on the assumption that the net charge is zero.

In line with one method in Section 2.3 the following procedure is suggested. Write the condition

$$V^i + V^r = V_0 = \text{constant},$$

where V^i is the potential of the point charge and V^r is the potential of the charge displaced on the wire; both are calculated on the axis of the wire. Take advantage of the thinness of the wire and express the preceding equation in an approximate form. Show that to this order of approximation the potential V_0 equals the average impressed potential

$$V_0 = \frac{1}{4\pi\epsilon l} \int_0^l \frac{dz}{\sqrt{s^2 + z^2}} = \frac{1}{4\pi\epsilon l} \ln \frac{l + \sqrt{s^2 + l^2}}{s}.$$

Finally, obtain the approximate displaced charge per unit length on the wire

$$q(z) = \frac{V_0}{A} - \frac{q}{4\pi\epsilon A \sqrt{s^2 + z^2}}$$

where

$$A = \frac{1}{2\pi\epsilon} \left(\ln \frac{4l}{a} - 1 \right)$$

is the average value of $A_1(z)$ in equation (2.18).

2.3–2   Consider a uniform flow of current in a dissipative medium such as soil or sea water. When a metal wire is inserted in the medium so that the wire is parallel to the lines of flow, the current takes advantage of the relatively low resistance of the wire and enters the wire along one half and leaves along the other half. The disparity between the conductivities of the wire and the surrounding medium is such that the wire may be regarded as a perfect conductor. Show that the situation is analoguous to an electrostatic problem considered in Section 2.3 [see Figure 2.8(b)] and that the current per unit length leaving the wire is given by equation (2.18) provided the dielectric constant ϵ in $A_1(z)$ is replaced by the conductivity σ of the medium.

Assume now that the wire is *insulated* from the medium except at the ends and that the ends are connected to small metal spheres of radius b. Calculate the following:

(a) the current in the wire when the spheres and the wire are perfectly conducting and E is the electric intensity impressed on the wire;

(b) the current in the wire when the spheres are perfectly conducting but the resistance of the wire is R_w;

(c) R_w for which the power dissipated in the wire is maximum.

Answer: (a) $I = El/R$, where $R = 1/2\pi\sigma b$ and l is the length of the wire; or more accurately,

$$R = (1/2\pi\sigma)(1/b - 1/l).$$

(b) $I = El/(R + R_w)$;

(c) $R_w = R$.

2.3-3   Two thin wires of length l are connected to a direct current generator as shown in Figure 2.8(a). Assume that the surrounding medium is conducting and that the wires are insulated from it except at the ends where they are connected to two spheres of very high conductivity and of radius b small compared with l. Let the resistance of the wires be negligible and the generator voltage be V. Show that the power delivered to the medium (and dissipated in it) is

$$P = V^2/R,$$

where

$$R = 1/2\pi\sigma b$$

or more accurately

$$R = \frac{1}{2\pi\sigma}\left(\frac{1}{b} - \frac{1}{2l}\right).$$

Consider a similar pair of wires, parallel to the first pair and perpendicular to the line joining the centers. Let this pair of wires be connected to a "load resistance" R_L rather than to a generator. Assume that the distance d between the two pairs of wires is large in comparison with l. Show that the power delivered to the load is

$$P_{\text{rec}} = \frac{V^2 l^4 R_L}{\pi^2\sigma^2 d^6 R^2 (R + R_L)^2},$$

where R is given above.

Obtain the ratio of the received power to the power delivered to the medium and show that the maximum power transfer ratio is

$$(P_{\text{rec}}/P)_{\max} = l^4/4\pi^2\sigma^2 d^6 R^2.$$

2.3–4   Assume that the potentials of the metal spheres in Problem 2.2–1 are equal. Find the charges.

Answer: $q_0 = \dfrac{4\pi\epsilon a V[1 - (3a/2s)]}{1 + (a/2s) - (2a^2/s^2)}$, on the middle sphere

$q_1 = q_0 \dfrac{1 - (a/s)}{1 - (3a/2s)}$, for an outside sphere.

2.3–5   Show that except for small quantities of the order $(a/s)^2$ the charges in Problem 2.3–1 are inversely proportional to the potentials in Problem 2.2–1. That is,

$$q_1/q_0 = V_0/V_1 = 1 + (a/2s).$$

This is not surprising since the potential of a sphere of radius a, under the conditions assumed in these problems, is determined largely by the charge on it. Hence we can equalize approximately the potentials in Problem 2.2–1 by assuming that the charge on the middle sphere is

$$q_0 = q \left/ \left(1 + \frac{2a}{s}\right)\right. \simeq q\left(1 - \frac{2a}{s}\right)$$

and on an outside sphere is

$$q_1 = q \left/ \left(1 + \frac{3a}{2s}\right)\right. \simeq q\left(1 - \frac{3a}{2s}\right).$$

2.3–6   Consider three infinite, coplanar, parallel, thin wires of radius a. Let q be the charge per unit length on one outside wire and $-q$ on the remaining two wires which are kept at the same potential. Let $s \gg a$ and $2s$ be the distances between the axis of the first wire and the axes of the other two. Find the ratio of the charge densities on the latter wires.

Answer: $\dfrac{\ln (s/a) + \ln 2}{\ln (s/a) - \ln 2}$, the larger charge is on the central wire.

2.3–7   Consider two parallel thin wires of radius a and length l shorted at one end as shown in Figure 2.3–7(a). Let $s \gg a$ be the distance between their axes. Find the transverse voltage V_{MN} due

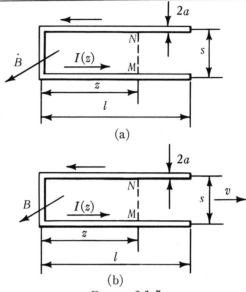

FIGURE 2.3–7

to the displaced charge, the charge $q(z)$ per unit length on the lower
wire, and the current $I(z)$ in the following two cases:

(a) The open loop is stationary in a slowly varying uniform
magnetic field perpendicular to the plane of the loop. The
time rate of change of the magnetic flux density is $\dot{B}$.

(b) The loop is moving parallel to the long wires in its plane with
a speed v in a uniform magnetic field perpendicular to the
plane of the loop. The flux density is B. See Figure 2.3–7 (b).

Answer: (a) $V_{MN} = -\dot{B}sz$, $q(z) = CV_{MN}$ where

$$C = \frac{\pi\epsilon}{\ln\,(s/a)}$$

$$I(z) = \tfrac{1}{2}C\dot{B}s(z^2 - l^2)$$

(b) $V_{MN} = Bsv$, $q(z) = CBsv$, $I(z) = CBs\dot{v}(l - z)$.

2.3–8   Answer the question in the preceding problem when the
loop is shorted at the other end. Let R be the resistance per unit
length of each long wire. Neglect the resistances of the short wires.

Answer: (a) $I(z) = I_0 = -Bs/2R$, $V_{MN} = 0$, $q(z) = 0$.

(b) $V_{MN} = Bsv$, $q(z) = CBsv$, $I(z) = CBs\dot{v}(\tfrac{1}{2}l - z)$.

2.3–9   Consider a closed loop as in Problem 2.3–8 except that the resistance per unit length is R_1 for $z < l/2$ and R_2 for $z > l/2$ as

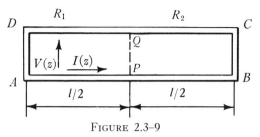

FIGURE 2.3–9

indicated in Figure 2.3–9. Answer the questions in Problem 2.3–7 and compare them with the case $R_1 = R_2 = R$.

Answer: (a) $I(z) = I_0 = -\dot{B}s/(R_1 + R_2),$
$\qquad V(z) = \dot{B}sz(R_1 - R_2)/(R_1 + R_2),$
$\qquad q(z) = CV(z).$

(b)   Same answer as in Problem 2.3–8(b).

Note: The answer in case (a) is exact when $\dot{B} = $ constant. Otherwise, it is the first approximation. If $\dot{B}$ varies with time, $V(z)$ and $q(z)$ also vary with time and charging or displacement currents should be added to $I(z)$. These currents in turn will affect $V(z)$ and $q(z)$. The step-by-step calculations may be continued.

2.3–10   Suppose that the thin wire shown in Figure 2.8(b) is moving to the right, with a speed v, in a uniform magnetic field perpendicular to the paper. Let B be the magnetic flux density pointing into the paper. Obtain the density of displaced charge.

Answer: The answer is given by equation (2.18) if we let $E_0 = Bv$. To compare with the results in Problem 2.3–7 note that $A(z)$ corresponds to the reciprocal of C. The calculation of current is more difficult unless $A(z)$ is approximated by its average value.

2.3–11   Let the plane $z = h$ be the surface of an ocean of uniform depth $H \gg h$ and conductivity σ. Consider two copper spheres of radius a, connected with insulated copper wires to a dc generator. Let the centers of these spheres be at points $(0, -l, 0)$ and $(0, l, 0)$ where $l > 2a$. Assume that two other copper spheres are centered at $(0, d - l, 0)$ and $(0, d + l, 0)$ and are connected with insulated copper wires to a resistance R_L ("load"). Let $h \ll d \ll H$. Find the following:

(a)   the current through the generator when the voltage between its terminals is V_0,

(b)   the power dissipated in the ocean,

(c)   the electric intensity at the second pair of spheres,

(d)   the current through R_L,

(e)   the maximum power which can be abstracted from the field by a proper load resistance R_L.

Answer: (a) $\dfrac{2\pi\sigma a V_0}{1 - (a/2l)}$,

(b) $\dfrac{2\pi\sigma a V_0}{1 - (a/2l)}$,

(c) $E_y = \dfrac{4alV_0}{[1 - (a/2l)]d^3}$,

(d) $8al^2d^{-3}[1 - (a/2l)]^{-1}\left[\dfrac{1 - (a/2l)}{2\pi\sigma a} + R_L\right]^{-1}V_0$,

(e) $32\pi\sigma a^3l^2d^{-6}[1 - (a/2l)]^3V_0^2$.

2.3–12   Consider five metal spheres of radius a, centered on the z axis at $z = 0, \pm c, \pm 2c$. Let the intensity of the incident field be $E_z = E_0$. Suppose that the spheres have been momentarily connected with conducting wires. Show that if q_1 and q_2 are the charges on the spheres centered at $z = c$ and $z = 2c$, respectively, then

$$q_2/q_1 = 2[1 - (5a/6c)]/[1 - (19a/12c)].$$

Note that as a approaches zero, the ratio approaches 2.

2.3–13   There is a fourth method of obtaining an approximate solution for the static configuration shown in Figure 2.8(a). It is based on an assumption that the electric lines of force run along the meridians on spheres concentric with the midpoint between the wires. This assumption enables us to obtain D_θ and the voltage between the wires along a typical meridian. Thus we find

$$q(z) = \pi\epsilon V_0/\ln(2z/a)$$

which agrees with equation (2.16) except for the last term in the expression for $A(z)$. This last term represents the "end effect" due to departure of electric lines of force from meridians as z approaches l.

2.3–14   Using the result of the preceding problem, show that an approximate charge per unit length of a thin wire, Figure 2.8 (b), in a uniform electric field of intensity E_0 is

$$q(z) = 2\pi\epsilon E_0 z/\ln\ (2z/a), \qquad z > 0,$$

$$\simeq 2\pi\epsilon E_0 z/[\ln\ (2l/a) - 1],$$

where in the second approximation the slowly varying (except in the vicinity of $z = 0$) denominator has been replaced by its average value.

Since this result, as well as equation (2.18), shows that $q(z)$ is approximately proportional to z, we can improve our approximation by assuming that

$$q(z) = E_0 z f(z)$$

where $f(z)$ is a slowly varying function. The equation which precedes equation (2.18) would then become

$$E_0 z = \int_{-l}^{l} \frac{E_0 u f(u)\ du}{4\pi\epsilon\sqrt{a^2 + (u - z)^2}}.$$

We now take advantage of the facts that $f(u)$ is a slowly varying function and that the greatest contribution to the integral comes from the vicinity of $u = z$: we replace $f(u)$ by $f(z)$, integrate, and obtain

$$f(z) \simeq 2\pi\epsilon \bigg/ \left[\ln\frac{2l}{a} - 1 + \tfrac{1}{2}\ln\left(1 - \frac{z^2}{l^2}\right)\right].$$

If the denominator is replaced by its average value, then

$$f(z) \simeq 2\pi\epsilon/[\ln\ (4l/a) - 2].$$

Since $\ln 2 = 0.693$ and $\ln 2 - 1 = -0.307$, the new value for the charge density is somewhat larger than that given by the preceding approximation.

2.3–15   Consider two thin wires of length l on the z axis, one going upward from a point A slightly above the origin and the other going downward from a point B slightly below the origin. Let a uniform field of intensity $E_z = E_0$ be impressed on the wires. Since the impressed potential is a linear function of z, the potential due to the displaced charge, on the surface of each wire, is also a linear function of z. Hence the density of displaced charge is approximately a linear function. Show that V_{BA} is then approximately equal to $E_0 l$ and that

$$q(z) = \tfrac{1}{2}\pi\epsilon E_0(-l + 2z)/[\ln (2l/a) - 1], \qquad z > 0,$$

and that $q(-z) = -q(z)$.

2.4–1   Consider an electric dipole of moment ql along the z axis at $z = 0$ and a concentric conducting sphere of radius b. Find the field and the surface density of charge displaced on the sphere.

Answer: In the interior of the sphere the field is the sum of the original field of the dipole and a "reflected" field due to electric charge displaced on the sphere. The reflected field is uniform and parallel to the z axis,

$$E_z^r = \frac{ql}{4\pi\epsilon b^3}.$$

Outside the sphere the field is zero. The surface density of charge on the sphere is

$$q_s = -\frac{3ql \cos\theta}{4\pi b^3}.$$

2.4–2   Suppose that instead of the dipole in Problem 2.4–1 there is a point charge q on the z axis at $z = l \ll b$. Obtain the field and the charge distribution on the sphere.

Answer: The interior field is the sum of the original field of the point charge and the reflected field equal to that in the preceding problem. The exterior field is radial and $E_r = q/4\pi\epsilon r^2$. The density of charge displaced on the sphere equals that in the preceding problem. *Note:* Use two methods:

  (1)   Expand the potential of the given point charge in a suitable power series.
  (2)   Replace the given point charge by a suitable point charge in the center of the sphere and a suitable dipole.

2.4–3   Solve the preceding problem when the sphere is grounded.

Answer: The interior field is the same as in the preceding problem, the exterior field is zero, and the charge density is

$$q_s = -\frac{q}{4\pi b^2}\left(1 + \frac{3l}{b}\cos\theta\right).$$

2.4–4   In Problem 2.4–3 assume that the charge q is on a sphere of radius $a \ll b$ with the center at $z = l$. Find the potential of the small sphere.

Answer: $V = \dfrac{q}{4\pi\epsilon a} - \dfrac{q}{4\pi\epsilon b}\left(1 + \dfrac{l^2}{b^2}\right).$

2.4–5   Suppose that the sphere in Section 2.4 is perfectly conducting and the conductivity of the medium around it is σ. In what way does the sphere affect the field?

2.4–6   Calculate the effect of a spherical airhole of radius a in a conducting medium on a uniform impressed field of intensity $E_z = E_0$, $E_x = E_y = 0$. Assume that the center of the hole is at the origin.

Answer: The field reflected from the hole is

$$E_r^r = -(a/r)^3 E_0 \cos\theta, \qquad E_\theta^r = -\tfrac{1}{2}(a/r)^3 E_0 \sin\theta$$

2.4–7   Using the answer of the preceding problem obtain the field in the hole.

Answer: $E_z = 1.5 E_0, \qquad E_x = E_y = 0.$

2.4–8   Consider a metal cylinder of radius a, coaxial with the z axis, and assume that a uniform field

$$E_x^i = E_0, \qquad E_y^i = E_z^i = 0$$

is impressed on it. Calculate the reflected field. Hint: Take advantage of the results obtained in Problem 2.1–2.

Answer: $E_\rho^r = (a/\rho)^2 E_0 \cos\varphi, \quad E_\varphi^r = (a/\rho)^2 E_0 \sin\varphi.$

2.4–9   Consider a thin cylindrical metal shell of radius a, coaxial with the z axis. Assume that along the z axis there is a double line source of moment qs per unit length (see Problem 2.1–2). Obtain the field and the charge density on the cylinder. Show that the reflected field is uniform and normal to the z axis.

Answer: $E_\rho = \dfrac{qs \cos\varphi}{2\pi\epsilon}\left(\dfrac{1}{\rho^2} + \dfrac{1}{a^2}\right), \qquad \rho < a$

$\qquad\qquad E_\varphi = \dfrac{qs \sin\varphi}{2\pi\epsilon}\left(\dfrac{1}{\rho^2} - \dfrac{1}{a^2}\right), \qquad \rho \le a$

$\qquad\qquad E_\rho = E_\varphi = 0, \qquad \rho > a,$

$\qquad\qquad q_s = -\dfrac{qs \cos\varphi}{\pi\epsilon a^2}.$

2.4–10   Assume that instead of the source in Problem 2.4–9 we have a charged filament parallel to the z axis which passes through point $x = s$, $y = z = 0$, where $s \ll a$. Find the field when the charge per unit length is q.

Answer: In the interior of the cylinder the field is the sum of the field of the line charge and the reflected field $E_x^r = qs/2\pi\epsilon a^2$, $E_y^r = E_z^r = 0$. Outside the cylinder the field is radial and $E_\rho = q/2\pi\epsilon\rho$.

2.4–11   Suppose that in Problem 2.4–10 the cylinder is grounded (at zero potential). Obtain the potential in the interior.

Answer: $V = -(q/2\pi\epsilon)[\ln\,(\rho_1/a) + sx/a^2]$,

where

$$\rho_1 = (\rho^2 - 2s\rho \cos\,\varphi + s^2)^{\frac{1}{2}}.$$

2.4–12   Suppose that in the preceding problem the charge is on a thin wire of radius $b \ll a$ rather than on a line. Find the potential of the wire.

Answer: $(q/2\pi\epsilon)[\ln\,(a/b) - (s/a)^2]$.

2.4–13   Assume that the moment of the electric dipole in Problem 2.4–1 is varying slowly and show that

$$H_\varphi = \frac{\dot{q}l \sin\theta}{4\pi r^2} + \frac{\dot{q}lr \sin\theta}{8\pi b^3}.$$

Suppose that b is very large; let a metal sphere of radius a be centered on the z axis far from the dipole so that the intensity E_0 of the incident field is sensibly uniform. Show that

$$H_\varphi = (\epsilon_0 a^3/r_1^2)\, \dot{E}_0 \sin\theta_1 + \tfrac{1}{2}\epsilon_0 r_1 \dot{E}_0 \sin\theta_1,$$

where (r_1, θ_1) are the spherical coordinates with reference to the center of the small sphere, provided the latter is not too close to the surface of the large sphere. When the small sphere is close to the surface of the large sphere, the field of the charge displaced on the small sphere will in its turn displace a charge on the large sphere and thus will generate an additional field.

If the small sphere is in a sensibly uniform time-varying field E_0 off the z axis, then the magnetic intensity due to the induced currents is still given by the first term in the above expression. The magnetic intensity of the incident field, however, is no longer given by the second term.

2.4–14   Suppose that a solid metal sphere of radius a is moving with a constant speed v_0 in the x direction in a uniform magnetic field parallel to the y direction, $B_y = B_0$. Calculate the intensity of the electric field outside the sphere and the density of charge on the sphere.

   Answer: If the origin of the spherical coordinate system is at the center of the sphere, then

$$E_r = 2v_0 B_0 (a/r)^3 \cos \theta, \qquad E_\theta = v_0 B_0 (a/r)^3 \sin \theta,$$

$$q_S = 2\epsilon_0 v_0 B_0 \cos \theta.$$

2.4–15   Show that if the solid sphere in the preceding problem is replaced by a thin spherical shell, the external electric field will be unaltered while an internal field $E_z = -v_0 B_0$ will appear. Show also that the charge density will be $q_S = 3\epsilon_0 v_0 B_0 \cos \theta$.

2.5–1   Consider an infinite medium of conductivity σ_0, supporting a uniform electric field of intensity E_0, parallel to the z axis, and therefore an electric current of density $J_0 = \sigma_0 E_0$. Suppose that within a sphere of radius a, concentric with the origin of the coordinate system, the medium is replaced by another medium of conductivity σ. The problem is to obtain the modification in the originally uniform field.

   Explain why the solution is essentially the same as that for a dielectric sphere in a dielectric medium (see Section 2.5) and that we need only substitute σ_0 and σ for ϵ_0 and ϵ, and J for D. In particular, show that the field inside the sphere is uniform, parallel to the impressed field, and equal to

$$E_z = \frac{3\sigma_0}{2\sigma_0 + \sigma} E_0, \qquad J_z = \frac{3\sigma}{2\sigma_0 + \sigma} J_0.$$

   Thus as $\sigma/\sigma_0 \to 0$, we have $E_z \to 1.5 E_0$, $J_z \to 1.5 (\sigma/\sigma_0) J_0$. That is, the electric intensity is not very different from the original intensity in the homogeneous medium. The current density, on the other hand, becomes vastly different. This is to be expected intuitively since the current tends to avoid entering the highly resistive sphere and tends to flow around it. Similarly, the electric flux tends to avoid a sphere whose dielectric constant is small in comparison with the dielectric constant of the surrounding medium.

On the other hand, if $\sigma/\sigma_0 \to \infty$, then

$$E_z \to 3(\sigma_0/\sigma)E_0, \qquad J_z \to 3J_0.$$

The electric intensity approaches zero. The current tends to seek the highly conducting sphere but only from a limited area. From regions more distant from the sphere the current takes longer paths in the original medium in order to reach the sphere and thus encounters too great a resistance to benefit from the low resistance of the sphere.

These considerations have an important bearing on the classical definitions of $\bar{E}$ and $\bar{D}$ in solid dielectric media. In vacuum, $\bar{E}$ is defined as the force acting on a unit stationary charge and it can be measured. In vacuum, $\bar{D}$ can be defined simply as $\epsilon_0\bar{E}$ since ϵ_0 is a universal constant. Thus $\bar{D}$ is also related simply to the force on a unit charge. In fact, in classical electrostatic units the two quantities are equal. In a solid dielectric medium the charge cannot move and the force on it cannot be measured directly. For this reason, the classical physicist defined $\bar{E}$ and $\bar{D}$ with the aid of *Kelvin cavities*. One of them was a long thin tunnel in the medium, [Figure 2.5–1 (a)] and the other a thin pancake-like cavity [Figure 2.5–1 (b)]. Noting that the tangential component of $\bar{E}$ and the normal component of D are continuous, one can argue that $\bar{E}$ in the dielectric can be measured by $\bar{E}$ in a thin tunnel (a) and $\bar{D}$ in the dielectric by $\epsilon_0\bar{E}$ in a pancake type of cavity (b). As far as the thin tunnel is concerned, we are on a solid ground. Intuitively, we feel that the field is not distorted much by the tunnel. In the case of the pancake cavity, however, it is evident that the field will be distorted considerably and that the electric flux will tend to avoid the cavity to an increasing extent as ϵ increases. Of course, by making the cavity sufficiently thin we can eventually make the distortion negligible; but the thickness will definitely depend on the ratio ϵ/ϵ_0 (where ϵ_0 is the dielectric constant of vacuum) and will have to be halved when ϵ is doubled. These conclusions can be verified by obtaining exact solutions for thin prolate and oblate spheroids. Thus if a and b are semi-major and semi-minor axes of a thin oblate spheroid, the quantity $b\epsilon/a\epsilon_0$ must be very small in comparison with unity to make $\bar{D}$ in the cavity approximately equal to $\bar{D}$ in the medium before the cavity has been hollowed out.

The definition of $\bar{D}$ in Section 1.14 of this book uses a thin *metal plate* [Figure 2.5–1 (c)]. It is evident intuitively that $\bar{D}$ is not appreciably affected by the plate. This also can be verified by solving the problem for an oblate metal spheroid.

(a)

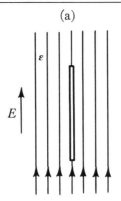

(b)

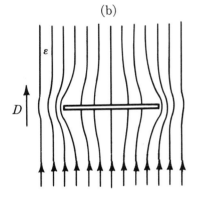

(c)

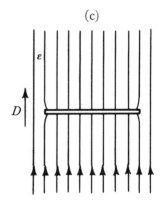

FIGURE 2.5-1

2.5–2   Consider a dielectric cylinder of radius a, coaxial with the z axis, in a uniform field of intensity $E_x = E_0$, $E_y = E_z = 0$. Let the dielectric constant of the cylinder be ϵ and that of the surrounding medium ϵ_0. Obtain the field inside the cylinder and the field reflected by the cylinder.

Answer: $$E_x = \frac{2\epsilon_0}{\epsilon + \epsilon_0} E_0, \qquad E_y = E_z = 0, \qquad \rho < a,$$

$$E_\rho^r = \frac{\epsilon - \epsilon_0}{\epsilon + \epsilon_0} E_0 \left(\frac{a}{\rho}\right)^2 \cos \varphi, \qquad \rho > a.$$

$$E_\varphi^r = \frac{\epsilon - \epsilon_0}{\epsilon + \epsilon_0} E_0 \left(\frac{a}{\rho}\right)^2 \sin \varphi.$$

2.5-3   Calculate the field of an electric dipole of moment ql at the center of a dielectric sphere of radius a. Assume that ϵ and ϵ_0 are dielectric constants of the sphere and the surrounding space and choose the coordinate system with the origin at the center of the sphere and the z axis along the dipole.

Answer:
$$E_r = \frac{ql \cos \theta}{2\pi\epsilon r^3} + \frac{(\epsilon_0 - \epsilon)ql \cos \theta}{2\pi\epsilon(2\epsilon_0 + \epsilon)a^3}, \qquad r < a,$$

$$= \frac{3ql \cos \theta}{2\pi(2\epsilon_0 + \epsilon)r^3}, \qquad r > a,$$

$$E_\theta = \frac{ql \sin \theta}{4\pi\epsilon r^3} - \frac{(\epsilon_0 - \epsilon)ql \sin \theta}{2\pi\epsilon(2\epsilon_0 + \epsilon)a^3}, \qquad r < a,$$

$$= \frac{3ql \sin \theta}{4\pi(2\epsilon_0 + \epsilon)r^3}, \qquad r > a.$$

2.5-4   Suppose that in Problem 2.5-3 the dipole moment is varying slowly with time. Obtain the magnetic intensity (assuming that the electric field is already known).

Answer:
$$H_\varphi = \frac{\dot{q}l \sin \theta}{4\pi r^2} + \frac{(\epsilon_0 - \epsilon)\dot{q}lr \sin \theta}{4\pi a^3(2\epsilon_0 + \epsilon)}, \qquad r \le a,$$

$$= \frac{3\epsilon_0 \dot{q}l \sin \theta}{4\pi(2\epsilon_0 + \epsilon)r^2}, \qquad r \ge a.$$

2.5-5   In Problem 2.5-3 replace the solid dielectric sphere by a spherical shell of radii a and $b > a$. Calculate the field.

Answer: Let $k = \dfrac{(\epsilon - \epsilon_0)(a/b)^3}{2\epsilon_0 + \epsilon}$,

$$M = \frac{3ql}{2(1 - k) + (1 + 2k)(\epsilon_0/\epsilon)},$$

$$A = \frac{M[(1 - k) - (1 + 2k)(\epsilon_0/\epsilon)]}{6\pi\epsilon_0 a^3},$$

$$P = \frac{3\epsilon_0 M}{2\epsilon_0 + \epsilon}.$$

Then,

$$E_r = \frac{ql \cos \theta}{2\pi\epsilon_0 r^3} + A \cos \theta, \qquad r < a,$$

$$= \frac{M \cos \theta}{2\pi\epsilon r^3} - \frac{kM \cos \theta}{2\pi\epsilon a^3}, \qquad a < r < b,$$

$$= \frac{P \cos \theta}{2\pi\epsilon_0 r^3}, \qquad b < r$$

$$E_\theta = \frac{ql \sin \theta}{4\pi\epsilon_0 r^3} - A \sin \theta, \qquad r < a,$$

$$= \frac{M \sin \theta}{4\pi\epsilon r^3} + \frac{kM \sin \theta}{2\pi\epsilon a^3}, \qquad a < r < b,$$

$$= \frac{P \sin \theta}{4\pi\epsilon_0 r^3}, \qquad b < r.$$

2.5–6   A dielectric sphere moving in a magnetic field is polarized. The polarization $\vec{P}$ equals $(\epsilon - \epsilon_0)\vec{E}$, where $\vec{E}$ is the total force per unit charge. Calculate the polarization, and the electric field outside the sphere, under the conditions specified in Problem 2.4–14.

Answer: $$P_z = \frac{2(\epsilon - \epsilon_0)v_0 B_0}{(\epsilon/\epsilon_0) + 1},$$

$$E_r = \frac{2(\epsilon - \epsilon_0)v_0 B_0}{\epsilon + \epsilon_0}\left(\frac{a}{r}\right)^3 \cos \theta,$$

$$E_\theta = \frac{(\epsilon - \epsilon_0)v_0 B_0}{\epsilon + \epsilon_0}\left(\frac{a}{r}\right)^3 \sin \theta.$$

2.5–7   In Section 2.4 we obtained the density of charge displaced on the surface of a conducting sphere of radius a by a uniform electric field. This charge produces an exterior field of the dipole type, which was also calculated. Since the total interior field must equal zero, the displaced charge must produce an interior field, equal and opposite to the impressed field. Verify this conclusion by direct calculation. That is, assume that on the surface of the sphere $r = a$

there is a thin layer of charge of density

$$q_S = 3\epsilon_0 E_0 \cos\theta$$

and calculate the field produced by this charge.

2.5–8   Consider two parallel conducting plates, uniformly and oppositely charged. Explain why a neutral metal sphere, introduced between the plates, will reduce the voltage between the plates, and hence, increase the capacitance between the plates.

Suppose now that the plates are connected to a source of constant voltage. Explain why a neutral metal sphere, introduced between the plates, will cause an additional displacement of negative charge from the positively charged plate to the negatively charged plate. Thus the capacitance between the plates will be increased.

Suppose that small metal spheres are scattered sparsely and uniformly between the plates. Let N be the number of spheres per unit volume and a be the radius of each sphere. Show that on the average the displacement density between the plates is

$$D = \epsilon_0 E_0 + 4\pi N a^3 \epsilon_0 E_0,$$

where E_0 is the electric intensity, that is, the impressed voltage per unit length between the plates. Thus the effective dielectric constant of the medium between the plates is

$$\epsilon = (1 + 4\pi N a^3)\,\epsilon_0.$$

2.6–1   Three conducting spheres of radius a are centered on the z axis at $z = 0$, $z = l$, and $z = 2l$. The first sphere has a charge q and potential V. The second and third spheres are at the same potential $-V_1$ and the total charge on them is $-q$. Find the approximate charges on each of these two spheres when $a \ll l$ and note the "proximity" effect.

Answer: The approximate charges on the spheres centered at $z = l$ and $z = 2l$ are, respectively,

$$-\tfrac{1}{2}q\,\frac{1 - (a/2l)}{1 - (a/l)} \simeq -\tfrac{1}{2}q[1 + (a/2l)],$$

and

$$-\tfrac{1}{2}q\,\frac{1 - (3a/2l)}{1 - (a/l)} \simeq -\tfrac{1}{2}q[1 - (a/2l)].$$

2.6–2   Solve the preceding problem for three infinitely long conducting wires which are parallel to the z axis and whose axes pass through points $(0, 0, 0)$, $(l, 0, 0)$, and $(2l, 0, 0)$. Assume that q is the charge per unit length.

Answer: The ratio of the charge densities on the last two wires is

$$\frac{\ln\ (l/a)\ +\ \ln\ 2}{\ln\ (l/a)\ -\ \ln\ 2}$$

and the charge densities are, respectively,

$$-\tfrac{1}{2}q\ \frac{\ln\ (l/a)\ +\ \ln\ 2}{\ln\ (l/a)},$$

and

$$-\tfrac{1}{2}q\ \frac{\ln\ (l/a)\ -\ \ln\ 2}{\ln\ (l/a)}.$$

2.7–1   Show that the magnetic intensity of an infinitely long current filament I along the z axis can be obtained from a potential function

$$U\ =\ -I\varphi/2\pi\ +\ \text{constant.}$$

2.8–1   Consider a straight electric current filament I of length l. Calculate the vector potential. In what way does it differ from the scalar potential of a similar filament of electric charge [see equation (2.11)]?

2.8–2   Show that the magnetic flux density around an infinitely long electric current filament I along the z axis may be obtained from the following logarithmic vector potential

$$A_\rho\ =\ A_\varphi\ =\ 0, \qquad A_z\ =\ -(\mu I/2\pi)\ \ln\ \rho\ +\ \text{constant.}$$

Note the resemblance to the scalar potential of an infinitely long filament of charge.

2.9–1   Consider a square current loop, length b on each side, made with a very thin wire of radius a. Find the magnetic intensity at the center of the loop.

Answer: $2\sqrt{2}I/\pi b.$

2.9-2   Find the fields at the center of a current loop in the shape of a regular polygon with n sides, inscribed in a circle of radii a or circumscribed about it.

$$Answer: \quad \frac{nI \tan (\pi/n)}{2\pi a} \quad and \quad \frac{nI \sin (\pi/n)}{2\pi a}.$$

2.9-3   Consider two thin parallel wires of radius a and length l, shorted at both ends to form a loop. Let $s \ll l$ be the distance between the axes of the wires. Suppose that the loop is perpendicular to a time-varying uniform magnetic field. In Problem 2.3–9 it was assumed that the time rate of change of magnetic flux density, that is, the magnetic current density $\dot{B}$, was constant. It was found that current in the loop is

$$I = \dot{B}s/2R,$$

where R is the resistance of the wire per unit length. This current generates a magnetic field which is superposed on the field given by B.

As long as $\dot{B}$, and hence I, are constant, the added field does not affect I. Otherwise, it will affect it. For instance, if the loop is brought into the field, the current I can not suddenly assume a value different from zero since this would mean an instantaneous creation of magnetic flux associated with the current, and therefore, an infinite electric field. Hence, the above equation can be true only in the steady state even when $\dot{B}$ is constant. Obtain the more exact equation for the current by taking into consideration its magnetic field. Assume that if the loop is in the plane of the paper, B is coming out of it and that consequently the positive direction of electric current in the above equation is clockwise.

$$Answer: \quad 2RI = \frac{d}{dt} (Bs - LI),$$

where

$$L = \frac{\mu}{\pi} \ln (s/a).$$

2.9-4   Note that if the loop in the preceding problem is perfectly conducting and is brought into the magnetic field from a field free region, no net magnetic flux will be linked with the loop and the current is determined by B and not by $\dot{B}$,

$$I = Bs/L.$$

Show that if the magnetic flux density is generated at a constant rate $\dot{B}$ from $t = 0$ and on, then

$$I(t) = \frac{\dot{B}s}{2R}\left(1 - e^{-2Rt/L}\right).$$

2.10–1   Consider a thin solenoid extending from $z = 0$ to $z = l$. Let C be the circulating current per unit length of the solenoid and S the cross-sectional area of the solenoid. Using equation (2.45) show that the magnetic potential *outside* the solenoid is

$$U = \frac{CS}{4\pi r_1} - \frac{CS}{4\pi r},$$

where r and r_1 are the distances from the origin and the point at $z = l$. To simplify the integration take advantage of the fact that the potential as given by equation (2.45) is the derivative with respect to z of the potential of a certain point source.

Show also that if Φ is the magnetic flux through the solenoid, not too near its ends, then the above equation becomes

$$U = \frac{\Phi}{4\pi\mu r_1} - \frac{\Phi}{4\pi\mu r},$$

as one would naturally expect on intuitive grounds.

2.10–2   Consider a thin spherical shell of mean radius a, thickness h, and conductivity σ. Let the center of the shell be at the origin. Assume that at t equal to zero a uniform magnetic field, parallel to the z axis is impressed on the shell at the rate $\dot{B}_0$. This time-varying magnetic field will generate an electric field of intensity E_φ. The latter will start circulating currents of density J_φ in the shell, which in their turn will generate a magnetic field, both inside and outside the shell. On account of the boundary conditions and symmetry, this magnetic field must conform to the original field. Following this line of thought derive the equations for the subsequent field, first for an arbitrary slowly varying impressed field B_0 and then for a field increasing at a constant rate. Calculate the current density in the shell. Obtain the field when the conductivity of the shell is infinite.

Answer: If $B_z = A$ is the magnetic flux density in the interior of the shell ($r < a$) due to the circulating currents in the shell, then

$$\dot{A} + (3/\mu_0 \sigma h a)\,A = -\dot{B}_0. \tag{1}$$

For $r < a$

$$B_z = B_0 + A, \qquad E_\varphi = -\tfrac{1}{2}(\dot{B}_0 + \dot{A})r\sin\theta,$$

and for $r > a$ the field is the sum of the impressed field $B_z = B_0$, $E_\varphi = -\frac{1}{2}\dot{B}_0 r \sin \theta$ and the induced field

$$B_r = A\,(a/r)^3 \cos \theta, \qquad B_\theta = \frac{1}{2}A\,(a/r)^3 \sin \theta,$$

$$E_\varphi = -\frac{1}{2}\dot{A}a\,(a/r)^2 \sin \theta.$$

The current density in the shell is

$$J_\varphi = -\frac{1}{2}\sigma a\,(\dot{B}_0 + \dot{A}) \sin \theta.$$

If $\sigma = \infty$, one obtains directly from equation (1)

$$A + B_0 = \text{constant} = 0, \tag{2}$$

which means that in this case there is no field inside the shell.

The general solution of equation (1) is

$$A = -\exp\,(-3t/\mu_0\sigma ha) \int_0^t \dot{B}_0 \exp\,(3t/\mu_0\sigma ha)\, dt.$$

If $\dot{B}_0 = \text{constant}$, then

$$A = -\frac{1}{3}\mu_0\sigma ha\dot{B}_0\,[1 - \exp\,(-3t/\mu_0\sigma ha)], \tag{3}$$

so that ultimately

$$A = -\frac{1}{3}\mu_0\sigma ha\dot{B}_0$$

unless $\sigma = \infty$. Derive equation (2) from equation (3).

2.11–1   Consider a sphere of radius a, centered at the origin. Let μ be the permeability of the sphere, and μ_0 that of the surrounding medium. A magnetic field is created by a closely wound solenoid, coaxial with the z axis and almost touching the sphere. Let C be the circulating current in the φ direction per unit length of the solenoid. Show that the magnetic intensity in the interior of the sphere is

$$H_z = \frac{3\mu_0 C}{2\mu_0 + \mu}$$

and that the intensity just outside the solenoid in the xy plane is

$$H_z = \frac{(\mu_0 - \mu)\,C}{2\mu_0 + \mu}.$$

Show that the sphere becomes a magnet of moment

$$\frac{4\pi a^3 \mu_0\,(\mu - \mu_0)\,C}{2\mu_0 + \mu}.$$

The sphere acts as if there were a layer of positive magnetic charge on its upper hemisphere and a layer of negative charge on the lower hemisphere which create the exterior field of the magnet and produce a *downward* magnetic intensity

$$\frac{(\mu - \mu_0) C}{2\mu_0 + \mu}$$

opposing the field of the solenoid inside the magnet ("demagnetizing" intensity).

Magnetic polarization is the dipole moment per unit volume

$$P = \frac{3\mu_0 (\mu - \mu_0) C}{2\mu_0 + \mu}.$$

Show that inside the sphere

$$B_z = \mu_0 H_z + P.$$

We can also write

$$B_z = \mu_0 (H_z + M),$$

where M is called the magnetization of the sphere. Here M is the *area moment* per unit volume of amperian currents induced in the sphere by the field of the solenoid, or the *magnetization* of the sphere.

2.11–2   Consider a spherical shell $a \le r \le b$ of permeability μ, imbedded in a medium of permeability μ_0. Assume a current loop of area moment IS centered at the origin and in the xy plane. Explain why the magnetic intensity may be obtained from the results of Problem 2.5–5 if ϵ and ϵ_0 are replaced by μ and μ_0, and ql by $\mu_0 I S$.

2.11–3   Suppose that a uniform magnetic field of intensity $H_z = H_0$, $H_x = H_y = 0$ is impressed on the shell in the preceding problem (without the current loop). Calculate the field inside the shell (where $r < a$).

Answer: $H_x = H_y = 0, H_z = kH_0,$

where

$$k = \frac{9(\mu_0/\mu)}{(2 + \mu_0/\mu)(1 + 2\mu_0/\mu) - 2(a/b)^3(1 - \mu_0/\mu)^2}.$$

The factor k represents magnetic shielding. The same factor represents the ratio of the external field in the preceding problem to that which would have existed there without the shield.

2.12–1   Obtain the potential of a charge q at point $(0, 0, 0)$ between conducting planes $z = -\frac{1}{2}a$ and $z = \frac{1}{2}a$.

$$Answer:\quad V = \frac{q}{4\pi\epsilon\sqrt{\rho^2 + z^2}} + \frac{q}{4\pi\epsilon}\sum_{n=1}^{\infty}(-)^n\left(\frac{1}{r_n} + \frac{1}{R_n}\right),$$

where

$$r_n = \sqrt{\rho^2 + (z - na)^2},\qquad R_n = \sqrt{\rho^2 + (z + na)^2}.$$

2.12–2   Find the potential of a uniform line charge on the z axis between conducting planes $y = -a/2$ and $y = a/2$. Let q be the charge per unit length.

$$Answer:\quad V = -\frac{q}{2\pi\epsilon}\ln\sqrt{x^2 + y^2} - \frac{q}{2\pi\epsilon}\ln\prod_{n=1}^{\infty}\frac{r_{2n}R_{2n}}{r_{2n-1}R_{2n-1}},$$

where

$$r_n = \sqrt{x^2 + (y - na)^2},\qquad R_n = \sqrt{x^2 + (y + na)^2}.$$

2.12–3   Consider a metal cylinder of radius a, coaxial with the z axis, and a uniform line charge of density q, parallel to the z axis and passing through point $(l, 0, 0)$ where $l > a$. The charge on the surface of the cylinder will be displaced in order to make its surface an equipotential surface. Show that a hypothetical *image* line charge of density $-q$, also parallel to the z axis and passing through $(a^2/l, 0, 0)$ actually accomplishes this effect and thus produces outside the cylinder the same field as the charge displaced on the cylinder. Hence, the density of the displaced charge equals $D_\rho(a, \varphi, z)$ where D_ρ is due to both the given line charge and the image charge.

Note that the result depends on the symmetry in the expression

$$(a^2 - 2al\cos\varphi + l^2)^{1/2}$$

for the distance between the given line charge and a typical generator of the cylinder.

Show that if the logarithmic potential of a line charge q is taken as

$$V = -\frac{q}{2\pi\epsilon}\ln\rho_0,$$

where ρ_0 is the distance from the line charge, then the potential of the metal cylinder is

$$V_2 = -\frac{q}{2\pi\epsilon}\ln\frac{l}{a}.$$

Show that the potential of a cylinder of radius $b \ll l - a$, coaxial with the line charge, is approximately

$$V_1 = -\frac{q}{2\pi\epsilon} \ln \frac{b}{l - (a^2/l)}$$

and that

$$V_1 - V_2 = \frac{q}{2\pi\epsilon} \ln \left[\frac{l^2}{ab} \left(1 - \frac{a^2}{l^2} \right) \right].$$

Show that if the metal cylinder is electrically neutral, its potential is $-(q/2\pi\epsilon) \ln l$ and that the potential of the cylinder of radius b is

$$\frac{q}{2\pi\epsilon} \ln \frac{1}{b} \left(1 - \frac{a^2}{l^2} \right).$$

Show that if charge of density per unit length, q, is placed on the metal cylinder, its potential will become $-(q/2\pi\epsilon) \ln (al)$ and that the potential of the cylinder of radius b will be

$$(q/2\pi\epsilon) \ln [l^{-1}b^{-1}(1 - a^2/l^2)]$$

and that the potential difference between the latter and the former is

$$\frac{q}{2\pi\epsilon} \ln \left[\frac{a}{b} \left(1 - \frac{a^2}{l^2} \right) \right].$$

2.12–4   Consider, as in the preceding problem, a line charge of density q and a metal cylinder with an equal and opposite charge. Show that the surface density of charge on the cylinder is

$$q_s = -\frac{q[(l^2/a) - a]}{2\pi\rho_1^2},$$

where ρ_1 is the distance from the line charge to a typical generating line of the cylinder.

Hence if the cylinder is neutral, the density of charge is

$$q_s = \frac{q}{2\pi} \left[\frac{1}{a} + \frac{a - (l^2/a)}{\rho_1} \right].$$

Show that the density of charge is zero when

$$\rho_1 = \sqrt{l^2 - a^2},$$

that is, where the planes tangent to the cylinder pass through the line charge.

When the cylinder is charged, as in the preceding case, the charge density at points of tangency is $-q/2\pi a$, the same as for uniform distribution of charge. When $l \gg a$, ρ_1 does not vary much with φ and the charge is almost uniformly distributed. But as l approaches a, the charge tends to concentrate on the side of the cylinder facing the line charge. Show that the densities at points nearest the line charge, at points of tangency, and at points farthest from the line charge are proportional to

$$\frac{l+a}{l-a}, \quad 1, \quad \frac{l-a}{l+a}.$$

Show that the charge per unit length of the cylinder between the planes $\varphi = -\varphi_0$ and $\varphi = \varphi_0$ is

$$q(\varphi_0) = -\frac{2q}{\pi} \tan^{-1} \left(\frac{l+a}{l-a} \tan \tfrac{1}{2}\varphi_0 \right).$$

Thus the charge on that half of the cylinder which faces the line charge is

$$q(\tfrac{1}{2}\pi) = -\frac{2q}{\pi} \tan^{-1} \frac{l+a}{l-a}$$

$$= -q + \frac{2q}{\pi} \left[\frac{l-a}{l+a} - \frac{(l-a)^3}{3(l+a)^3} + \cdots \right].$$

2.12–5   Consider two parallel metal cylinders of radii a and b. Let q be the charge per unit length on the first cylinder and $-q$ that on the second. Assume that the distance between the axes is d. When d is very large, there is little interaction between the charges. On each cylinder the charge distribution is essentially uniform. As d diminishes, the interaction becomes more important. Thus if the charge on cylinder B (the one of radius b) is uniformly distributed, its exterior field equals that of a line charge on its axis. Cylinder A will then be equipotential if its field equals that of a line charge at distance $s_1 = a^2/d$ from its axis. This field acts on cylinder B which will become equipotential if its field is not that of initially assumed axial line charge but that of a line charge at distance $c_1 = b^2/(d - s_1)$ from its axis. To make cylinder A equipotential, the image charge must be shifted to distance $s_2 = a^2/(d - c_1)$. Similarly, the image charge inside cylinder B must be shifted to distance $c_2 = b^2/(d - s_2)$. This iterative process can be continued indefinitely and the limiting positions of the image charges

$$s = \lim s_n, \qquad c = \lim c_n$$

can be expressed as periodic continued fractions. Show that the limit of the potential difference between the cylinders is

$$V_1 - V_2 = \frac{q}{2\pi\epsilon} \ln \frac{(d-s)(d-c)}{ab}.$$

Show that s and c are roots of a certain quadratic equation. Thus

$$s^2 d + s(b^2 - a^2 - d^2) + a^2 d = 0.$$

This equation has two roots, one of which must be rejected on physical grounds. What is the condition which the correct root must satisfy?

Once proper values for s and c are obtained, $V_1 - V_2$ is determined. A simpler expression for this potential difference can be obtained if we establish

$$s = \frac{a^2}{d-c}, \qquad c = \frac{b^2}{d-s}$$

and note that

$$(d-s)(d-c) = d^2 - sd - b^2.$$

In this manner show that

$$V_1 - V_2 = \frac{q}{2\pi\epsilon} \ln \frac{d^2 - a^2 - b^2 + \sqrt{(d^2 - a^2 - b^2)^2 - 4a^2 b^2}}{2ab}.$$

Show that approximately

$$V_1 - V_2 = \frac{q}{\pi\epsilon} \ln \frac{d}{\sqrt{ab}} - \frac{q}{2\pi\epsilon} \ln \left(1 - \frac{a^2 + b^2}{d^2}\right).$$

2.12–6   Show that a sphere of radius a, centered at the origin and in the presence of a point charge q at point $(0, 0, l)$ becomes an equipotential surface if we introduce a charge $-qa/l$ at point $(0, 0, a^2/l)$. Hence, this sphere may be replaced by a thin metal sphere without disturbing the field. Show that the surface density of charge on the metal sphere which produces the same exterior field as the *image charge* $-qa/l$ is

$$q_s = -\frac{q[(l^2/a) - a]}{4\pi r_1^3},$$

where r_1 is the distance between a point on the sphere and the point charge.

If a *uniform* distribution of charge qa/l is superposed on this charge distribution, the sphere becomes electrically neutral. Show that the potential of the sphere is

$$V = q/4\pi\epsilon l.$$

Show that the charge density vanishes when

$$r_1 = 3\sqrt{l(l^2 - a^2)} = l\left(1 - \frac{a^2}{3l^2} - \frac{a^4}{9l^2} - \cdots\right).$$

The locus of these points on the sphere divides the sphere into positively and negatively charged parts.

2.12–7   Show that if a charge $-q$ is placed on the neutral sphere in the preceding problem, then the potential of the sphere and the charge density will be

$$V = -\frac{q}{4\pi\epsilon}\left(\frac{1}{a} - \frac{1}{l}\right),$$

$$q_s = -\frac{q(l - a)}{4\pi a}\left(\frac{l + a}{r_1^3} + \frac{1}{al}\right).$$

Show that the charge on the surface of the sphere intercepted by the cone $\theta = \theta_0$ is

$$q(\theta_0) = -q\left[1 - \frac{l - a}{2l}\cos\theta_0 - \frac{l^2 - a^2}{2l\sqrt{a^2 + l^2 - 2al\cos\theta_0}}\right].$$

The charge on the hemisphere facing the point charge is

$$q(\tfrac{1}{2}\pi) = -q\left[1 - \frac{l^2 - a^2}{2l\sqrt{l^2 + a^2}}\right].$$

This equation may be used for studying the proximity effect. Thus if l equals two diameters, the charge on the hemisphere facing the point charge is $-(18/33)q$, which is about 4.5 percent in excess of one-half of the total charge. If $l = 3a$, the charge on the hemispheres is distributed in the ratio of 11 to 8. When $l - a \ll a$, only $-0.35q(l - a)/a$ is on the hemisphere looking away from the point charge.

2.12–8   Show that if the charge on the metal sphere equals that of the point charge, the potential of the sphere is

$$V = \frac{q}{4\pi\epsilon}\left(\frac{1}{a} + \frac{1}{l}\right).$$

2.12–9   Consider two metal spheres of radius a, with a charge q on one and $-q$ on the other. Let l be the distance between their centers. The potentials of these spheres may be obtained by successive approximations, based on the results of Problems 2.12–6 and 2.12–7. Thus starting with the assumption that in the first approximation the charges are distributed uniformly so that their fields outside the spheres are the same as the fields of equal charges located at the centers of the spheres, one obtains the first image charges and the compensating uniformly distributed charges. The potential of the positive sphere will then be

$$V = \frac{q}{4\pi\epsilon}\left(\frac{1}{a} - \frac{1}{l}\right).$$

Note that this agrees with the equation following equation (2.31) except for the term of order $(a/l)^4$.

Applying the method of images for the second time, one obtains

$$V = \frac{q}{4\pi\epsilon}\left[\frac{1}{a} - \frac{1}{l} - \frac{a}{l}\left(\frac{1}{l} - \frac{1}{l_1}\right)\right],$$

where $l_1 = l - (a^2/l)$. Hence

$$V = \frac{q}{4\pi\epsilon}\left[\frac{1}{a} - \frac{1}{l} - \frac{a^3}{l^2(l^2 - a^2)}\right].$$

This agrees with the result in Section 2.6 as far as the term of order $(a/l)^4$.

The method of successive images can be applied indefinitely. After the first term, the terms in the expression for V will be of the same sign.

2.12–10   Show that if the spheres in the preceding problem are equally charged, then

$$V = \frac{q}{4\pi\epsilon}\left[\frac{1}{a} + \frac{1}{l} - \frac{a^3}{l^2(l^2 - a^2)} + \cdots\right].$$

2.12–11   Show that the next application of the method of images will introduce inside the brackets in the expression for V for two equally charged spheres (Problem 2.12–10) the following term:

$$\frac{2a^6}{l^3(l^2 - a^2)(l^2 - 2a^2)}.$$

The same term with the negative sign will appear in the potential of two equally and oppositively charged spheres.

2.15–1   Show that the resistance between two perfectly conducting spheres of radius a imbedded in a conducting medium is approximately

$$R = \frac{1}{2\pi\sigma} \left[\frac{1}{a} - \frac{1}{l} - \frac{a^3}{l^2(l^2 - a^2)} \right],$$

where l is the distance between the centers.

2.15–2   Show that the power contributed to the conducting medium by the generators between conducting bodies K_1 and K_2 (Section 2.15) and a point at infinity or ground is

$$P = r_{11}I_1^2 + 2r_{12}I_1I_2 + r_{22}I_2^2.$$

2.15–3   Show that the currents in two resistive rods, connected to a generator in parallel, are so distributed that the dissipated power is minimum, and that a greater current is in the rod with the smaller resistance.

2.15–4   Consider two perfectly conducting spheres of radius a, imbedded in a conducting medium. Let their centers be on the z axis at $z = a + h$ and $z = -a - h$ where $h \ll a$. From the results of Problem 2.12–7 (as well as the principle established in Problem 2.15–3) we conclude that current will flow largely between the hemispheres facing each other. One should be able, therefore, to obtain the approximate conductance between the spheres by assuming that the lines of flow between the hemispheres are straight lines parallel to the z axis. The greatest deviation from straightness will occur in the region where the current is small so that the resulting effect on the conductance is small. Based on this approximation show that

$$G = \pi\sigma \left[(a + 2h) \ln \frac{a + 2h}{h} - (a + h) \right].$$

An estimate of the conductance between the remaining hemispheres is $G_1 = 1.5\pi\sigma a$. This should be added to the preceding expression for a better approximation.

2.15–5   Explain why the mutual resistance coefficient r_{12} of two conducting bodies is approximately independent of their size and shape as long as the mean distance l between them is large in comparison with their linear dimensions.

2.16–1   Show that the work done by the generators when placing charges q_1 and q_2 on the conducting bodies K_1 and K_2 (Section 2.16) is

$$W = \tfrac{1}{2}p_{11}q_1^2 + p_{12}q_1q_2 + \tfrac{1}{2}p_{22}q_2^2.$$

2.16–2   Show that the work done by the generators when raising the potentials of the conducting bodies K_1 and K_2 from zero to V_1 and V_2, respectively, is

$$W = \tfrac{1}{2}c_{11}V_1^2 + c_{12}V_1V_2 + \tfrac{1}{2}c_{22}V_2^2.$$

2.16–3   Show from the results of Section 2.2 that the total capacitance of a prolate spheroid whose focal distance is l, and whose major and minor axes are, respectively, $2a$ and $2b$, is

$$C_t = \frac{2\pi\epsilon l}{\coth{(2a/l)}} = \frac{4\pi\epsilon l}{\ln{(2a+l)} - \ln{(2a-l)}}$$

$$= \frac{2\pi\epsilon l}{\ln{(2a+l/2b)}}.$$

Thus, for thin spheroids

$$C_t \simeq \frac{2\pi\epsilon l}{\ln{(l/b)} + (b/l)^2}.$$

Show from equation (2.12) that the approximate capacitance of a thin cylinder of radius b and length l is

$$C_t \simeq \frac{2\pi\epsilon l}{\ln{(l/b)} - 1 + \ln 2}.$$

Show that as l approaches zero, prolate spheroids approach a sphere and

$$C_t \rightarrow 4\pi\epsilon a,$$

where a is the radius of the sphere.

More advanced methods are needed to obtain the capacitance of an oblate spheroid

$$C_t = \frac{2\pi\epsilon l}{\cot^{-1}{(l/2b)}},$$

where l is the focal distance and $2b$ is the minor axis. The oblate spheroid of zero minor axis is a *disk* and the above formula gives

$$C_t = 8\epsilon a,$$

where a is the radius of the disk.

2.16–4   Suppose that the conducting bodies K_1 and K_2 have equal and opposite charges so that all tubes of displacement originating on K_1 end on K_2. Consider two tubes of displacement whose capacitances are C_1 and C_2 so that the charges intercepted by the tubes on K_1 are

$$q_1 = C_1 V, \qquad q_2 = C_2 V,$$

where V is the voltage from K_1 to K_2. Show that the charge $q_1 + q_2$ intercepted by both tubes is so distributed that the work done in placing these charges on the bodies is minimum.

2.17–1   Show that the work needed to establish currents I_1 and I_2 in two perfectly conducting loops, Figure 2.30, is

$$W = \tfrac{1}{2}L_{11}I_1^2 + L_{12}I_1I_2 + \tfrac{1}{2}L_{22}I_2^2.$$

2.17–2   Using the results of Section 2.8 show that the inductance of a square loop is

$$L = \frac{\mu}{\pi} \int_0^a \int_0^a \left[\frac{1}{\sqrt{c^2 + (\xi - z)^2}} - \frac{1}{\sqrt{a^2 + (\xi - z)^2}} \right] d\xi \, dz,$$

where c is the radius of the wire and a is the side of the square.
Integrate and show that

$$L = \frac{2\mu a}{\pi} \left[\ln (a/c) + \ln \frac{1 + \sqrt{1 + (c/a)^2}}{1 + \sqrt{2}} - 1 + \sqrt{2} \right.$$

$$\left. - \sqrt{1 + (c/a)^2} + (c/a) \right]$$

or approximately

$$L = (2\mu a/\pi)[\ln (a/c) + \ln 2(\sqrt{2} - 1) - 2 + \sqrt{2}].$$

Using the result of Section 2.9, show that

$$L = \frac{2\mu}{\pi} \int_c^a \int_c^a \frac{z}{\rho\sqrt{\rho^2 + z^2}} \, d\rho \, dz.$$

If the terms of order c/a are neglected, we shall obtain the same result as above.

2.17–3   Consider a tube of magnetic flux Φ between two equipotential end surfaces. If U is the mmf between these ends, the ratio $R = U/\Phi$ is called the *reluctance* of the tube. In the analysis of magnetic circuits it plays the same role the resistance does in the analysis of direct current electric circuits.

Show that the reluctance of a toroidal solenoid of length l and radius a is $R = l/\mu\pi a^2$.

Assume that the solenoid is divided into two sections, one of length l_1 and the other of length $l_2 = l - l_1$. Assume that the first section is filled with substance of permeability μ_1 and the remaining section with substance of permeability μ_2. Let I be the *total* circulating current. Obtain the magnetic flux Φ, the magnetomotive force U_1 across the first section, and the magnetomotive force U_2 across the second.

Answer:

$$\Phi = \frac{\pi a^2 \mu_1 \mu_2 I}{\mu_2 l_1 + \mu_1 l_2}, \qquad U_1 = \frac{\mu_2 l_1 I}{\mu_2 l_1 + \mu_1 l_2}, \qquad U_2 = I - U_1.$$

2.17–4   Consider a solenoid of radius a, coaxial with the z axis, extending from $z = 0$ to $z = l \gg a$. In its interior the magnetic flux is substantially parallel to the z axis and distributed uniformly except near one end where the flux leaks out into the outer space and near the other where the flux re-enters the solenoid. The magnetic intensity on the axis of the solenoid was calculated in Problem 1.22–2 and may be taken as indicative of the flux passing through the corresponding cross section of the solenoid. Thus only about one-half of the total flux Φ_0 actually comes from one end turn and enters through the other. Show that the flux $\Phi(z)$ in the solenoid at distance z from the lower end varies approximately as follows:

$$\Phi(0) = 0.5\Phi_0, \qquad \Phi(a) = 0.85\Phi_0, \qquad \Phi(2a) = 0.95\Phi_0$$

$$\Phi(3a) = 0.97\Phi_0, \qquad \Phi(4a) = 0.985\Phi_0.$$

Show that the magnetomotive force between $z = Na$ and $z = l - Na$ when $Na \ll l$ is

$$U \simeq C(l - 2Na),$$

where C is the circulating current per unit length of the solenoid. In view of the foregoing results we may subdivide the solenoid into an inner "air-core," extending from $z = 4a$ to $z = l - 4a$, and two "poles" of the solenoid at the ends. Show that the reluctance of the core is $(l - 8a)/\pi\mu_0 a^2$ and that the external reluctance between the poles is $8/\pi\mu_0 a$.

If the solenoid has a magnetizable core of permeability $\mu \gg \mu_0$, extending the entire length of the solenoid, the flux density will be substantially uniform all the way to the ends $z = 0$ and $z = l$. In this case the external reluctance between these ends (constituting two faces of two circular disks) may be obtained by analogy with the capacitance of a circular disk (Problem 2.16–3). Show that this reluctance equals approximately $1/2\mu_0 a$, assuming that $l \gg a$. Show that a more accurate reluctance is $(1/2\mu_0 a) - (1/\pi\mu_0 l)$. Show that the flux through the solenoid is

$$\Phi = \frac{\pi\mu a^2 C}{1 + (\pi\mu a/2\mu_0 l)}.$$

This means that the magnetic intensity inside the core is

$$H_z = C[1 + (\pi\mu a/2\mu_0 l)]^{-1}$$

as contrasted with the value C in absence of the core.

2.18–1   Consider a direct current generator imbedded in a dissipative medium of conductivity σ_0 and insulated from the medium except at its terminals. Suppose that these terminals are highly conducting spheres of radius b. Assume that the distance s between the centers of the terminals is equal to or larger than two diameters. Two infinitely long parallel rods of radius $a < b$ and conductivity $\sigma \gg \sigma_0$ are connected to the terminals. These rods are not insulated from the medium. The distance between their axes is also s. The problem is to find the current in the rods.

Since σ is much larger than σ_0 the current entering one rod slowly leaks out essentially at right angles to the rod, enters the other rod, and returns to the generator. Assuming that $I(z)$ is the current in one rod at distance z from the terminal and that $V(z)$ is the transverse voltage from this rod to the other rod show that

$$\Delta V = -2R_{se}I\Delta z, \qquad \Delta I = -G_{sh}V\Delta z,$$

where

$$R_{se} = 1/\pi\sigma a^2, \qquad G_{sh} = \pi\sigma_0/\ln{(s/a)},$$

so that as Δz approaches zero

$$\frac{dV}{dz} = -2R_{se}I, \qquad \frac{dI}{dz} = -G_{sh}V.$$

Examine the solution for infinitely long rods when $\sigma = 10^7$ mho per meter (iron) and $\sigma_0 = 0.01$ mho per meter (soil). Assume that $a = 1$ cm, $b = 2$ cm, $s = 8$ cm.

Show that if V_0 is the voltage between the terminals, the current entering one rod is $(G_{sh}/2R_{se})^{\frac{1}{2}}V_0$. Compare this current with direct leakage current between the terminals.

2.18–2   In the preceding problem it was assumed that the shunt current emerging from a rod (or converging to it) is essentially perpendicular to the rod. This is true to the extent that the ratio, E_z/E_ρ, of the longitudinal to the radial component of electric intensity at the surface of the rod is small in comparison with unity. Using the solution obtained on this assumption show that

$$E_z/E_\rho = [2(\sigma_0/\sigma) \ \ln \ (s/a)]^{1/2}.$$

2.18–3   Consider two solid conducting cones, whose boundaries are $\theta = \vartheta$ and $\theta = \pi - \vartheta$, with their apexes at the origin. Let their conductivity be σ. Assume that the conductivity of the medium between the cones is $\sigma_0 \ll \sigma$. Show that the approximate differential equations for the current $I(r)$ in the upper cone and the transverse voltage $V(r)$ along the meridians from the upper cone to the lower are

$$\frac{dV}{dr} = -2R_{se}I, \qquad \frac{dI}{dr} = -G_{sh}V,$$

where

$$R_{se} = 1/\sigma\Omega r^2, \qquad G_{sh} = \frac{\pi\sigma_0}{\ln \ \cot \ (\vartheta/2)}$$

and

$$\Omega = 2\pi(1 - \cos \vartheta)$$

is the solid angle of the upper cone.
    Show that

$$r^2 \frac{d^2I}{dr^2} = kI, \qquad k = \frac{2\pi\sigma_0}{\sigma\Omega \ln \ \cot \ (\vartheta/2)}.$$

Show that the solution is

$$I = Ar^{n_1} + Br^{n_2}, \qquad n_{1,2} = \tfrac{1}{2} \pm \sqrt{\tfrac{1}{4} + k}.$$

For infinitely long cones I must vanish at infinity and therefore A must equal zero. If the medium beyond $r = l$ is nonconducting, the ratio A/B will be obtained from the condition $I(l) = 0$.

2.18–4   A rod of radius a and permeability μ is bent into a long rectangular loop $ABCD$ (see Figure 2.18–4) of mean dimensions s and $l \gg s$. A solenoid is wound round one short side of the loop

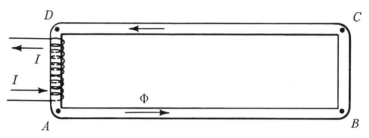

FIGURE 2.18–4

AD. Assuming the direction of current as shown, the magnetic flux in the solenoid will be from D to A. If the permeability μ_0 of the surrounding medium is much smaller than μ, this flux will follow the highly permeable loop but gradually will leak out from the lower rod, substantially at right angles to it, and enter the upper rod to return to the solenoid. Show that if $\Phi(z)$ is the magnetic flux in the lower rod at distance z from the solenoid and $U(z)$ is the magneto-motive force from the lower rod to the upper, then

$$\frac{dU}{dz} = -2R_{se}\Phi, \qquad \frac{d\Phi}{dz} = -\frac{U}{R_{sh}}$$

where $R_{se} = 1/\mu\pi a^2$ is the reluctance per unit length of the rod and

$$R_{sh} = \frac{\ln\,(s/a)}{\pi\mu_0},$$

is the reluctance per unit length between the lower and the upper sections of the loop.

   Show that in general

$$\Phi(z) = Ae^{-\Gamma z} + Be^{\Gamma z}, \qquad \Gamma = \sqrt{2R_{se}/R_{sh}},$$

$$U(z) = KAe^{-\Gamma z} - KBe^{\Gamma z}, \qquad K = \sqrt{2R_{se}R_{sh}}.$$

Thus

$$\Gamma a = \sqrt{\frac{2\mu_0}{\mu\,\ln\,(s/a)}}, \qquad K = \frac{1}{\pi a}\sqrt{\frac{2\,\ln\,(s/a)}{\mu\mu_0}}.$$

Show that

$$B = Ae^{-2\Gamma l} \frac{K - R_t}{K + R_t},$$

where $R_t = s/\pi \mu a^2$ is the relcutance of BC.

Show that if I is the current in the winding and N is the number of turns, then

$$I(0) = NI - R_s \Phi(0),$$

where $R_s = s/\pi \mu a^2$ is the reluctance of AD. Hence, show that

$$A = \frac{NI}{K + R_s} + \frac{K - R_s}{K + R_s} B.$$

2.18–5   If the winding is extended to AB and DC and if n is the number of turns per unit length, show that the flux transmission equations become

$$\frac{dU}{dz} = -2R_{se}\Phi + 2nI, \qquad \frac{d\Phi}{dz} = -\frac{U}{R_{sh}}.$$

Solve these equations and show that if the winding is over the entire loop (n turns per unit length over AD and BC as well), then

$$\Phi(z) = nI/R_{se}, \qquad U(z) = 0.$$

3.4–1   Consider a circularly symmetric perfectly conducting cavity whose cross section and dimensions are shown in Figure 3.4–1. Obtain the first approximation to the natural frequency of oscillations.

Answer: $\omega = (L_t C_t)^{-1/2}$

where

$$L_t = \frac{\mu(h - s)}{2\pi} \ln \frac{b}{c} + \frac{\mu s}{2\pi} \ln \frac{b}{a}, \qquad C_t = \frac{\epsilon \pi a^2}{s}.$$

3.8–1   Consider two perfectly conducting spheres, of radii a and $b > a$, concentric with the origin. Assume that a/b is not too small. Suppose that segments of these spheres inside the cone $\theta = \vartheta$ are removed and a voltage is impressed uniformly round the periphery

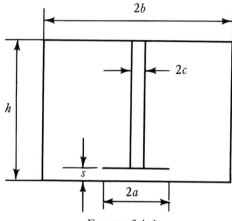

FIGURE 3.4–1

between the edges of the spheres. Show that the low-frequency equivalent circuit for this structure is a capacitance

$$C_t = \frac{2\pi\epsilon ab(1 + \cos\vartheta)}{b - a}$$

in series with an inductance

$$L_t = \frac{2\mu(b - a)(\ln csc \tfrac{1}{2}\vartheta - \tfrac{1}{2}\cos^2 \tfrac{1}{2}\vartheta)}{\pi(1 + \cos\vartheta)^2}.$$

As ϑ approaches 0, L_t approaches

$$\frac{\mu(b - a)}{2\pi}\left(\ln\frac{2}{\vartheta} - \frac{1}{2}\right).$$

3.9–1   Consider a circular parallel plate capacitor as shown in Figure 3.5 (Section 3.8) and assume that the plates are connected with a coaxial conducting rod of radius c. Show that the equivalent circuit for this structure is an inductance $L_t = (\mu/2\pi)\ln(a/c)$ shunted by a capacitance

$$C_t = \frac{2\pi\epsilon P}{h[\ln(a/c)]^2},$$

where

$$P = \tfrac{1}{4}(a^2 - c^2) - \tfrac{1}{2}c^2\ln(a/c) - \tfrac{1}{2}c^2[\ln(a/c)]^2.$$

3.9–2   Consider the structure in Problem 3.8–1 and assume that the spheres are shorted with a section of a perfectly conducting cone $\theta = \pi - \psi$. Show that the low-frequency equivalent circuit is an inductance

$$L_t = \frac{\mu(b - a)}{2\pi} \ln \frac{\cot (\psi/2)}{\tan (\vartheta/2)}$$

is parallel with a capacitance

$$C_t = \frac{2\pi\epsilon abP}{(b - a)[\ln \cot (\psi/2) + \ln \cot (\vartheta/2)]^2},$$

$$P = \int_\vartheta^{\pi-\psi} [\ln \cot (\psi/2) + \ln \cot (\theta/2)]^2 \sin^2 \theta \, d\theta.$$

To evaluate the integral, substitute $\cot (\theta/2) = u$. The integration is laborious.

3.12–1   Consider a perfectly conducting cylindrical cavity of radius a and height h. This is a special case of the cavity in Figure 3.2(a) (Section 3.4) in which $s = h$ and $b = 2a$. If we use equation (3.26), the natural frequency is given by $\omega a \sqrt{\mu\epsilon} = 3.4$; the exact natural frequency is given by $\omega a \sqrt{\mu\epsilon} = 2.40 \cdots$. Equation (3.26) becomes more accurate as s becomes smaller. When s is smaller one region of the cavity is occupied primarily by an electric field and the other primarily by a magnetic field; this was the assumption in the derivation of equation (3.26). This equation is even more accurate for the cavity described in Problem 3.4–1.

Obtain an improved approximation for the cylindrical cavity by using the low-frequency equivalent circuits for the central portion of the cavity, given by $a = 0.5b$, and for the remaining "slotted toroid."

Answer: $\omega b \sqrt{\mu\epsilon} = 2.36$ (as compared with the exact value $2.40 \cdots$).

4.2–1   Consider two parallel perfectly conducting planes, $z = 0$ and $z = h$, with circular holes extending from $\rho = 0$ to $\rho = \rho_0$. Assume that a voltage $V(\rho_0)$ is applied uniformly between the edges of the planes and that the resulting radial current in the plane $z = 0$ is $I(\rho_0)$. Obtain the integral equations for the voltage and current in this *disk transmission line* at distances $\rho \geq \rho_0$. Compare these equations with equations (4.11) and draw conclusions about L and C.

Answer:
$$V(\rho) = V(\rho_0) - (j\omega\mu h/2\pi) \int_{\rho_0}^{\rho} \rho^{-1}I(\rho)\, d\rho.$$

$$I(\rho) = I(\rho_0) - (2\pi j\omega\epsilon/h) \int_{\rho_0}^{\rho} \rho V(\rho)\, d\rho.$$

4.2–2   Consider two perfectly conducting spheres, concentric with the origin of a spherical coordinate system. Let a be the radius of the inner sphere and b the radius of the outer sphere. Assume that $b - a \ll (b + a)/2$. Suppose that there are circular holes in these spheres, concentric with the z axis, and that the edges of the sphere are given by $\theta = \theta_0$. Let a voltage $V(\theta_0)$ be applied uniformly between the edges and assume that the resulting current along the meridians on the inner sphere is $I(\theta_0)$. Show that the integral equations for $V(\theta)$ and $I(\theta)$, when $\theta \geq \theta_0$, are approximately

$$V(\theta) = V(\theta_0) - j\omega \int_{\theta_0}^{\theta} L_1(\theta)I(\theta)\, d\theta,$$

$$I(\theta) = I(\theta_0) - j\omega \int_{\theta_0}^{\theta} C_1(\theta)V(\theta)\, d\theta,$$

where the inductance $L_1(\theta)$ and capacitance $C_1(\theta)$ per radian are

$$L_1(\theta) = \mu(b - a)/2\pi \sin\theta,$$
$$C_1(\theta) = (2\pi\epsilon ab \sin\theta)/(b - a).$$

Show that if s is the distance from the z axis along a meridian of radius $c = \sqrt{ab}$ [which is approximately equal to $(a + b)/2$], then the transmission equations become

$$V(s) = V(s_0) - j\omega \int_{s_0}^{s} L(s)I(s)\, ds,$$

$$I(s) = I(s_0) - j\omega \int_{s_0}^{s} C(s)V(s)\, ds,$$

where the inductance $L(s)$ and capacitance $C(s)$ per unit length along the mean meridian are

$$L(s) = \mu(b - a)/2\pi c \sin(s/c),$$
$$C(s) = [2\pi\epsilon \sin(s/c)]/(b - a).$$

What happens when $s/c \ll 1$?

4.2-3   Consider a perfectly conducting cylinder of radius b and a closely wound coaxial solenoid of mean radius $a < b$. Assume that the wire with which the solenoid is wound is very thin and perfectly conducting. Let c be the radius of the wire and t the thickness of the insulation. Find an approximate value of $E_z(a, z)$ in equation (4.5). What is its effect on the parameters in equation (4.12)?

> *Answer:* $E_z(a, z) = j\omega L_1 I(z)$, where $L_1 = \mu\pi a^2/4(c + t)^2$.

4.2-4   Consider two parallel solenoids whose dimensions are the same as those in the preceding problem. Assume that the interaxial distance s is larger than $4a$. Show that approximate equations for the transverse voltage between the solenoids and the current $I(z)$ are equations (4.11) in which

$$Z = j\omega(2L_1 + L), \qquad Y = \frac{j\omega\pi\epsilon}{\ln(s/a)},$$

where L_1 is given in the answer to the preceding problem and $L = (\mu/\pi)\ln(s/a)$.

4.2-5   Suppose that the outer cylinder of a coaxial pair (Figure 4.1, Section 4.1) is perfectly conducting and that the inner cylinder is made of thin wafers which are alternately perfectly conducting and dielectric. Let h be the thickness of a conducting wafer and s the thickness of a dielectric wafer. Assume that the dielectric constant of the wafer is ϵ_1 and that of the medium between the cylinders is ϵ. Show that approximate equations for the transverse voltage and longitudinal current are still equations (4.11) with

$$Z = j\omega L + \frac{1}{j\omega C_{se}}, \qquad Y = j\omega C_{sh},$$

where

$$L = \frac{\mu}{2\pi}\ln\frac{b}{a}, \qquad C_{sh} = \frac{2\pi\epsilon}{\ln(b/a)}, \qquad C_{se} = \frac{\epsilon_1\pi a^2(s + h)}{s};$$

more accurately

$$L = \frac{\mu}{2\pi}\ln\frac{b}{a} + \frac{\mu s}{8\pi(s + h)}.$$

4.4-1   Consider two perfectly conducting circular disks, coaxial with the z axis, in the planes $z = 0$ and $z = h$. Assume that a voltage is applied uniformly between the edges of these disks. Show that in this case the answer to Problem 4.2–1 becomes

$$V(\rho) = V(0) - (j\omega\mu h/2\pi) \int_0^\rho \rho^{-1} I(\rho) \, d\rho,$$

$$I(\rho) = -(2\pi j\omega\epsilon/h) \int_0^\rho \rho V(\rho) \, d\rho.$$

Apply the step-by-step method for calculating $V(\rho)$ and $I(\rho)$ and show that

$$V(\rho) = V(0) \left[1 - (\beta\rho/2)^2 + \frac{(\beta\rho/2)^4}{(1.2)^2} - \frac{(\beta\rho/2)^6}{(3!)^2} + \cdots \right],$$

$$I(\rho) = -V(0) \, (j\omega\epsilon\pi\rho^2/h) \left[1 - \frac{(\beta\rho/2)^2}{2} + \frac{(\beta\rho/2)^4}{(1.2)(2.3)} \right.$$

$$\left. - \frac{(\beta\rho/2)^6}{(1.2.3)(2.3.4)} + \cdots \right],$$

where $\beta = \omega\sqrt{\mu\epsilon}$.

4.4–2   Suppose that along the axis of the structure in the preceding problem there is a perfectly conducting wire of radius a, connecting the plates. Express $V(\rho)$ and $I(\rho)$ in terms of the current I_0 in the wire.

Answer: $$V(\rho) = -(j\omega\mu h/2\pi) \int_a^\rho \rho^{-1} I(\rho) \, d\rho,$$

$$I(\rho) = I_0 - (2\pi j\omega\epsilon/h) \int_a^\rho \rho V(\rho) \, d\rho.$$

4.6–1   Show that the differential equations for the disk transmission line are

$$\frac{dV}{d\rho} = -(j\omega\mu h/2\pi\rho) I$$

$$\frac{dI}{d\rho} = -(2\pi j\omega\epsilon\rho/h) V.$$

Show that V and I satisfy the following second-order differential equations

$$\rho \frac{d^2 V}{d\rho^2} + \frac{dV}{d\rho} + \beta^2 \rho V = 0, \qquad \beta^2 = \omega^2 \mu \epsilon,$$

$$\rho \frac{d^2 I}{d\rho^2} - \frac{dI}{d\rho} + \beta^2 \rho I = 0.$$

The first equation is Bessel's equation of order zero; the second may be reduced to Bessel's equation of order one if we choose a new dependent variable $u = I/\rho$.

4.6–2 Show that propagation of voltage along the meridians in Problem 4.2–2 is described by

$$\frac{d^2 V}{ds^2} + c^{-1} \cot (s/c) \frac{dV}{ds} + \beta^2 V = 0, \qquad \beta^2 = \omega^2 \mu \epsilon.$$

If this equation is expressed in terms of the polar angle θ, it becomes Legendre's equation

$$\sin \theta \frac{d^2 V}{d\theta^2} + \cos \theta \frac{dV}{d\theta} + \beta^2 c^2 \sin \theta V = 0.$$

Usually, the constant $\beta^2 c^2$ is written as $n(n + 1)$, where n is called the *order* of Legendre's equation.

4.6–3 Suppose that a distributed voltage, $E^i(z)$ per unit length, is impressed on the conductor carrying current $I(z)$. Show that the transmission line equations (4.22) become

$$\frac{dV}{dz} = -ZI + E^i(z), \qquad \frac{dI}{dz} = -YV.$$

Similarly, if $C^i(z)$ is the current per unit length, forced against the transverse voltage $V(z)$ from one conductor to the other, then

$$\frac{dV}{dz} = -ZI, \qquad \frac{dI}{dz} = -YV + C^i(z).$$

4.6–4 Derive from equations (4.22) the following relation

$$V(0)I^*(0) - V(l)I^*(l) = \int_0^l [ZI(z)I^*(z) + Y^*V(z)V^*(z)] \, dz,$$

where the asterisks denote conjugate complex numbers.

Show that if the line is either open or shorted at $z = l$, then

$$Z_{in}I_{in}I_{in}^* = Y_{in}^*V_{in}V_{in}^* = \int_0^l [ZII^* + Y^*VV^*]\,dz,$$

where Z_{in}, I_{in}, and V_{in} are, respectively, the input impedance, the input current, and the input voltage.

4.7–1   Consider a transmission line extending from $z = 0$ to $z = l$. Let it be terminated into its characteristic impedance at both ends. Let V_0 be the voltage impressed in series with the line at $z = \xi$ so that there will be a discontinuity in the transverse voltage, $V(\xi + 0) - V(\xi - 0) = V_0$. Show that at other points

$$I(z) = (V_0/2K)e^{-j\beta(z-\xi)}, \qquad z > \xi,$$

$$= (V_0/2K)e^{-j\beta(\xi-z)}, \qquad z < \xi,$$

$$V(z) = \tfrac{1}{2}V_0 e^{-j\beta(z-\xi)}, \qquad z > \xi,$$

$$= -\tfrac{1}{2}V_0 e^{-j\beta(\xi-z)}, \qquad z < \xi.$$

4.7–2   Suppose that in the preceding problem I_0 is the shunt current forced from one conductor into the other. Show that

$$I(z) = \tfrac{1}{2}I_0 e^{-j\beta(z-\xi)}, \qquad z > \xi,$$

$$= -\tfrac{1}{2}I_0 e^{-j\beta(\xi-z)}, \qquad z < \xi,$$

$$V(z) = \tfrac{1}{2}KI_0 e^{-j\beta(z-\xi)}, \qquad z > \xi,$$

$$= \tfrac{1}{2}KI_0 e^{-j\beta(\xi-z)}, \qquad z < \xi.$$

4.9–1   Obtain the propagation constant and the characteristic impedance of the coaxial structure described in Problem 4.2–5. Discuss their behavior as the frequency increases from zero to infinity. Discuss the conditions for the existence of waves on the one hand, and for the concentration of energy in the neighborhood (small or relatively large) of the source on the other hand.

4.12–1   Suppose that in Problem 4.7–1 the line is shorted at $z = 0$ and terminated into its characteristic impedance at $z = l$. Assume proper forms for the current and voltage distributions on either side of the source, determine the arbitrary constants from the given conditions, and show that

$$I(z) = (V_0/K)e^{-j\beta\xi}\cos\beta z, \qquad z < \xi,$$

$$= (V_0/K)\cos\beta\xi\, e^{-j\beta z}, \qquad z > \xi,$$

$$V(z) = -jV_0\, e^{-j\beta\xi}\sin\beta z, \qquad z < \xi,$$

$$= V_0\cos\beta\xi\, e^{-j\beta z}, \qquad z > \xi.$$

Alternatively, derive these expressions from those in Problem 4.7–1 by noting that the wave traveling in the negative z direction is totally reflected from the shorted end.

4.13–1   Show that the input impedance of a nondissipative line may be expressed as

$$Z_i = K\,\frac{Z_t\cos\beta l + jK\sin\beta l}{K\cos\beta l + jZ_t\sin\beta l}.$$

What are the input impedances when $l = \lambda/4$ and $l = \lambda/2$? Show that if Z_t is a pure resistance and $l = \lambda/8$, then the magnitude of the input impedance is K. Show also that as βl varies, the locus of Z_i in the complex plane is a circle of radius $\frac{1}{2}\,|\,R_t - K^2R_t^{-1}\,|$ centered at $\frac{1}{2}(R_t + K^2R_t^{-1})$ on the real axis. Even if Z_t is complex, the locus is still a circle; but the proof is less simple.

4.16–1   Consider two perfectly conducting coaxial cylinders of radii a and $b > a$. Let the medium between them be nondissipative from the generator at $z = 0$ to $z = l$ and highly dissipative from $z = l$ to $z = l + h$. Show that if h is infinite, the field in the dissipative medium decays at the rate α nepers per meter, where $\alpha = \sqrt{\pi f\mu\sigma}$, and that $V(l)/I(l) = \sqrt{j\omega\mu/\sigma}\,(1/2\pi)\ln(b/a)$.
    Show that for a finite h,

$$V(l)/I(l) = \sqrt{j\omega\mu/\sigma}\,(1/2\pi)\ln(b/a)\coth h\sqrt{j\omega\mu\sigma}.$$

4.16–2   Consider three thin parallel wires of radius a. Two of these wires are shorted at frequent intervals and serve as a return path for the current in the third wire. Let s be the interaxial distance from the latter to the wire nearest to it and h the interaxial distance

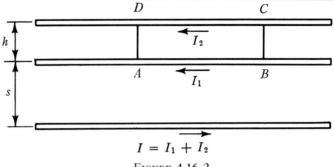

$$I = I_1 + I_2$$

FIGURE 4.16–2

to the remaining wire as shown in the figure. Apply the Faraday-Maxwell law to the rectangle $ABCD$ and show that

$$\left[R + \frac{j\omega\mu}{2\pi} \ln \frac{h(s+h)}{as}\right] I_2 = \left[R + \frac{j\omega\mu}{2\pi} \ln \frac{hs}{(s+h)a}\right] I_1$$

where $R = 1/\pi\sigma a^2$. Thus at very low frequencies the resistances of the wires control the distribution of current and $I_2 = I_1$. At high frequencies the inductive effects control the distribution and

$$\frac{I_2}{I_1} = \frac{\ln (h/a) - \ln (s + h/s)}{\ln (h/a) + \ln (s + h/s)}.$$

These equations express the *proximity effect*. The skin effect is evidently related to it.

4.17–1   The disk transmission line, considered in Problems 4.2–1 and 4.6–1 is nonuniform. Apply the transformation introduced in Section 4.17 and show that if

$$\vartheta = \beta\rho, \qquad K(\vartheta) = \eta\beta h/\vartheta,$$

$$V(\vartheta) = (\eta\beta h/\vartheta)^{\frac{1}{2}}\hat{V}(\vartheta),$$

$$I(\vartheta) = (\vartheta/\eta\beta h)^{\frac{1}{2}}\hat{I}(\vartheta),$$

then

$$\frac{d\hat{V}}{d\vartheta} = -j\hat{I} + (1/2\vartheta)\hat{V},$$

$$\frac{d\hat{I}}{d\vartheta} = -j\hat{V} - (1/2\vartheta)\hat{I}.$$

Hence, show that when $\beta\rho \gg 0.5$, that is, when $\rho/\lambda \gg 1/4\pi$, approximate expressions for the voltage and current in the disk transmission line are

$$I(\rho) = (\rho/\eta h)^{\frac{1}{2}}[Ae^{-j\beta\rho} + Be^{j\beta\rho}],$$
$$V(\rho) = (\eta h/\rho)^{\frac{1}{2}}[Ae^{-j\beta\rho} - Be^{j\beta\rho}].$$

For $\beta\rho \ll 0.5$, an approximate solution may best be obtained in the form of power series in $\beta\rho$ by using the step-by-step method. The intermediate section, on both sides of $\beta\rho = 0.5$, can be similarly treated.

Of course, in the present case, a complete solution may be expressed in terms of Bessel functions whose properties are now well known and tables are available. Here, this case has been used for two reasons:

(1) to illustrate the phase integral method of Section 4.17, and
(2) to show by a concrete case that when the parameters of a transmission line vary slowly, the line acts as an impedance transformer.

4.17-2   Show that when the inductance and capacitance per unit length vary in the same manner, that is, when $L = L_0 F(z)$ and $C = C_0 F(z)$, then equation (4.56) can be solved exactly and that the solution is

$$I(z) = Ae^{-j\vartheta} + Be^{j\vartheta}, \qquad V(z) = K(Ae^{-j\vartheta} - Be^{j\vartheta}),$$

where

$$K = \sqrt{L_0/C_0} \quad \text{and} \quad \vartheta = \omega\sqrt{L_0 C_0} \int_0^z F(z)\,dz.$$

4.17-3   Find an approximate solution for wave propagation along meridians (see Problem 4.2–2), when θ is neither small nor near π. What is the criterion of "smallness" of θ and of its "nearness" to π?

Answer:

$$I(\theta) = \sqrt{\frac{2\pi(ab)^{\frac{1}{2}}\sin\theta}{\eta(b-a)}}\,(Ae^{-jk\theta} + Be^{jk\theta}),$$

$$V(\theta) = \sqrt{\frac{\eta(b-a)}{2\pi(ab)^{\frac{1}{2}}\sin\theta}}\,(Ae^{-jk\theta} - Be^{jk\theta}),$$

where $k = \omega\sqrt{\mu\epsilon ab}$. For these approximations to hold we should have $k\theta \gg 0.5$ and $k(\pi - \theta) \gg 0.5$.

4.17-4   Consider a section of length l of a nonuniform transmission line and assume that it is shorted at both ends. Show that if $K'/2K \ll 1$, then the natural frequencies are given by

$$\omega_n \int_0^l \sqrt{L(z)\,C(z)} \; dz = n\pi, \qquad n = 1, 2, \cdots.$$

4.17-5   In Section 4.17 we obtained an approximate solution of nonuniform transmission line equations when $K' \ll 2K$. An improved approximation may be obtained from the results of problems 4.7-1 and 4.7-2 as follows: Start with the first approximation

$$\hat{I} = Ae^{-j\vartheta}, \qquad \hat{V} = Ae^{-j\vartheta}$$

for the progressive wave propagating in the direction of increasing ϑ. The last terms in equations (4.61) may be interpreted as the impressed series voltage $-(K'/2K)\,\hat{V}$ per unit length and shunt current $(K'/2K)\,\hat{I}$, also per unit length. Thus at a typical point $\vartheta = \varphi$ we may assume an impressed infinitesimal series voltage $-(K'/2K)Ae^{-j\varphi}\,d\varphi$ and an impressed shunt current $(K'/2K)Ae^{-j\varphi}$. The response to these may be obtained from the results of Problems 4.7-1 and 4.7-2. Then we integrate over the given length of the line from $\varphi = 0$ to $\varphi = \Theta$, for example. Following this procedure show that the improved approximations are

$$\hat{I}(\vartheta) = Ae^{-j\vartheta} - Ae^{j\vartheta} \int_\vartheta^\Theta (K'/2K)e^{-2j\varphi}\,d\varphi,$$

$$\hat{V}(\vartheta) = Ae^{-j\vartheta} + Ae^{j\vartheta} \int_\vartheta^\Theta (K'/2K)e^{-2j\varphi}\,d\varphi.$$

The second terms represent reflections which are inevitable when K is not a constant.

4.17-6   Prove that

$$\frac{K'(\vartheta)}{2K(\vartheta)} = \frac{K'(z)}{2\omega L(z)},$$

where $K(z)$ is, of course, $K[\vartheta(z)]$. This shows that $K'(\vartheta)/2K(\vartheta)$ decreases with increasing frequency.

4.18-1   As ω approaches zero, the ratio $K'(\vartheta)/2K(\vartheta)$ increases and the approximations involved in equations (4.62) become invalid.

Show that in this case approximate values of the image parameters are (for a nondissipative line)

$$K_1 = K_2 = \sqrt{L_t/C_t}, \qquad \tan\theta \simeq \theta = \omega\sqrt{L_tC_t},$$

where

$$L_t = \int_0^l L(z)\, dz, \qquad C_t = \int_0^l C(z)\, dz.$$

4.18–2   Show that improved approximations for the image parameters (at "low frequencies") may be obtained from

$$Y_{1,sh} = \frac{1}{j\omega L_t} + j\omega L_t^{-2} \int_0^l C(z)\left[\int_z^l L(z)\, dz\right]^2 dz,$$

$$Z_{1,op} = \frac{1}{j\omega C_t} + j\omega C_t^{-2} \int_0^l L(z)\left[\int_z^l C(z)\, dz\right]^2 dz,$$

$$Y_{2,sh} = \frac{1}{j\omega L_t} + j\omega L_t^{-2} \int_0^l C(z)\left[\int_0^z L(z)\, dz\right]^2 dz,$$

$$Z_{2,op} = \frac{1}{j\omega C_t} + j\omega C_t^{-2} \int_0^l L(z)\left[\int_0^z C(z)\, dz\right]^2 dz.$$

5.1–1   In Section 2.10 expressions were derived for the magnetic intensity of an infinitesimal circulating current. In Section 2.11 the expression for the electric intensity was obtained on the assumption that the circulating current varies slowly. Show that if this current varies rapidly, then the field components must satisfy the following differential equations:

$$\frac{\partial}{\partial\theta}(\sin\theta E_\varphi) = -j\omega\mu r \sin\theta H_r,$$

$$\frac{\partial}{\partial r}(rE_\varphi) = j\omega\mu r H_\theta, \qquad \frac{\partial}{\partial r}(rH_\theta) = j\omega\epsilon r E_\varphi + \frac{\partial H_r}{\partial\theta}.$$

5.1–2   In Section 1.16 it was found that for a static infinitesimal electric dipole, along the z axis, at the origin, the field components E_r and E_θ are proportional to $\cos\theta$ and $\sin\theta$, respectively. In Section 1.23 it was further found that if the charge is flowing slowly between the ends of such a dipole, there is a magnetic field of intensity H_φ which is proportional to $\sin\theta$. The results so obtained should be approximate solutions of equations (5.1), (5.2), and (5.3) when ω is "sufficiently small." We are now in a position to look for exact field intensities at all frequencies. Show that if

$$E_\theta(r, \theta) = \bar{E}_\theta(r) \sin \theta, \qquad E_r(r, \theta) = \bar{E}_r(r) \cos \theta,$$

$$H_\varphi(r, \theta) = \bar{H}_\varphi(r) \sin \theta,$$

then

$$\frac{d}{dr} (r\bar{E}_\theta) = -\left(j\omega\mu + \frac{2}{j\omega\epsilon r^2} \right) (r\bar{H}_\varphi),$$

$$(1)$$

$$\frac{d}{dr} (r\bar{H}_\varphi) = -j\omega\epsilon(r\bar{E}_\theta).$$

Comparing with the transmission line equations (4.22) we find that with the dipole (current element), at the origin, space acts as a radial transmission line with distributed parameters for rE_θ and rH_φ:

$$L_{se} = \mu, \qquad C_{sh} = \epsilon, \qquad C_{se} = \tfrac{1}{2}\epsilon r^2.$$

The radial current in this line is entirely a displacement current. Show that if $I(r)$ is the total radial displacement current in the northern hemisphere, then

$$I(r) = 2\pi r\bar{H}_\varphi.$$

If $V(r)$ is the voltage along the meridians from the northern axis to the southern, then

$$V(r) = 2r\bar{E}_\theta.$$

The transmission equations will then become

$$\frac{dV}{dr} = -\left(\frac{j\omega\mu}{\pi} + \frac{2}{j\omega\epsilon\pi r^2} \right) I,$$

$$(2)$$

$$\frac{dI}{dr} = -j\omega\epsilon\pi V$$

so that in this case

$$L_{se} = \mu/\pi, \qquad C_{sh} = \pi\epsilon, \qquad C_{se} = \tfrac{1}{2}\pi\epsilon r^2.$$

Note that if the radial displacement currents were distributed uniformly in each hemisphere, the series capacitance per unit length, in each hemisphere, would be $\epsilon 2\pi r^2$ [see equation (2.33)] and the capacitance of both hemispheres in series would be $\pi\epsilon r^2$. The factor $\frac{1}{2}$ is the result of the cosine distribution of the radial current density. Also, for a uniform current distribution, the series inductance of each hemisphere would be $\mu/8\pi$ [see equation (3.36)] and that of both hemispheres in series $\mu/4\pi$. The factor 4 is also the effect of nonuniform current distribution.

Of course, we would not have made such assumptions unless we were completely ignorant of the fact that in the static case D_r varies as $\cos\theta$. Even if we were ignorant of this fact, we would have thought of better approximations. But once we know that D_r is proportional to $\cos\theta$, the exact values of transmission line parameters are obtained immediately.

5.1–3   When $\beta r \gg 1.41$ in equations (1) of the preceding problem, we have differential equations with constant parameters and the general solutions are

$$r\bar{H}_\varphi = Ae^{-j\beta r} + Be^{j\beta r}, \qquad \beta = \omega\sqrt{\mu\epsilon},$$

$$r\bar{E}_\theta = \eta Ae^{-j\beta r} - \eta Be^{j\beta r}, \qquad \eta = \sqrt{\mu/\epsilon}.$$

For outward bound waves, B is equal to zero. We also know that as $\beta r \to 0$, $r\bar{H}_\varphi$ approaches $Il/4\pi r$. These facts should help in finding the exact solution of equations (1). Tentatively assume that

$$r\bar{H}_\varphi = \frac{Il}{4\pi r} e^{-j\beta r} + Ae^{-j\beta r}.$$

The reason for including the exponential factor in the first term is this: If this term does not have the exponential factor while the second does, there can be no hope to satisfy equations (1). We need only try the substitution. There is no risk in the above tentative assumption since the next step is to substitute $r\bar{H}_\varphi$ in

$$\frac{d^2}{dr^2}(r\bar{H}_\varphi) = -\beta^2(r\bar{H}_\varphi) + \frac{2}{r^2}(r\bar{H}_\varphi).$$

This will enable us either to express A in terms of Il or disprove the conjecture. Find A and note the agreement with equation (5.23).

5.3–1   Assume a perfectly conducting sphere of radius l, concentric with the apexes of the cones in Figure 5.4 (Section 5.3). Show that the current in the cones and the transverse voltage between them are

$$I(r) = [I(0) \cos \beta(l - r)]/\cos \beta l,$$

$$V(r) = [V(0) \sin \beta(l - r)]/\sin \beta l,$$

where the ratio of the input voltage $V(0)$ to the input current is

$$V(0)/I(0) = jK \tan \beta l,$$

where K is given by equation (5.12).

What is the magnetic intensity between the cones?

5.3–2   Obtain the natural frequencies of the cones in the preceding problem:

    (a) when the apexes of the cones are insulated and
    (b) when they are shorted.

  Answer: (a) $\omega_n = (2n + 1)\pi/2l\sqrt{\mu\epsilon}$, $n = 0, 1, 2, \cdots$,

               (b) $\omega_n = n\pi/l\sqrt{\mu\epsilon}$, $n = 0, 1, 2, \cdots$.

5.3–3   Consider two perfectly conducting coaxial cones, $\theta = \theta_1$ and $\theta = \theta_2 > \theta$. Assume that a voltage is impressed between their apexes and that consequently there is a current $I(r)$ in the cone $\theta = \theta_1$ at distance r from the source. Since there is no radial displacement current, we have

$$2\pi r \sin \theta H_\varphi = I(r).$$

Using this equation show that the inductance per unit length of the cone is

$$L = \frac{\mu}{2\pi} \ln [\tan (\theta_2/2) \cot (\theta_1/2)].$$

Similarly assuming a charge per unit length, $q(r)$, on the cone $\theta = \theta_1$ calculate D_θ, E_θ, the voltage $V(r)$ along the meridians and show that the capacitance per unit length is

$$C = \frac{2\pi\epsilon}{\ln [\tan (\theta_2/2) \cot (\theta_1/2)]}.$$

5.8–1   Using the results in Section 2.10, the equations in Problem 5.1–1, and the analogy between the fields of a current element and an infinitesimal circulating current, show that the exact field of the latter, for all frequencies is

$$E_\varphi = \frac{\eta\beta^2 I S}{4\pi r}\left(1 + \frac{1}{j\beta r}\right)e^{-j\beta r}\sin\theta,$$

$$H_\theta = -\frac{\beta^2 I S}{4\pi r}\left(1 + \frac{1}{j\beta r} - \frac{1}{\beta^2 r^2}\right)e^{-j\beta r}\sin\theta,$$

$$H_r = \frac{j\beta I S}{2\pi r^2}\left(1 + \frac{1}{j\beta r}\right)e^{-j\beta r}\cos\theta,$$

where I is the current and S is the area of the loop.

Show that the field of an infinitesimal solenoid of moment Vl, that is, a *magnetic current element*, may be obtained from the above if IS is replaced by $Vl/j\omega\mu$. (Here V is the magnetic current in the solenoid and can be measured by the voltage induced in a *single* turn of the solenoid.) Show that the distant field in this case is

$$H_\theta = \frac{j\omega\epsilon Vl}{4\pi r}e^{-j\beta r}\sin\theta, \qquad E_\varphi = -\eta H_\theta.$$

5.8–2 Show that equations (5.1), (5.2), and (5.3) are invariant under the following transformation:

$$r \to -r, \qquad H_\varphi \to -H_\varphi, \qquad E_r \to E_r, \qquad E_\theta \to E_\theta.$$

Use this fact to obtain the following expressions for the field of a converging spherical wave

$$E_r = \frac{A\eta}{2\pi r^2}\left(1 - \frac{1}{j\beta r}\right)e^{j\beta r}\cos\theta,$$

$$E_\theta = -\frac{j\omega\mu A}{4\pi r}\left(1 - \frac{1}{j\beta r} - \frac{1}{\beta^2 r^2}\right)e^{j\beta r}\sin\theta,$$

$$H_\varphi = \frac{j\beta A}{4\pi r}\left(1 - \frac{1}{j\beta r}\right)e^{j\beta r}\sin\theta.$$

5.8–3 Use the expressions for the diverging and converging spherical waves to obtain the following expressions for standing waves:

(a) $$E_\theta = -\frac{\eta A}{\lambda r}\left[\frac{\cos \beta r}{\beta r} + \left(1 - \frac{1}{\beta^2 r^2}\right)\sin \beta r\right]\sin \theta,$$

$$H_\varphi = j\frac{A}{\lambda r}\left(\frac{\sin \beta r}{\beta r} - \cos \beta r\right)\sin \theta,$$

$$E_r = \frac{\eta A}{\pi r^2}\left(\frac{\sin \beta r}{\beta r} - \cos \beta r\right)\cos \theta,$$

and

(b) $$E_\theta = -\frac{\eta B}{\lambda r}\left[\left(1 - \frac{1}{\beta^2 r^2}\right)\cos \beta r - \frac{\sin \beta r}{\beta r}\right]\sin \theta,$$

$$H_\varphi = j\frac{B}{\lambda r}\left(\sin \beta r + \frac{\cos \beta r}{\beta r}\right)\sin \theta,$$

$$E_r = \frac{\eta B}{\pi r^2}\left(\sin \beta r + \frac{\cos \beta r}{\beta r}\right)\cos \theta.$$

The field given by (a) is finite at $r = 0$. The field given by (b) is singular at $r = 0$. Show that the latter implies a current element of moment $Il = 2jB$ at $r = 0$.

5.8–4   Using an appropriate equation from the preceding problem, obtain the equation for natural frequencies of oscillations of electric charge in a cavity bounded by a perfectly conducting sphere of radius a, centered at the origin, when the charge density on the sphere varies as $\cos \theta$.

    Answer: $\omega_n = k_n/a\sqrt{\mu\epsilon}$,
        where k_n is the nth root of $\cot k = k - k^{-1}$.

5.8–5   Calculate the smallest root of the equation in the preceding problem.

    Answer: $k_1 = 2.74371$.

5.8–6   Obtain the natural frequency and the damping constant of external oscillations on a perfectly conducting sphere of radius a when the charge distribution on it is proportional to $\cos \theta$.

    Answer: $\omega = \sqrt{3}/2a\sqrt{\mu\epsilon}$, $\xi = 1/2a\sqrt{\mu\epsilon}$.

5.8–7   Using the energy method and the low-frequency field in the spherical cavity (that is, the static field distribution for E and the effect of its time derivative on H), show that the lowest natural frequency is given by

$$\omega = \sqrt{10}/a\sqrt{\mu\epsilon} \simeq 3.16/a\sqrt{\mu\epsilon}.$$

This is 11.6 per cent higher than the exact natural frequency obtained in Problem 5.8–5. A better approximation would have been obtained if the sphere were divided into two parts by a cylindrical surface $\rho = a/2$ and the low-frequency equivalent circuits for each part obtained by the energy method.

5.8–8   Show that the method suggested in the preceding problem, when applied to external oscillations on a perfectly conducting sphere yields $\omega\sqrt{\mu\epsilon}\, a = \sqrt{2} = 1.414 \cdots$, as compared with the exact value $\omega\sqrt{\mu\epsilon}\, a = 0.866 \cdots$. The reason for a much poorer result in this case is that a very substantial loss of power by radiation is neglected when we apply equation (3.17) with $R_t = 0$.

5.8–9   Show that the natural frequencies of gyrations of currents circulating in a perfectly conducting sphere of radius a are given by $\omega_n\sqrt{\mu\epsilon}\, a = k_n$, $\tan k = k$, if we assume that these gyrations have been excited from *inside* the sphere in such a way that the density of circulating current is proportional to $\sin\theta$.
    Show that $k_1 = 4.4934 \cdots$.

5.8–10   Circulating currents, proportional to $\sin\theta$, may be excited on a perfectly conducting sphere by an appropriate outside source. Show that they would be exponentially damped at the rate $1/a\sqrt{\mu\epsilon}$ nepers per second.

5.8–11   Fill in the details in the solution of the following problem. In Section 5.2 we obtained the field of a semi-infinite progressive current wave along the z axis and issuing from the origin. From equations (5.9) we find that on the positive z axis, E_θ and H_φ are infinite and that E_r is finite (except at the origin). This means that as we approach the positive z axis, the ratio E_r/E_θ approaches zero and it would appear that we have a limit field of a progressive current wave on a thin perfectly conducting wire as the radius of the wire approaches zero.
    Consider now a thin perfectly conducting cone $\theta = \psi \ll 1$ and a current wave on it. How can we obtain the field? On account of symmetry E_r, E_θ, and H_φ must satisfy Maxwell's equations (5.1), (5.2),

and (5.3). In addition, the radial electric intensity must vanish on the surface of the cone,

$$E_r(\psi) = 0.$$

We would expect that if θ is large in comparison with ψ, E_r will be approximately the same as in the case $\psi = 0$ [see equation (5.5)]. This suggests that E_r for the new arrangement may be given by

$$E_r = \frac{R(r)\Theta(\theta)}{j\omega\epsilon r}, \tag{1}$$

where $\Theta(\theta)$ is almost unity for $\theta \gg \psi$ and reduces to zero for $\theta = \psi$,

$$\Theta(\psi) = 0. \tag{2}$$

Function $R(r)$ would probably be almost sinusoidal [see equation (5.8)]. Our problem now is to find out whether the assumption (1) is consistent with Maxwell's equations and calculate $R(r)$ and $\Theta(\theta)$ if it is.

To obtain the answer to the question we substitute E_r from equation (1) into equation (5.1), integrate from $\theta = \pi$ to $\theta = \theta$, note that $H\varphi(r, \pi) = 0$, and find

$$H\varphi = \frac{R(r)}{\sin\theta} \int_{\pi}^{\theta} \sin\theta\Theta(\theta) \, d\theta.$$

We substitute this in equation (5.2) to obtain rE_θ. Then we substitute E_θ, H_φ, and E_r in equation (5.3), multiply the result by $j\omega\epsilon \sin\theta$, differentiate with respect to θ, and rearrange the terms to find

$$\left[\frac{d^2(rR)}{dr^2} + \beta^2(rR)\right] \sin\theta\,\Theta = -Rr^{-1}\frac{d}{d\theta}\left(\sin\theta\frac{d\Theta}{d\theta}\right).$$

We observe that if we divide by $Rr^{-1}\Theta \sin\theta$, the left side of the equation will be a function of r only and the right side a function of θ only. The equality is possible only if each side reduces to a constant, k let us say. Thus, we find

$$\frac{d}{d\theta}\left(\sin\theta\frac{d\Theta}{d\theta}\right) = -k\sin\theta\,\Theta, \tag{3}$$

$$\frac{d^2(rR)}{dr^2} = -\beta^2(rR) + (k/r^2)(rR). \tag{4}$$

The consistency of assumption (1) with Maxwell's equations has now been demonstrated and it remains to solve the preceding equations.

We know that in the limiting case $\psi = 0$, the constant k is zero. The general solution of equation (3) is then

$$\Theta(\theta) = M \ln \tan (\theta/2) + N,$$

where M and N are constants of integration. For our physical arrangement M must equal zero since E_r must be finite at $\theta = \pi$. Indeed in equation (5.5), $\Theta(\theta) = 1$ [the constant N may be absorbed in $R(r)$]. When ψ does not vanish but is small, k must be small. Hence the right-hand side of equation (3) is small. If we replace Θ by unity, on the right-hand side, the error will be the product of one small quantity k and another small quantity, namely, the deviation of Θ from unity. Thus we have an approximate equation

$$\frac{d}{d\theta} \left(\sin \theta \frac{d\Theta}{d\theta} \right) = -k \sin \theta.$$

Integrating from $\theta = \pi$ to $\theta = \Theta$, etc., we find

$$\Theta = 1 + 2k \ln \sin (\theta/2).$$

The boundary condition (2) is satisfied if

$$k = \tfrac{1}{2} \ln \csc (\psi/2),$$

that is, for $\psi \ll 1$

$$k = \tfrac{1}{2} \ln (2/\psi).$$

Function Θ is

$$\Theta = 1 - \frac{\ln \sin (\theta/2)}{\ln \sin (\psi/2)}.$$

We observe that as ψ approaches zero, Θ approaches unity.

When $k = 0$, function rR is given by equation (5.8). If $k \neq 0$, then equation (4) shows that the fractional deviation from equation (5.8) depends on $k/\beta^2 r^2$. This quantity approaches zero as βr increases, and, of course, k itself is small. It is only when $\beta r \ll k$ that the last term in equation (4) becomes dominant and we have approximately

$$\frac{r^2 d^2(rR)}{dr^2} = k(rR).$$

The general solution is

$$rR = Pr^{n_1} + Qr^{n_2},$$

where

$$n_{1,2} = \tfrac{1}{2} \pm \sqrt{\tfrac{1}{4} + k} \simeq 1 + k, \, -k.$$

This solution may be compared with equation (5.8) if we expand the exponential function in power series in r.

5.10–1   Obtain the average power contributed by the generator to the field produced by a circular current loop of *area moment IS*.

$$Answer:\quad P = \frac{\eta}{12\pi}\,\beta^4 S^2 II^*.$$

5.10–2   Calculate the power crossing a sphere of large radius, concentric with the current loop in the preceding problem. Compare this power with the average power contributed to the field.

5.10–3   Show by the method used in the preceding problem that the power radiated by a magnetic current element of *dipole moment Vl* is

$$P = \frac{1}{12\pi\eta}\,(\beta l)^2 VV^*.$$

5.10–4   Consider two current elements of moment Il, coaxial with the z axis, one at the origin and the other separated by distance r. Show that in addition to the self-radiated power, equal to $2P$, where P is given by equation (5.27), there is a mutual radiated power

$$P_M = \frac{\eta l^2 II^*}{2\pi r^2}\left(\frac{\sin \beta r}{\beta r} - \cos \beta r\right).$$

This formula can be derived most readily from equation (5.24). It can also be obtained by integrating equation (5.29) over a sphere of large radius (in fact, of any radius, except that the integration will be more complicated). The mutual power may be either positive or negative.

5.10–5   Show that if one current element is at the origin and the other at $(r, \pi/2, 0)$, then the mutual power is

$$P_m = \frac{\eta l^2 II^*}{2\lambda r}\left(\sin \beta r + \frac{\cos \beta r}{\beta r} - \frac{\sin \beta r}{\beta^2 r^2}\right)$$

assuming that the elements are parallel.

5.10–6   Show that if the currents in the preceding problems are in quadrature, then $P_m = 0$.

5.10–7   A charged particle q is oscillating about the origin, along the z axis, with an angular frequency ω. Let a be the amplitude of oscillations. Show that the radiated power equals $10\omega^4 a^2 q^2/c^2$, where c is the velocity of light.

5.12–1   Apply the approximate equation (5.32) to obtain the inductance of a square loop. First, imagine that the generator is inserted at some corner and obtain the total inductance

$$L_t = \frac{2\mu a}{\pi} \left[\ln \left(a/c \right) - 1 + \tfrac{1}{2} \ln 2 \right]$$

$$= \frac{2\mu a}{\pi} \left[\ln \left(a/c \right) - 0.65 \right],$$

where c is the radius of the wire and a is the side of the square.

Next imagine that the generator is inserted in the middle of a side of the square and obtain

$$L_t = \frac{2\mu a}{\pi} \left[\ln \left(a/c \right) - 0.5 \right].$$

Of course, the difference between the constants in the brackets is due to somewhat different methods of approximation. The exact value of the constant is $-0.78 \cdots$. (See Problem 2.17–2).

5.12–2   Obtain an approximate value of the average character-istic impedance of two thin wires of radius a and length l, diverging from a common apex and making an angle ϑ.

Answer: $K_{\text{av}} = \frac{\eta}{\pi} \left[\ln \left(2l/a \right) - 1 + \ln \sin \left(\vartheta/2 \right) \right].$

5.12–3   Derive equations 5.32 by the method suggested in Problem 5.3–3.

5.14–1   Show that at large distances the magnetic intensity of a full-wave antenna $(l = \tfrac{1}{2}\lambda)$ is

$$H_\varphi = \frac{j I_0 e^{-j\beta r} \left[1 + \cos \left(\pi \cos \theta \right) \right]}{2\pi r \sin \theta}.$$

5.14–2   Show that the power radiated by a full-wave antenna in free space is

$$P = 60I_0^2 \int_0^{2\pi} \frac{1 - \cos t}{t}\, dt - 15I_0^2 \int_0^{4\pi} \frac{1 - \cos t}{t}\, dt$$

$$= (60 \operatorname{Cin} 2\pi - 15 \operatorname{Cin} 4\pi)\, I_0 I_0^*.$$

6.1–1   Consider direct current in a homogeneous medium. Show that the Cartesian components of electric intensity and current density satisfy Laplace's equation. Show that

$$\frac{\partial E_x}{\partial y} = \frac{\partial E_y}{\partial x}, \qquad \frac{\partial E_y}{\partial z} = \frac{\partial E_z}{\partial y}, \qquad \frac{\partial E_z}{\partial x} = \frac{\partial E_x}{\partial z}$$

whether the medium is homogeneous or not. If the medium is homogeneous, similar equations connect the components of current density.

6.1–2   Consider a thin conducting plate bounded by planes $z = 0$, $z = h$, $y = 0$, and $y = b \gg h$. Suppose that current I is injected into the plate uniformly by an infinitely thin blade of width s piercing the plate. Let the edges of the blade pass through points $(0, y_0 - \frac{1}{2}s)$ and $(0, y_0 + \frac{1}{2}s)$. Show that if $x > 0$

$$J_x = \frac{I}{2bh} + \sum_{n=1}^{\infty} \frac{2I}{n\pi hs} \sin \frac{n\pi s}{2b} \cos \frac{n\pi y_0}{b} \cos \frac{n\pi y}{b} e^{-n\pi x/b},$$

$$J_y = \sum_{n=1}^{\infty} \frac{2I}{n\pi hs} \sin \frac{n\pi s}{2b} \cos \frac{n\pi y_0}{b} \sin \frac{n\pi y}{b} e^{-n\pi x/b},$$

and that

$$J_x(-x, y) = -J_x(x, y)$$
$$J_y(-x, y) = J_y(x, y).$$

Obtain J_x and J_y when $s = 0$.

6.1–3   Consider two parallel resistive wires, shunted at equal distances by other resistive wires as shown in Figure 6.1–3. Let R_{se} be the resistance of each section of the long wires and R_{sh} the resistance of each shunting wire. There are two simple types of current distribution in such a wire network. If equal currents are injected into the terminals A and B, there will be no current in the shunting wires and the current in all series sections will be the same. See part (a) of the figure. In this case there will be no voltage either between

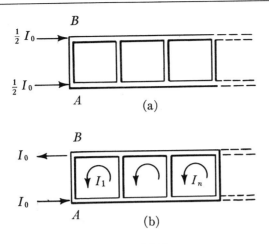

$$\text{Figure 6.1–3}$$

A and B or across any shunting wire. Another possibility is shown in part (b) of the figure where current I_0 enters the terminal A of the lower wire and leaves through the terminal B of the upper wire. Show that in this case the following relation exists between the currents in the successive meshes

$$I_{n-1} - 2pI_n + I_{n+1} = 0, \qquad p = 1 + (R_{se}/R_{sh}).$$

Show that it is possible for the ratio $k = I_{n+1}/I_n$ of the successive mesh currents to be constant, and that

$$k_{1,2} = p \pm \sqrt{p^2 - 1}. \tag{1}$$

Show that the product of k_1 and k_2 is unity and that therefore one value is smaller than unity and the other greater than unity. Show that the current in the nth mesh, given by

$$I_n = A k_1^n + B k_2^n = A k_1^n + B k_1^{-n}, \tag{2}$$

where A and B are arbitrary constants, satisfies the foregoing relation between mesh currents. Explain why A must equal zero, when the network is continued indefinitely. In this case show that if current I_{in} is injected only into the A-terminal, then the currents in the nth sections of the upper and lower wires are, respectively,

$$\tfrac{1}{2}I_{in}(1 + k_1^{-n}) \quad \text{and} \quad \tfrac{1}{2}I_{in}(1 - k_1^{-n}).$$

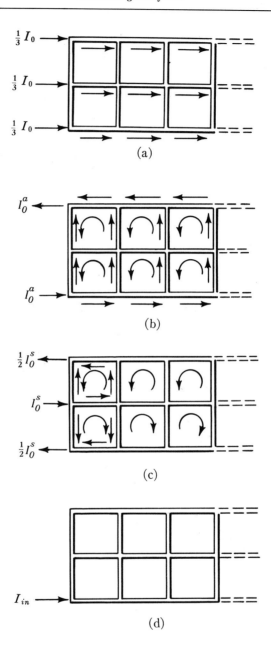

FIGURE 6.1–4

6.1–4   Three long wires shunted across at regular intervals are shown in Figure 6.1–4. If we assume that all series resistances are equal and all shunt resistances are also equal, we anticipate from symmetry considerations the following three regular types of current distribution [see parts (a), (b), and (c) of the figure]: type (a) in which the input current I_0 is equally distributed between the wires and there are no shunt currents; anti-symmetric type (b) in which the current I_0^a enters the lower wire and leaves the upper; there is no net current in the middle wire; the symmetric type (c) in which the current I_0^s enters the middle wire and leaves the screen by way of the other two. Any other current distribution is a linear combination of these three types. Show, for example, that if the current I_{in} enters the lower wire as shown in part (d) of the figure, then the resulting current distribution may be obtained by superposition of these three types with

$$I_0 = I_{in}, \qquad I_0^a = \tfrac{1}{2}I_{in}, \qquad I_0^s = -\tfrac{1}{3}I_{in}.$$

Show that the current in the nth mesh for the anti-symmetric distribution is given by equation (2) of the preceding problem in which $k_{1,2}$ are given by equation (1) with

$$p = 1 + (R_{se}/2R_{sh}).$$

Show that for the symmetric type

$$p = 1 + (3R_{se}/2R_{sh}).$$

In the case of four parallel wires there are four types of current distribution for each of which the current in the nth mesh in the longitudinal direction is given by equation (2) of Problem 6.1–3. Only two of these types are readily obtained from symmetry considerations. The remaining two can be determined by solving the three mesh equations for the nth *section* of the screen.

6.1–5   Show that the two dimensional Laplace's equation

$$\frac{\partial^2 V}{\partial x^2} + \frac{\partial^2 V}{\partial y^2} = 0$$

may be transformed into

$$\frac{\partial^2 V}{\partial \zeta \partial \zeta^*} = 0,$$

where ζ is the complex variable

$$\zeta = x + jy$$

and ζ^* is its conjugate

$$\zeta^* = x - jy.$$

Therefore the general solution of Laplace's equation is

$$V = f(\zeta) + g(\zeta^*),$$

where f and g are arbitrary functions. Of course, V can always be made real by a proper choice of g in relation to f.

6.1–6   Show that the real and imaginary parts of an arbitrary function of the complex variable, $W(\zeta) = V(x, y) + jU(x, y)$, satisfy Laplace's equation. The function W is called the *complex potential*.

6.1–7   Show that the real part of the complex logarithmic potential

$$W = -(q/2\pi\epsilon) \ln (\zeta - \zeta_0)$$

is the true potential of a line charge of density q, parallel to the z axis and passing through point $(x_0, y_0, 0)$.

Since we are dealing here with essentially two-dimensional problems, we may concentrate our attention on the complex plane where points are represented by a single complex number ζ.

6.1–8   Show that the complex potential of a line charge passing through $\zeta = \zeta_0$ in the presence of a conducting plane $y = 0$ is

$$W = -\frac{q}{2\pi\epsilon} \ln \frac{\zeta - \zeta_0}{\zeta - \zeta_0^*}.$$

The point ζ_0^* is the image of ζ_0.

Show that if the conducting plane is $x = 0$, then the image point is $-\zeta_0^*$ and

$$W = -\frac{q}{2\pi\epsilon} \ln \frac{\zeta - \zeta_0}{\zeta + \zeta_0^*}.$$

6.1–9   Suppose that there are two perfectly conducting planes, $x = 0$ and $y = 0$, and that the line charge is in the first quadrant $(x_0 > 0, y_0 > 0)$. Show that the complex potential is

$$W = -\frac{q}{2\pi\epsilon} \ln \frac{(\zeta - \zeta_0)(\zeta + \zeta_0)}{(\zeta - \zeta_0^*)(\zeta + \zeta_0^*)} = -\frac{q}{2\pi\epsilon} \ln \frac{\zeta^2 - \zeta_0^2}{\zeta^2 - (\zeta_0^*)^2}.$$

6.1–10   Suppose that the conducting half-planes are $\varphi = 0$ and $\varphi = \pi/3$, so that they form a 60° wedge. Show that the complex potential of a line charge, passing through point ζ_0 in the interior of the wedge $(0 < \varphi < \pi/3)$, is

$$W = -\frac{q}{2\pi\epsilon} \ln \frac{\zeta^3 - \zeta_0^3}{\zeta^3 - (\zeta_0^*)^3}.$$

6.1–11   Show that if the wedge is formed by half-planes $\varphi = 0$ and $\varphi = \pi/n$, where n is an integer, then the number of images is $2n - 1$ and

$$W = -\frac{q}{2\pi\epsilon} \ln \frac{\zeta^n - \zeta_0^n}{\zeta^n - (\zeta_0^*)^n}.$$

6.1–12   Show that the complex logarithmic potential in Problem 6.1–7 may be expressed as

$$W = (q/2\pi\epsilon) \sum_{m=1}^{\infty} (1/m)(\zeta/\zeta_0)^m - (q/2\pi\epsilon) \ln(-\zeta_0),$$

when $|\zeta| < |\zeta_0|$, and

$$W = -(q/2\pi\epsilon) \ln \zeta + (q/2\pi\epsilon) \sum_{m=1}^{\infty} (1/m)(\zeta_0/\zeta)^m,$$

when $|\zeta| > |\zeta_0|$. Show that consequently the true potential may be expressed as

$$V = (q/2\pi\epsilon) \sum_{m=1}^{\infty} (1/m)(\rho/\rho_0)^m \cos m(\varphi - \varphi_0) - (q/2\pi\epsilon) \ln \rho_0,$$

$$\rho < \rho_0,$$

$$= -(q/2\pi\epsilon) \ln \rho + (q/2\pi\epsilon) \sum_{m=1}^{\infty} (1/m)(\rho_0/\rho)^m \cos m(\varphi - \varphi_0),$$

$$\rho > \rho_0.$$

6.1–13   Show that the complex potential in Problem 6.1–11 may be expanded in two power series, one converging when $\rho < \rho_0$ and the other when $\rho > \rho_0$. From these series show that the true potential may be expressed as follows:

$$V(\rho, \varphi) = (q/\pi\epsilon) \sum_{m=1}^{\infty} (1/m)(\rho/\rho_0)^{mn} \sin(mn\varphi) \sin(mn\varphi_0)$$

$$= (q/\pi\epsilon) \sum_{m=1}^{\infty} (1/m)(\rho_0/\rho)^{mn} \sin(mn\varphi) \sin(mn\varphi_0)$$

depending on whether $\rho < \rho_0$ or $\rho > \rho_0$. Since $V(\rho, 0) = V(\rho, \pi/n) = 0$, irrespective of the value of n, the complex potential in Problem 6.1–11 must hold for a wedge of any angle. A half-plane is a "wedge" of angle 2π, for which $n = 1/2$.

6.1–14   Show that in the vicinity of $\zeta = \zeta_0$ the complex potential derived in Problem 6.1–11 is

$$W = -\frac{q}{2\pi\epsilon} \ln \frac{n\zeta_0^{n-1}\Delta\zeta}{\zeta_0^n - (\zeta_0^*)^n}$$

and that consequently the capacitance per unit length of a thin wire of radius a inside the wedge and parallel to its edge is

$$C = \frac{2\pi\epsilon}{\ln(2\rho_0 a^{-1}n^{-1} \sin n\varphi_0)}.$$

6.1–15   Given a conducting cylinder, coaxial with the z axis, and a uniform line charge parallel to it. Let a be the radius of the cylinder. Assume that the line charge is passing through the point $(l, 0, 0)$ where $l > a$. Using the result of Problem 6.1–12, show that the potential of the charge displaced on the cylinder is

$$V^r = -(q/2\pi\epsilon) \sum_{m=1}^{\infty} (1/m)(a^2/l\rho)^m \cos m\varphi, \qquad \rho \geq a.$$

Show that the density of displaced is

$$q_s = -(q/\pi l) \sum_{m=1}^{\infty} (a/l)^{m-1} \cos m\varphi.$$

6.1–16   By referring to Problems 2.7–1 and 2.8–2 show that the real part of

$$W = -(\mu I/2\pi) \ln(\zeta - \zeta_0)$$

is the vector potential of an infinitely long current filament passing through point ζ_0 and that the imaginary part is the scalar potential, multiplied by μ. Note the resemblance of the former to the scalar potential of a line charge and use this resemblance to show that the real vector potential of a current filament in a wedge of angle ψ formed by perfectly conducting half-planes, is

$$A = -\frac{\mu I}{2\pi} \text{ re} \left[\ln \frac{\zeta^n - \zeta_0^n}{\zeta^n - (\zeta_0^*)^n} \right],$$

where $n = \pi/\psi$.

Further, show that if the radius of a *thin* current filament is a, then the inductance per unit length, L, is

$$L = (\mu/2\pi) \ln (2\rho_0 a^{-1} n^{-1} \sin n\varphi_0).$$

Explain why in two dimensional situations the product of the inductance and capacitance per unit length is independent of the geometry and that

$$LC = \mu\epsilon.$$

6.1–17   Consider two parallel conducting planes given by $\text{im}(\zeta) = 0$ and $\text{im}(\zeta) = jh$. Show that the image of *any* point ζ in the plane $\zeta = jh$ is $\zeta^* + 2jh$. Use this result to show that the complex potential is

$$W = -\frac{q}{2\pi\epsilon} \ln \sum_{n=0}^{\infty} \frac{[(\zeta - \zeta_0)^2 + 4n^2h^2]}{[(\zeta - \zeta_0^*)^2 + 4n^2h^2]}$$

$$= -\frac{q}{2\pi\epsilon} \ln \frac{\sinh [\pi(\zeta - \zeta_0)/2h]}{\sinh [\pi(\zeta - \zeta_0^*)/2h]}.$$

6.1–18   Let a third conducting plane, re $(\zeta) = 0$, be added to the two planes in the Problem 6.1–17. Show that the complex potential will be the sum of the complex potential given above and

$$\frac{q}{2\pi\epsilon} \ln \frac{\sinh [\pi(\zeta + \zeta_0^*)/2h]}{\sinh [\pi(\zeta + \zeta_0)/2h]}.$$

6.10–1   Derive equations (6.102) and (6.104) as suggested in the text.

6.15–1   Consider a perfectly conducting rectangular waveguide as described in Section 6.10. At point $(x_0, y_0, 0)$ there is a current element of moment Il, parallel to the z axis. Show that only TM waves are excited and that for the (m, n) mode

$$E_{z,mn} = \frac{2Il\chi_{mn}^2 \sin (m\pi x_0/a) \sin (n\pi y_0/b)}{K_{mn}\omega^2\epsilon^2 ab} e^{\mp \Gamma_{mn}z},$$

where the upper sign corresponds to $z > 0$. Show that the power radiated into each mode is

$$P_m = \frac{II^* l^2 \chi_{mn}^2 \sin^2 (m\pi x_0/a) \sin^2 (n\pi y_0/b)}{K_{mn}\omega^2\epsilon^2 ab}.$$

7.1–1 Consider a transmission line whose characteristic impedance is K_1. Suppose that a section of it from $z = 0$ to $z = l$ is replaced by a line with the characteristic impedance K_2. Assume that a progressive wave

$$I^i(z) = I_0 e^{-j\beta_1 z}$$

is coming from $z = -\infty$. Find the reflected and transmitted waves.

Answer: If $u = (K_2 - K_1)/(K_2 + K_1)$ and $k = ue^{-2j\beta_2 l}$, then

$$I^r(z) = \frac{(k - u)I_0 e^{j\beta_1 z}}{1 - uk}, \qquad z \leq 0,$$

$$I(z) = Ae^{-j\beta_2 z} + Be^{j\beta_2 z}, \qquad 0 \leq z \leq l,$$

$$= Ce^{-j\beta_1(z-l)}, \qquad z \geq l,$$

where

$$A = \frac{(1 - u)I_0}{1 - \mu k}, \qquad B = kA,$$

$$C = \frac{(1 - u^2)I_0}{1 - uk}.$$

7.1–2 Equation (7.3) shows that there is no reflection at the junction of two transmission lines with equal characteristic impedances even though their phase constants are different. Similarly, equation (4.61) shows that there are no reflections in a nonuniform transmission line if the characteristic impedance K is constant. Suppose now that K is not constant and that a section of this line from $z = 0$ to $z = l$ is sandwiched in between two uniform lines whose characteristic impedances are $K(0)$ and $K(l)$. Assume that a progressive wave is coming from $z = -\infty$. Find the voltage and current in the interval $(0, l)$ taking into account the first-order reflections. Note the results of Problem 4.17–5.

7.2–1 Suppose that instead of a lumped series impedance at $z = \xi$ of the line in Figure 7.2 we have a lumped shunt admittance Y_l. Discuss the problem of reflection and find voltage and current distributions.

Answer:
$$I(z) = Ae^{-j\beta z} + \frac{AKY_l}{2 + KY_l} e^{-2j\beta\xi}e^{j\beta z}, \qquad z < \xi,$$

$$= \frac{2A}{2 + KY_l} e^{-j\beta z}, \qquad z > \xi,$$

$$V(z) = KAe^{-j\beta z} - \frac{AK^2Y_l}{2 + KY_l} e^{-2j\beta\xi}e^{j\beta z}, \qquad z \leq \xi,$$

$$= \frac{2KA}{2 + KY_l} e^{-j\beta z}, \qquad z \geq \xi.$$

7.3–1 Suppose that a wave given by equations (7.16) is incident on a thin resistive sheet in the plane $z = 0$. Let R be the resistance between the opposite sides of a unit square in the sheet. Show that

$$H_y = H_0 e^{-j\beta z} + \frac{(\eta/R)H_0}{2 + (\eta/R)} e^{j\beta z}, \qquad z < 0,$$

$$= \frac{2H_0}{2 + (\eta/R)} e^{-j\beta z}, \qquad z > 0;$$

$$E_x = \eta H_0 e^{-j\beta z} - \frac{(\eta^2/R)H_0}{2 + (\eta/R)} e^{j\beta z}, \qquad z \leq 0,$$

$$= \frac{2\eta H_0}{2 + (\eta/R)} e^{-j\beta z}, \qquad z \geq 0.$$

Compare this problem with Problem 7.2–1.

7.3–2   Suppose that in the preceding problem we add a perfectly conducting sheet in the plane $z = \lambda/4$. Assume that $R = \eta$. Show that there is no reflected wave in the region $z < 0$ and that between the resistive sheet and the perfectly conducting plane

$$E_x = \eta H_0 \cos \beta z,$$

$$H_y = -j H_0 \sin \beta z.$$

7.7–1   Discuss the situation in Problem 7.2–1 from the point of view of scattering and obtain the expressions for the scattered waves.

Answer: $I^s(z) = \dfrac{A K Y_l}{2 + K Y_l} e^{-2j\beta\xi} e^{j\beta z}, \qquad z < \xi,$

$$= -\frac{2A}{2 + K Y_l} e^{-j\beta z}, \qquad z > \xi,$$

$$V^s(z) = -\frac{A K^2 Y_l}{2 + K Y_l} e^{-2j\beta\xi} e^{j\beta z}, \qquad z \le \xi,$$

$$= -\frac{A K^2 Y_l}{2 + K Y_l} e^{-j\beta z}, \qquad z \ge \xi.$$

8.4–1   Show that equation (8.29) for the input admittance of the line shown in Figure 8.4(a) may be expressed as

$$Y_{in} = \frac{1}{j\omega L_0} + \sum_{n=1}^{\infty} \frac{j\omega}{L_n(\omega_n^2 - \omega^2)}$$

$$= \frac{1}{j\omega 2 \mathcal{E}_0} + \sum_{n=1}^{\infty} \frac{j\omega}{2 \mathcal{E}_n(\omega_n^2 - \omega^2)}$$

where: L_n is the inductance of the nth branch of the equivalent network and $\mathcal{E}_n$ *is the energy stored in the line at nth resonance when the amplitude of the current through the input terminals is unity.* Here $\mathcal{E}_0$ is the energy stored in the loop, Figure 8.4(b), when a direct current of unit magnitude is circulating in it.

8.4–2   Consider a transmission line of length l, shorted at both ends, $z = 0$ and $z = l$, Figure 8.4(b). Assume that a voltage V^i is impressed in series with the line at point $z = \xi$. This introduces a discontinuity in the transverse voltage, $V(\xi + 0) - V(\xi - 0) = V^i$. To satisfy the boundary conditions at $z = 0, l$ we expand $V(z)$ into a sine series, equation (8.19) in the text. We express $I(z)$ by a cosine series, equation (8.17) in the text. Show that

$$I(z) = \frac{V^i}{j\omega L_0} + \sum_{n=1}^{\infty} \frac{j\omega V^i \cos(n\pi\xi/l) \cos(n\pi z/l)}{j\omega L_n(\omega_n^2 - \omega^2)},$$

where L_n and ω_n are still given by equations (8.27) and (8.28).

Show that in this case the inductance and capacitance in the nth branch of the equivalent network, Figure 8.5, are

$$L'_n = \tfrac{1}{2} Ll \sec^2(n\pi\xi/l), \qquad C'_n = \frac{2Cl \cos^2(n\pi\xi/l)}{n^2\pi^2}.$$

8.4–3   Assume that the line in Figure 8.4 is open at $z = l$ and that a voltage V^i is impressed in series at $z = \xi$. Show that the current in the line may be expressed as

$$I(z) = \sum_{n=0}^{\infty} \frac{j\omega V^i \cos[(2n+1)\pi\xi/2l] \cos[(2n+1)\pi z/2l]}{L_n(\omega_n^2 - \omega^2)},$$

where

$$L_n = \tfrac{1}{2} Ll, \qquad C_n = 8Cl/(2n+1)^2\pi^2,$$

$$\omega_n = (2n+1)\pi/2l\sqrt{LC}.$$

The corresponding equivalent network is of the type in Figure 8.5 with

$$L'_n = \tfrac{1}{2} Ll \sec^2[(2n+1)\pi\xi/2l],$$

$$C'_n = \frac{8Cl \cos^2[(2n+1)\pi\xi/2l]}{(2n+1)^2\pi^2}.$$

Here again L'_n equals twice the energy stored in the line at nth resonance when the current through the source is unity.

8.5–1   Show that equation (8.38) for the input impedance of the line in Figure 8.6(a) is equivalent to

$$Z_{in} = \sum_{n=0}^{\infty} \frac{j\omega}{2\mathcal{E}_n(\omega_n^2 - \omega^2)},$$

where $\mathcal{E}_n$ is the *energy stored at nth antiresonance when the voltage amplitude across the input terminals is unity*.

8.5–2   Show that if the shunt current I^i is injected at $z = \xi$, Figure 8.6(a), rather than at $z = 0$, then the transverse voltage is given by

$$V(z) = \sum_{n=0}^{\infty} \frac{j\omega I^i \cos\left[(2n+1)\pi\xi/2l\right] \cos\left[(2n+1)\pi z/2l\right]}{C_n(\omega_n^2 - \omega^2)}.$$

8.5–3   Show that if the line is open at both ends and the shunt current is injected at $z = \xi$, then

$$V(z) = \frac{I^i}{j\omega C_0} + \sum_{n=1}^{\infty} \frac{j\omega I^i \cos(n\pi\xi/l) \cos(n\pi z/l)}{C_n(\omega_n^2 - \omega^2)},$$

where

$$C_0 = Cl, \qquad C_n = \tfrac{1}{2}Cl, \qquad \omega_n = n\pi/l\sqrt{LC}.$$

The corresponding equivalent network is of the type shown in Figure 8.7.

8.5–4   A shunt current I^i is injected at $z = \xi$ of a line shorted at both ends, Figure 8.4(b). Show that

$$V(z) = \sum_{n=1}^{\infty} \frac{j\omega I^i \sin(n\pi\xi/l) \sin(n\pi z/l)}{C_n(\omega_n^2 - \omega^2)},$$

where

$$C_n = \tfrac{1}{2}Cl \quad \text{and} \quad \omega_n = n\pi/l\sqrt{LC}.$$

Show that the input impedance seen by the shunt generator may be expressed as

$$Z_{\text{in}} = j\omega L_0 + \sum_{n=1}^{\infty} \frac{j\omega^3 L_{M,n}^2}{L_n(\omega_n^2 - \omega^2)}$$

where

$$L_0 = L\xi(l - \xi)/l$$

is the dc inductance of the two loops of lengths ξ and $l - \xi$ in parallel while

$$L_n = \tfrac{1}{2}Ll \quad \text{and} \quad L_{M,n} = \frac{Ll \sin(n\pi\xi/l)}{n\pi}.$$

The equivalent network is of the type shown in Fig. 8.8.

8.5–5   Solve the preceding problem when the line is shorted at $z = 0$ and open at $z = l$.

Obtain the solution when the line is open at both ends and a voltage V^i is impressed in series at $z = \xi$.

8.5-6   In the preceding problems ω_n is a typical natural frequency of the corresponding section of the line when the line is nondissipative. This suggests that the expressions for the input impedance and admittance may be generalized by substituting $-\xi_n + j\omega_n$ for $j\omega_n$, where ξ_n is the damping constant of corresponding free oscillations. This substitution is equivalent to the substitution of $\omega_n + j\xi_n$ for ω_n or approximately $\omega_n^2 + 2j\xi_n\omega_n$ for ω_n^2. In the latter approximation it is assumed that ξ_n^2 is negligible in comparison with ω_n^2. Another approximation may and usually is involved in the substitution: the coupling between various modes of oscillation, usually produced by the resistance and conductance, is neglected.

The damping constants may be calculated from energy considerations as explained in Sections 3.5 and 6.13. Show for instance that if R is the resistance per unit length of the line shown in Figure 8.4(a), then the expression for the input admittance given in Problem 8.4–1 becomes

$$Y_{in} = \frac{1}{2\mathcal{E}_0[j\omega + (R/L)]} + \sum_{n=1}^{\infty} \frac{j\omega}{2\mathcal{E}_n[\omega_n^2 - \omega^2 + (j\omega_n R/L)]}.$$

8.5-7   Consider a cavity bounded by planes $x = 0, a; y = 0, b;$ and $z = 0, h$. Assume that h is small in comparison with either a or b. Around a point $(x_0, y_0, 0)$ there is a small hole through which the inner conductor of a coaxial line enters the cavity and joins the upper wall at (x_0, y_0, h). Thus the current in the protruding post excites the cavity. At an antiresonant frequency the current in the post is zero and the post has a negligible effect on the antiresonant frequency. Therefore the frequencies can be calculated as in Section 6.11 by ignoring the post. The equation for the input impedance in Problem 8.5–1 is thus suitable for the present case. Show that

$$\omega_{mn}^2 = [(m\pi/a)^2 + (n\pi/b)^2]/\mu\epsilon,$$

$$2\mathcal{E}_{mn} = \epsilon ab/4h \, \sin^2 (m\pi x_0/a) \, \sin^2 (n\pi y_0/b).$$

As ω approaches zero,

$$Z_{in} \to j\omega \sum_{m,n=1}^{\infty} \frac{1}{2\omega_{mn}^2 \mathcal{E}_{mn}}$$

and the summation represents the direct current inductance L_0 of the post in the cavity. This inductance may be calculated from static considerations. Then

$$Z_{\text{in}} = j\omega L_0 + \sum_{m,n=1}^{\infty} \frac{j\omega^3 L_{M,mn}^2}{L_{mn}(\omega_{mn}^2 - \omega^2)},$$

where

$$\frac{L_{M,mn}^2}{L_{mn}} = \frac{4h \sin^2{(m\pi\alpha_0/a)} \sin^2{(n\pi y_0/b)}}{\epsilon a b \omega_{mn}^2}.$$

The equivalent network is of the type shown in Figure 8.8.

8.5–8   Consider the cavity in the preceding problem and assume that a given shunt current of density $J_z(x, y)$ is forced to flow from the lower face $z = 0$ to the upper face $z = h$. Show that in this case Maxwell's differential equations are

$$\frac{\partial E_z}{\partial y} = -j\omega\mu H_x, \qquad \frac{\partial E_z}{\partial x} = j\omega\mu H_y,$$

$$\frac{\partial H_y}{\partial x} - \frac{\partial H_x}{\partial y} = j\omega\epsilon E_z + J_z(x, y).$$

The electric intensity in the cavity may be represented by a double Fourier series.

$$E_z = \sum_{m,n} E_{mn} \sin{(m\pi x/a)} \sin{(n\pi y/b)}.$$

Show that

$$E_{mn} = -\frac{4j\omega}{\epsilon a b (\omega_{mn}^2 - \omega^2)} \int_0^b \int_0^a J_z(x, y) \sin{(m\pi x/a)} \sin{(n\pi y/b)} \, dx \, dy$$

where ω_{mn} is given in the preceding problem. From these equations one obtains the input impedance seen by the coaxial line in the preceding problem.

8.6–1   From a purely mathematical point of view the method presented in Section 8.6 is a method for solving transmission line equations (8.43) and (8.44). Another such method is based on calculus of variations. Suppose that we wish to determine natural frequencies of a nonuniform transmission line which is either open or shorted at its ends $z = 0$ and $z = l$. From equations (8.43) and (8.44) we then have

$$\frac{d}{dz}\left[\frac{1}{C(z)}\frac{dI}{dz}\right] = -\omega^2 L(z)I, \tag{1}$$

$$\frac{d}{dz}\left[\frac{1}{L(z)}\frac{dV}{dz}\right] = -\omega^2 C(z)V. \tag{2}$$

Multiplying equation (1) by $I(z)$, integrating from $z = 0$ to $z = l$, and using the boundary conditions, we find that the following integral,

$$P = \int_0^l \left[\frac{1}{C(z)}\left(\frac{dI}{dz}\right)^2 - \omega^2 L(z)I^2\right] dz, \tag{3}$$

vanishes. Furthermore, taking the variation of P, we obtain

$$\delta P = \int_0^l \left[\frac{1}{C(z)}2\frac{dI}{dz}\delta\frac{dI}{dz} - 2\omega^2 L(z)I\,\delta I\right] dz$$

$$= 2\int_0^l \left[\frac{1}{C(z)}\frac{dI}{dz}\frac{d}{dz}(\delta I) - 2\omega^2 L(z)I\,\delta I\right] dz.$$

Integrating the first term by parts and taking into account the boundary conditions, we have

$$\delta P = -2\int_0^l \left[\frac{d}{dz}\left\{\frac{1}{C(z)}\frac{dI}{dz}\right\} + \omega^2 L(z)I\right] \delta I\,dz.$$

Thus if $I(z)$ satisfies equation (1), then $\delta P = 0$. Conversely, if $\delta P = 0$ for an arbitrary variation in $I(z)$ but subject to the given end conditions, then $I(z)$ satisfies equation (1). Thus, we have

$$P = 0 \quad \text{and} \quad \delta P = 0. \tag{4}$$

The first of these equations expresses the physical fact that if the oscillations are free, the maximum electric energy in the line must equal the maximum magnetic energy. Similar equations are obtained for equation (2).

Equations (4) are suitable for approximate calculation of natural frequencies. Suppose, for example, that the line is open at $z = 0$ and $z = l$. If the parameters L and C are independent of z, then we know that for the lowest mode $I(z)$ is proportional to $\sin(\pi z/l)$. If we use this function to approximate $I(z)$ in the general case, we find

$$P = \int_0^l \left[\frac{\pi^2}{l^2 C(z)} \cos^2 (\pi z/l) - \omega^2 L(z) \sin^2 (\pi z/l) \right] dz.$$

The condition $P = 0$ then yields

$$\omega^2 = \frac{\displaystyle\int_0^l \pi^2 l^{-2} [C(z)]^{-1} \cos^2 (\pi z/l) \ dz}{\displaystyle\int_0^l L(z) \sin^2 (\pi z/l) \ dz}.$$

We could have used a different approximation to $I(z)$, $1 - (z/l)^2$, for instance. The choice of the first approximation depends on the physical insight in any specific case. If L and C are nearly independent of z, the sine approximation would be quite good since it would yield the exact answer when L and C are constants while other functions would yield only approximate answers.

To improve the approximation we should introduce more disposable parameters. Thus we could assume

$$I(z) = a_1 \sin (\pi z/l) + a_2 \sin (2\pi z/l).$$

If we calculate P, then δP, and equate to zero the coefficients of δa_1, and δa_2, we obtain two linear homogeneous equations for the two unknowns a_1 and a_2. From these equations we can determine ω and the ratio a_2/a_1. We can keep adding more sine functions for better approximations. We also can select a different set of approximating functions.

9.4–1 Obtain the solution of equation (9.27) for the principal mode, $m = 0$, when

$$\mu = \mu_0, \qquad \epsilon(z) = \epsilon_0[1 + k(z/\lambda_0)], \qquad z \geq 0, \qquad (1)$$

where k is a constant and λ_0 is the free space wavelength. At first use the approximate method of Section 4.17. The following substitution of the new dependent variable W, defined by

$$\frac{dZ}{dz} = -j\omega\epsilon(z) W \qquad (2)$$

will transform equation (9.27) into a pair of the first-order equations of the type (4.56).

Answer: $Z(z) = [K(z)]^{-1/2}(Ae^{-j\vartheta} + Be^{j\vartheta})$,

where

$$K(z) = \eta_0[1 + k(z/\lambda_0)]^{-1/2},$$

$$\vartheta(z) = (4\pi/3k)[1 + k(z/\lambda_0)]^{3/2} - (4\pi/3k).$$

9.4–2   The solution of the preceding problem is good to the extent to which $K'(\vartheta)/2K(\vartheta)$ is negligible in comparison with unity. Show that for equations (4.56)

$$K'(\vartheta)/2K(\vartheta) = K'(z)/2\omega L(z),$$

and use this result to show that the solution is good when $k \ll 1$ or when $k \gg 1$ and z is relatively large in comparison with λ_0.
Show that

$$K'(\vartheta)/2K(\vartheta) = -(k/4\pi)[1 + k(z/\lambda_0)]^{-3/2},$$

that the magnitude of this ratio for $z = z_0$ is maximum when

$$k = 2\lambda_0/z_0,$$

and that

$$|[K'(\vartheta)/2K(\vartheta)]_{\max}| = (\lambda_0/z_0)/6\pi\sqrt{3}.$$

If the approximation is considered good enough in the vicinity of $z = z_0$, it will be just as good or better for *all* k when $z > z_0$. Note that the maximum ratio is relatively small even when $z_0 = \lambda_0/4$. Since the section from $z = 0$ to $z = \lambda_0/4$ is relatively short, the appropriate solution may be found by successive integrations as in Section 4.4.

9.4–3   Show that the exact solution of the Problem 9.4–1 is

$$W(z) = Au^{1/3}J_{1/3}(u) + Bu^{1/3}N_{1/3}(u),$$

where

$$u = \vartheta + (4\pi/3k),$$

and

$$Z(z) = -(1/j\omega\mu_0)\frac{dW}{dz}.$$

Progressive waves are obtained when $B = \mp jA$. If $u \gg 1$, then the Bessel functions may be approximated by the first terms of their asymptotic expansions and the approximate solutions given in Problem 9.4 − 1 are obtained. The quantity u is large when either $k \ll 1$ or $\vartheta \gg 1$.

9.4-4   If the stratification is at right angles to the direction of propagation and we have to solve equations (9.28) subject to the boundary conditions (9.29), we may use either the method of Section 4.17 or the variational method. In the latter case show that if

$$ P = \int_0^a \left[\frac{1}{\epsilon(x)} \left| \frac{dX}{dx} \right|^2 - \omega^2 \mu X^2 - \frac{\Gamma^2}{\epsilon(x)} X^2 \right] dx, $$

then

$$ P = 0 \quad \text{and} \quad \delta P = 0. $$

Since $X(x)$ is proportional to $\cos(m\pi x/a)$ when $\epsilon(x) = $ const, we may use these functions for obtaining the approximate values of the propagation constants. Show that for the principal mode we have

$$ \Gamma_0 = \frac{j\omega\sqrt{\mu}}{\sqrt{(1/a) \int_0^a [\epsilon(x)]^{-1} \, dx}}. $$

List of Symbols

B	magnetic flux density
C	capacitance, linear current density
c	speed of light in vacuum
D	electric displacement (or flux) density
E	electric intensity
ε	energy
F	force
f	frequency
G	conductance
H	magnetic intensity
I	electric current
J	electric current density
K	characteristic impedance
L	inductance
M	magnetization
m	mass
P	power, polarization
p	moment
q	electric charge
R	resistance
S	area
s	distance
t	time
U	magnetic potential, magnetomotive force
V	electric potential, electromotive force (voltage)

v	speed, volume
W	work
X	reactance
Y	admittance
Z	impedance
α	attenuation constant
β	phase constant
Γ, γ	propagation constant
ϵ	dielectric constant
ϵ_0	dielectric constant of vacuum
$\epsilon_r = \epsilon/\epsilon_0$	relative dielectric constant
η	intrinsic impedance
λ	wavelength
μ	permeability
μ_0	permeability of vacuum
$\mu_r = \mu/\mu_0$	relative permeability
ρ	charge density, cylindrical coordinate
σ	conductivity
φ	phase, cylindrical coordinate
Φ	magnetic flux
Ψ	electric flux
Ω	solid angle
ω	angular frequency
(x, y, z)	Cartesian coordinates
(ρ, φ, z)	cylindrical coordinates
(r, θ, φ)	spherical coordinates
(u, v, w)	general coordinates

Index

409

A Note About the Author

Professor Sergei A. Schelkunoff, born in Russia on January 27, 1897, emigrated to the United States in 1921. Having majored in mathematics, he received both his B.A. and M.A. degrees from the State College of Washington in 1923 and his Ph.D. degree from Columbia University in 1928. Until 1960, he was with Bell Telephone Laboratories, doing research in electromagnetic field theory. In 1956 he became the Assistant Director of Mathematical Research and in 1958, Assistant Vice President. At various times he lectured on mathematics and field theory at the State College of Washington, Brown University, University of California at Low Angeles, New York University, and Columbia University. In 1960, he was appointed Professor of Electrical Engineering at Columbia University.

Professor Schelkunoff is author of *Electromagnetic Waves* (1943), *Applied Mathematics for Scientists and Engineers* (1948), *Antennas: Theory and Practice* (with Harald T. Friis, 1952), and *Advanced Antenna Theory* (1952).

A Note on the Production and Design

The text of this book is set in a monotype face called Bruce Old Style No. 31. It is a compact close-fitting letter that permits more copy in a given space than the average transitional or old style type. It was adapted by Sol Hess from the Old Style Series No. 21, originally cut by the George Bruce's Son & Company. In the first quarter of the nineteenth century, George Bruce first formulated the modern system whereby body sizes of type increase by arithmetical progression. This system, which De Vinne called ingenious and scientific, was first adopted by Bruce's own foundry.

The book was composed by Mono of Maryland, Inc., Baltimore, Maryland, printed by Halliday Lithograph Corporation, West Hanover, Massachusetts, and bound by The Colonial Press, Clinton, Massachusetts. The paper was manufactured by Warrens Paper Company, Boston, Massachusetts and supplied by Lindenmeyr Schlosser Company, Long Island City, New York. The illustrations were drawn by Versatron Technical Corporation, Hicksville, New York. Alfred Manso of New York City designed the book.